N
Quote You!

Be a part of
ZAGAT SURVEY®

If you would like to participate in one of our Surveys or be added to our mailing list, please fill out this card and send it back to us.

☐ Mr.   ☐ Mrs.   ☐ Ms.
_____
Your Name

_____
Street Address   Apt #

_____
City   State   Zip

_____
e-mail Address

_____
Occupation

I'd like to be a surveyor for the following city:

_____

or a surveyor for U.S. Hotels, Resorts & Spas ☐

The city I visit most is: _____

My favorite restaurant is: _____

_____
                        City

My favorite hotel is: _____

_____
                        City

I eat roughly _____ lunches and dinners out per week.

☐ This book was a gift   ☐ Bought by me   ☐ Surveyor copy

The title of this book is: _____

ZAGATSURVEY®

2000

SAN FRANCISCO BAY AREA RESTAURANTS

Edited by Anthony Dias Blue

Coordinated by Carol Seibert
and David Gadd

Published and distributed by
ZAGAT SURVEY, LLC
4 Columbus Circle
New York, New York 10019
Tel: 212 977 6000
E-mail: zagat@zagatsurvey.com
Web site: zagat.com

Acknowledgments

First of all, we want to thank the over 2,800 respondents who took the time to fill out the San Francisco Bay Area questionnaire: without you there would be no *Zagat Survey*. Thank you for your intrepid restaurant-going and for your keen wit. Special thanks are also due to Patrick Anglin, Kate Black, Kathy Blue, Paul Bourbin, Jenn Callum, Mary Dorst and Ann Rudorf. Finally, a warm thank you to all the San Francisco Bay Area chefs and restaurateurs whose dedication makes this the best place on earth to find a great meal.

Contents

Starters

Here are the results of our *2000 San Francisco Bay Area Restaurant Survey* covering some 799 restaurants from the wine country in the north to the Monterey Peninsula in the south.

By regularly surveying large numbers of local restaurant-goers, we think we have achieved a uniquely current and reliable guide. We hope you agree. More than 2,810 people participated. Since the participants dined out an average of 3.3 times per week, this *Survey* is based on about 482,000 meals per year.

We want to thank each of our participants. They are a widely diverse group in all respects but one – they are food lovers all. This book is really "theirs."

Of the surveyors, 50% are women, 50% are men; the breakdown by age is 17% in their 20s, 28% in their 30s, 22% in their 40s, 22% in their 50s and 11% in their 60s or above.

To help guide our readers to The Bay Area's best meals and best buys, we have prepared a number of lists. See, for example, The Bay Area's Most Popular Restaurants (page 11), Top Ratings (pages 12–16) and Best Buys (pages 17–18). On the assumption that most people want a quick fix on the places at which they are considering eating, we have tried to be concise and to provide handy indexes.

We are particularly grateful to our editor, Anthony Dias Blue, the nationally syndicated food and wine radio and television commentator and columnist, and to his associates, Carol Seibert and David Gadd.

We invite you to be a reviewer in our next *Survey*. To do so, simply send a stamped, self-addressed, business-size envelope to ZAGAT SURVEY, 4 Columbus Circle, New York, NY 10019, so that we will be able to contact you. Each participant will receive a free copy of the next *San Francisco Bay Area Restaurant Survey* when it is published.

Your comments, suggestions and even criticisms of this *Survey* are also solicited. There is always room for improvement with your help.

New York, New York
October 13, 1999

Nina and Tim Zagat

What's New

Whew! Keeping up with the San Francisco restaurant scene can be exhausting. I didn't say it wasn't fun, though. Next to Giants statistics and trying to predict the next fog-free day (whether by magic or meteorology), poring over the figures in each year's *Survey* is a favorite past time of many Bay Area residents.

I get a real charge of energy out of the incredible interest in food that keeps San Franciscans alive, not only in a bodily sense but in a spiritual sense as well. When surveyors in this *Survey* are exclaiming "heavenly", "ecstatic", and "miraculous" over the likes of a well-made soufflé, such quotes are, of course, meant to be taken lightly. But beneath the surface they indicate that people in this town take food seriously indeed. They hint that nourishment and the life of the spirit are closely intertwined, an idea that any anthropologist would have to acknowledge. (And, in a sense, the *Survey* itself is a work of anthropology.)

On a more mundane level, food is business – and a very lucrative one at times. And, as in any business, change is not only inevitable, but essential. If it weren't, we'd all still be eating the kind of fare we ate in the '50s and '60s (any volunteers?). This means that some of our restaurants have departed, while others have emerged.

Major losses this past year include Mark Miller's short-lived Loongbar in Ghirardelli Square, Nancy Mootz's dramatic Vertigo in the Transamerica Pyramid and Michel Elkaim's beloved Chez Michel near Fisherman's Wharf. Taking the place of the latter and generating some big buzz is chef Gary Danko's eponymous French-accented New American. Also on the to-be-watched list are Gordon Drysdale's (ex BIX) Gordon's House of Fine Eats, the tony Gramercy Grill on Nob Hill, the sleek Montage at the Sony Metreon complex and the resuscitated Ondine, with its spectacular Bay and skyline views, in Sausalito.

In addition, the proliferation of refined hotel restaurants, thank God, seems to be a certified trend, and I say it's about time. A city such as ours that attracts a wealth of world travelers deserves some fabulous hotel dining rooms. While there have been some long-standing stalwarts such as Fournou's Ovens in the Stanford Court and the Redwood Room in the Clift (as well as a few underappreciated gems like Pacific in the Pan Pacific Hotel and Silks in the Mandarin Oriental Hotel), the new spate of establishments should help stamp out the notion that such places serve nothing more ambitious than worse-for-the-wear Continental cuisine. Among those debuting now are the promising Anzu in the Hotel Nikko; Paul Arenstam's (ex Rubicon) Belon in the hip

Hotel Metropolis; George Morrone's Fifth Floor in the urbane Palomar Hotel; James Ormsby's hot Red Herring in the Hotel Griffon and the edgy XYZ at the W Hotel. Look for a renewed commitment to excellence at the Campton Place Hotel as chef Laurent Manrique mans the stoves and brings a French touch to this classic. And South of SF, star-chef Carl Stamenov (ex Pacific Edge in the Highlands Inn) heads up Marinus in the luxurious Bernardus Lodge in Carmel Valley.

In general, it seems that food quality has never been higher than it is now, both in the Bay Area and nationwide. America is becoming a nation of sophisticated eaters, and San Francisco continues to be a major locus of this encouraging trend. Maybe that's why we eat out here an average of 3.3 times a week, despite the fact that we spend a not-inexpensive average of $30.12 to do so (our fellow diners in LA pay $26.28 per meal). The people who dine in San Francisco – and if you're reading this you're most likely one of them – make an incredible difference in how chefs approach their professions and how restaurant workers perform their jobs. Your opinions matter. Your voices count. This is what the *Zagat Survey* is all about. To paraphrase Thomas Jefferson: People usually get the restaurants they deserve.

One restaurant gripe from this year's respondents that caught and held my attention throughout the *Survey* had to do with noise. Complaints of "deafening" or "thunderous" were common, even to the point of surveyors saying that they would not return to a particular place. Could it be all those cutting-edge industrial spaces that enhance rather than dampen sound? (I was praying that we might be spared a full-fledged revival of the "high-tech" '80s for another few years!) Maybe it's that people are just talking – and eating – louder these days, letting out all the stops as the millennium approaches. Maybe dishes and flatware just make more noise than they used to in my college busboy days. And then there are the saxophones.... We can only hope that architects and interior designers, restaurateurs and managers, will take note of a problem that seems to be near the top of diners' list of complaints these days.

In the meantime, with this, the foodies' Little Burgundy Book as your guide, I wish you delightful, delicious and decibel-controlled dining in the wonderful San Francisco Bay Area.

San Francisco, CA   Anthony Dias Blue
October 13, 1999

Key to Ratings/Symbols

This sample entry identifies the various types of information contained in your Zagat Survey.

(1) Restaurant Name, Address & Phone Number

(2) Hours & Credit Cards

(3) ZAGAT Ratings

F	D	S	C
23	5	9	$19

Tim & Nina's ◖ⓈⓂ⊄

4 Columbus Circle (8th Ave.), 212-977-6000

◪ "What a dump!" – open 7 days a week, 24 hours a day, this successful "deep dive" started the "deli-tapas craze" (i.e., tidbits of pastrami, corned beef, etc. on cracker-size pieces of stale rye); though the place looks like a "none-too-clean garage" and T & N "never heard of credit cards or reservations", "dirt cheap" prices for "great eats" draw demented crowds.

(4) Surveyors' Commentary

The names of restaurants with the highest overall ratings, greatest popularity and importance are printed in **CAPITAL LETTERS**. Address and phone numbers are printed in *italics*.

(2) Hours & Credit Cards

After each restaurant name you will find the following courtesy information:

◖	....	*serving after 11 PM*
Ⓛ	....	*open for lunch*
Ⓢ	....	*open on Sunday*
Ⓜ	....	*open on Monday*
⊄	....	*no credit cards accepted*

8

(3) ZAGAT Ratings

Food, **Decor** and **Service** are each rated on a scale of **0** to **30**:

F	D	S	C

F	....	*Food*
D	....	*Decor*
S	....	*Service*
C	....	*Cost*

23	5	9	$19

0 - 9	....	*poor to fair*
10 - 15	....	*fair to good*
16 - 19	....	*good to very good*
20 - 25	....	*very good to excellent*
26 - 30	....	*extraordinary to perfection*

▽ 23	5	9	$19

| ▽ | .... | *Low number of votes/less reliable* |

The **Cost (C)** column reflects the estimated price of a dinner with one drink and tip. Lunch usually costs 25% less.

A restaurant listed without ratings is either an important **newcomer** or a popular **write-in**. The estimated cost, with one drink and tip, is indicated by the following symbols.

–	–	–	VE

I	....	*$15 and below*
M	....	*$16 to $30*
E	....	*$31 to $50*
VE	....	*$51 or more*

(4) Surveyors' Commentary

Surveyors' comments are summarized, with literal comments shown in quotation marks. The following symbols indicate whether responses were mixed or uniform.

| ◪ | .... | *mixed* |
| ◼ | .... | *uniform* |

Most Popular Restaurants

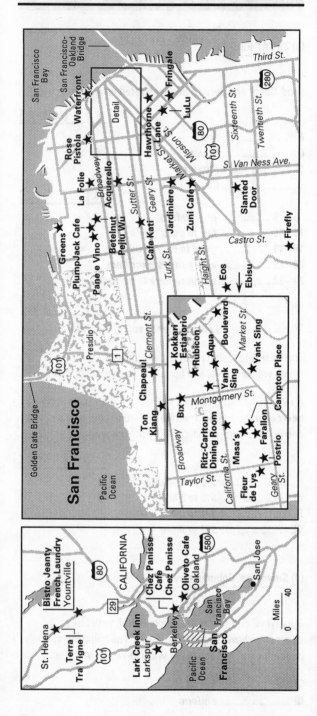

Most Popular Restaurants*

Each of our reviewers has been asked to name his or her five favorite restaurants. The 40 spots most frequently named, in order of their popularity, are:

1.	Boulevard	21.	Betelnut Pejiu Wu
2.	Aqua	22.	Bistro Jeanty/N
3.	French Laundry/N	23.	Rose Pistola
4.	Fleur de Lys	24.	Acquerello
5.	Postrio	25.	Campton Place
6.	Jardinière	26.	Terra/N
7.	Hawthorne Lane	27.	Bix
8.	Farallon	28.	Cafe Kati
9.	Chez Panisse/E	29.	Oliveto Cafe/E
10.	Ritz-Carlton Din. Rm.	30.	Firefly
11.	Fringale	31.	Pane e Vino
12.	Masa's	32.	Yank Sing**
13.	Slanted Door	33.	LuLu
14.	La Folie	34.	Greens
15.	Eos	35.	Ebisu
16.	Zuni Cafe	36.	Lark Creek Inn/N
17.	Chez Panisse Cafe/E	37.	Rubicon
18.	Tra Vigne/N	38.	Kokkari Estiatorio
19.	PlumpJack Cafe	39.	Waterfront**
20.	Chapeau!	40.	Ton Kiang

It's obvious that many of the restaurants on the above list are among the most expensive, but San Franciscans also love a bargain. Were popularity calibrated to price, we suspect that a number of other restaurants would join the above ranks. Thus, we have listed over 150 Best Buys on pages 17–18.

---

* All restaurants are in the City of San Francisco unless otherwise noted (E=East of San Francisco; N=North of San Francisco and S=South of San Francisco).
** Tied with the restaurant listed directly above it.

Top Ratings*

Top 40 Food Ranking

29 French Laundry/N	Pacific
28 Sent Sovi/S	Hawthorne Lane
Masa's	Jardinière
Ritz-Carlton Din. Rm.	Sushi Ran/N
27 La Folie	Chapeau!
Fleur de Lys	Kyo-Ya
Chez Panisse/E	**25** Rivoli/E
Terra/N	Acquerello
Aqua	Bistro Jeanty/N
Boulevard	Le Mouton Noir/S
Chez Panisse Cafe/E	Delfina
26 Campton Place	Foothill Cafe/N
Charles Nob Hill	Willowside Cafe/N
Erna's Elderberry/S	L'Amie Donia/S
Domaine Chandon/N	Slanted Door**
Pacific's Edge/S	Downtown Bakery/N
Postrio	231 Ellsworth/S
Emile's/S	Thep Phanom
Woodward's Garden	Fresh Cream/S
Fringale	Meetinghouse

Top Spots by Cuisine

American (New)
29 French Laundry/N
27 Terra/N
Boulevard
26 Erna's Elderberry/S
Woodward's Garden

American (Regional)
25 Foothill Cafe/N
Rest. at Meadowood/N
23 John Ash & Co./N
Catahoula/N
22 Manka's Inverness/N

American (Traditional)
24 Lark Creek Inn/N
22 JoAnn's Cafe/S
Mama's/Washington Sq.
Hayes St. Grill
Tarpy's Roadhouse/S

Breakfast†
25 Downtown Bakery/N
24 Oliveto Cafe/E
Citizen Cake
23 Universal Cafe
Zuni Cafe

Brunch
26 Campton Place
Erna's Elderberry/S
Pacific's Edge/S
Postrio
Pacific

Californian
27 Chez Panisse/E
Chez Panisse Cafe/E
26 Charles Nob Hill
Domaine Chandon/N
Pacific's Edge/S

---

* Excluding restaurants with low voting; all restaurants are in the City
of San Francisco unless otherwise noted (E=East of San Francisco;
N=North of San Francisco and S=South of San Francisco).
** Tied with the restaurant listed directly above it.
† Other than hotels.

Chinese
25 Ton Kiang
   Tommy Toy's
23 Fook Yuen/S
   Eliza's
22 Harbor Village

Continental
22 Fournou's Ovens
   Bella Vista/S
21 Rocco's Seafood
   Eulipia/S
   Ovation

Dim Sum
25 Ton Kiang
24 Yank Sing
23 Fook Yuen/S
22 Harbor Village
21 Hong Kong Flower/S

Eclectic/International
24 Café La Haye/N
   Celadon/N
   Cafe Beaujolais/N
23 Wappo Bar Bistro/N
22 Firefly

Family Dining
23 House of Prime Rib
22 Rio Grill/S
21 Lark Creek/E
20 Rutherford Grill/N
19 Park Chow

French Bistro
26 Fringale
   Chapeau!
25 Bistro Jeanty/N
   L'Amie Donia/S
23 Cafe Marcella/S

French Classic
26 Campton Place
   Emile's/S
25 Le Mouton Noir/S
   231 Ellsworth/S
24 Citron/E

French New
28 Sent Sovi/S
   Masa's
   Ritz-Carlton Din. Rm.
27 La Folie
   Fleur de Lys

Hotel Dining
28 Masa's/
   Vintage Court
   Ritz-Carlton Din. Rm./
   Ritz-Carlton
26 Campton Place/
   Campton Place
   Pacific's Edge/S
   Highlands Inn
   Postrio/
   Prescott

Indian
23 Amber India/S
   Ajanta/E
22 Indian Oven
20 North India
   Swagat/S

Italian
25 Acquerello
   Delfina
24 Tra Vigne/N
   Bistro Don Giovanni/N
   Oliveto Cafe/E

Japanese
26 Sushi Ran/N
   Kyo-Ya
24 Hamano Sushi
   Kirala/E
   Ebisu

Late Night
23 Bouchon/N
   Zuni Cafe
   Scala's Bistro
22 Park Grill
21 Globe

Mediterranean
25 Rivoli/E
   Ritz-Carlton Terrace
   Zaré
24 PlumpJack Cafe
   Lalime's/E

Mexican/Tex-Mex
23 La Taqueria
22 Maya
   Las Camelias/N
21 Casa Aguila
   La Cumbre

Top Food

Newcomers/Rated
26 Sushi Ran/N
25 Delfina
Kokkari Estiatorio
A.P. Stump's/S
La Toque/N

Newcomers/Unrated
Fifth Floor
Gary Danko
Gordon's Hse./Fine Eats
Ondine/N
Rest. Marais

Offbeat
24 Helmand
23 Flying Saucer
22 Cafe Fanny/E
Plouf
Dottie's True Blue

Pacific Rim/Euro-Asian
26 Pacific
25 Roy's at Pebble Beach/S
Eos
24 Bridges
Oritalia

People Watching
27 Chez Panisse/E
26 Postrio
Jardinière
24 Farallon
Rubicon

Pizza
24 Zachary's/E
22 Tommaso's
21 Pauline's
20 Vicolo
17 Mozzarella Di Bufala

Seafood
27 Aqua
25 Swan Oyster Depot
24 Farallon
Yabbies Coastal Kit.
22 Hayes St. Grill

Spanish
22 César/E
21 Zarzuela
19 Iberia/S
Vinga
Alegrias

Steakhouses
23 Harris'
House of Prime Rib
22 Morton's of Chicago
21 Izzy's
Alfred's

Thai
25 Thep Phanom
23 Marnee Thai
22 Royal Thai/N
21 Manora's
Khan Toke

Vegetarian
27 Fleur de Lys
22 Greens
Millennium
21 Bontà
19 Valentine's Cafe

Vietnamese
25 Slanted Door
22 Crustacean
21 Le Colonial
Golden Turtle
La Vie

Wild Card
24 Helmand/Afghan
22 Straits Cafe/Singaporean
21 Ti Couz/Crêpes
Angkor Wat/Cambodian
20 Massawa/Ethiopian

Worth a Trip
29 French Laundry/N
Yountville
28 Sent Sovi/S
Saratoga
27 Chez Panisse/E
Berkeley
Terra/N
St. Helena
26 Erna's Elderberry/S
Oakhurst

Top 40 Decor Ranking

28 Pacific's Edge/S
Ritz-Carlton Din. Rm.
Auberge du Soleil/N
Farallon

27 Erna's Elderberry/S
Ovation
Fleur de Lys
Garden Court
Kokkari Estiatorio

26 Jardinière
Top of the Mark
French Laundry/N
Aqua
Le Colonial
Chateau Souverain/N
Grand Cafe
Carnelian Room
El Paseo/N
Postrio
Cypress Club

Boulevard
Club XIX/S
Roy's at Pebble Beach/S
Tra Vigne/N

25 Wente Vineyards/E
Domaine Chandon/N
Campton Place
Bouchon/N
Rest. at Meadowood/N
Bix
Nepenthe/S
Charles Nob Hill
Big Four
Ritz-Carlton Terrace
Caprice/N
Masa's
Hawthorne Lane
Napa Valley Wine Train/N
Silks
Terra/N

Outdoor

Auberge du Soleil/N
Bay Wolf/E
Bistro Jeanty/N
Bouchon/N
Brava Terrace/N
Chez Renee/S
Domaine Chandon/N
Erna's Elderberry/S
Insalata's/N
Kenwood/N

Left Bank/N
Le Mouton Noir/S
MoMo's
Park Grill
Roy's at Pebble Beach/S
Sent Sovi/S
Sonoma Mission/Grille/N
Spago Palo Alto/S
Tra Vigne/N
Xanadu/E

Romantic

Acquerello
Casanova/S
Cassis
Chez Renee/S
Erna's Elderberry/S
Fleur de Lys
Jardinière

Julius' Castle
Pacific's Edge/S
Ritz-Carlton Din. Rm.
Sierra Mar/S
Terra/N
Venticello
Zax

Rooms

Aqua
Big Four
Boulevard
Campton Place
Cypress Club
Farallon
Fleur de Lys
Fournou's Ovens
French Laundry/N

Garden Court
Grand Cafe
Jardinière
Lark Creek Inn/N
mc²
Postrio
Rest. at Meadowood/N
Ritz-Carlton Din. Rm.
Ritz-Carlton Terrace

Views

Alta Mira/N	Julius' Castle
Auberge du Soleil/N	Mandarin
Caprice/N	McCormick & Kuleto's
Carnelian Room	Mikayla/N
Cielo/S	Moss Beach Distillery/S
Cliff House	Nepenthe/S
dalla Torre	Pacific's Edge/S
Domaine Chandon/N	Pier 23 Cafe
Gaylord India	Rest. at Meadowood/N
Greens	Sam's Anchor Cafe/N
Harbor Village	Sierra Mar/S
Horizons/N	Waterfront

Top 40 Service Ranking

28	Ritz-Carlton Din. Rm.	Chapeau!
27	Erna's Elderberry/S	Silks
	French Laundry/N	Rest. at Meadowood/N
26	Masa's	La Toque/N
	Fleur de Lys	Auberge du Soleil/N
	Ritz-Carlton Terrace	Celadon/N*
	Charles Nob Hill	Plumed Horse/S*
	Campton Place	Fresh Cream/S
25	Chez Panisse/E	Postrio
	La Folie	Le Mouton Noir/S
	Domaine Chandon/N	Aqua
	Sent Sovi/S	231 Ellsworth/S
	Terra/N	Chez Panisse Cafe/E
	Acquerello	Hawthorne Lane
	Club XIX/S	**23** Albona
24	Tommy Toy's	Jardinière
	Pacific's Edge/S	Emile's/S
	Boulevard	Big Four
	Pacific	Albion River Inn/N
	Meetinghouse	El Paseo/N

---

* Tied with the restaurant listed directly above it.

Best Buys

80 Top Bangs For The Buck

This list reflects the best dining values in our *Survey.* It is produced by dividing the cost of a meal into the combined ratings for food, decor and service.

1. La Cumbre
2. El Balazo
3. Citizen Cake
4. Downtown Bakery/N
5. La Taqueria
6. Pancho Villa
7. Dottie's True Blue
8. Mama's Royal Cafe/E
9. Mo's Burgers
10. JoAnn's Cafe/S
11. Picante Cocina/E
12. Kate's Kitchen
13. Caffe Greco
14. Cafe Fanny/E
15. Dragon Well
16. Bette's Oceanview/E
17. Pluto's
18. Barney's Gourmet
19. Alice's
20. Zachary's/E
21. Blue Nile/E
22. World Wrapps
23. Mario's Bohemian Cigar
24. Sweet Heat
25. Saul's/E
26. Mifune
27. Bill's Place
28. Wa-Ha-Ka Oaxaca
29. FatApple's/E
30. Roosevelt Tamale
31. Eliza's
32. Park Chow
33. Doidge's Cafe
34. Cafe Flore
35. Mama's/Washington Sq.
36. Miss Millie's
37. Hamburger Mary's
38. Ti Couz
39. Hotei
40. Tu Lan
41. Eric's
42. Connecticut Yankee
43. Cha Am Thai
44. Khan Toke
45. Nan Yang Rockridge/E
46. Massawa
47. Mom is Cooking
48. Ella's
49. Savor
50. Pasta Pomodoro
51. Thep Phanom
52. Chow
53. Marnee Thai
54. Angkor Wat
55. Sears Fine Food
56. Neecha Thai
57. Le Cheval/E
58. Fuzio
59. Mel's Drive-In
60. La Mediterranée
61. Pauline's
62. Mandalay
63. Tommy's Joynt
64. Michelangelo Cafe
65. Magnolia Pub
66. Firewood Cafe
67. Food Inc.
68. Bubba's Diner/N
69. Mozzarella Di Bufala
70. Royal Thai/N
71. Long Life Noodle Co.
72. Casa Aguila
73. Manora's
74. Taiwan
75. Swan Oyster Depot
76. Firecracker
77. César/E
78. Zazie
79. Grandeho's Kamekyo
80. Las Camelias/N

Additional Good Values

(A bit more expensive, but worth every penny)

Ajanta/E	La Vie
Alamo Square	Lhasa Moon
Alegrias	Liberty Cafe & Bakery
Amber India/S	Little Italy
Aperto	L'Osteria Del Forno
Avenue 9	Meetinghouse
Baker St. Bistro	Mescolanza
Bistro Aix	Millennium
Blue Point	Narai
Bocca Rotis	North India
Boonville Hotel/N	O Chamé/E
Cafe Akimbo	Pacific Cafe
Cafe Bastille	Pane e Vino
Cafe For All Seasons	Parma
Cafe Marimba	Pasta Moon/S
Caffe Delle Stelle	PJ's Oyster Bed
Caffe Macaroni	Plearn Thai/E
Cassis	Plouf
Celadon/N	Rose's Cafe
Cha Cha Cha	Slanted Door
Chapeau!	Straits Cafe
Clement St. B&G	Suppenküche
Curbside Cafe	Sushi Ran/N
Delfina	Tin-Pan Asian
Duarte's Tavern/S	Tommaso's
E'Angelo	Ton Kiang
Enrico's	Tortola
Ernesto's	Town's End
Esperpento	Trattoria Contadina
Fountain Court	Universal Cafe
Gira Polli	Valentine's Cafe
Golden Turtle	Venezia/E
Grandview/S	Venticello
Harbor Village	Vicolo
Helmand	Yank Sing
House	Zaré
Indigo	Zarzuela
Kasbah Moroccan/N	Zinzino
La Ginestra/N	Zza's Trattoria/E

Alphabetical Directory of Restaurants

San Francisco

F	D	S	C

Absinthe ●ⓁⓈ
19 | 23 | 19 | $36

398 Hayes St. (Gough St.), 415-551-1590

☑ "Leave the world behind" as you enter this "dark", "decadent", "very fin de siècle" Hayes Valley French bistro, with murals, "fantastic velvety" booths and a "stylish bar" offering "boozy" antiquarian cocktails; detractors say it's "glitz without substance", but concede that the location is "ideal" for a pre-symphony poulet frites.

Ace Wasabi's ⓈⓂ
20 | 14 | 15 | $24

3339 Steiner St. (bet. Chestnut & Lombard Sts.), 415-567-4903

■ Watch out for "raucous yuppies on the make" at this "deafening" Marina sushi bar where the "people-watching" clientele looks like a "90210 casting call", the "creative" "specialty rolls rule" and everyone "loves that bingo" game; it's definitely a "fun joint to go to with a group", but expect "long waits" for a table.

ACQUERELLO
25 | 22 | 25 | $52

1722 Sacramento St. (bet. Polk St. & Van Ness Ave.), 415-567-5432

■ Most surveyors "never regret" a meal at this Van Ness/Polk "oasis", with "heavenly service" and a "blissfully subdued" atmosphere that's made for romance (though "you'll pay for it!"); in addition to an "excellent wine list", there's "impeccable" cuisine of the red, white and green, including a "spectacular" seasonal white truffle menu; even the few who find it "stuffy" agree that it's the "best fussy Italian" in town.

Alamo Square ⓈⓂ
18 | 15 | 18 | $25

803 Fillmore St. (bet. Fulton & Grove Sts.), 415-440-2828

☑ Fans say "seafood is the star" ("get the sturgeon") at this "quaint" Alamo Square French bistro where you get to choose your fish, preferred cooking style and sauce; it's a cool concept, made even more appetizing by the "bargain prices" and "exceedingly friendly service."

Albona Ristorante Istriano
23 | 16 | 23 | $32

545 Francisco St. (bet. Mason & Taylor Sts.), 415-441-1040

■ Host-owner Bruno Viscovi "attends to every detail" and "makes you feel at home" at his moderately priced North Beach Italian, which also offers "something a little different" in the form of Istrian cuisine from the Adriatic coast of what was formerly Yugoslavia; "if it's your first time let them order for you" – otherwise, you already know that this "satisfying dining experience" should start with the gnocchi appetizer.

Alegrias, Food From Spain S M   19 | 17 | 18 | $25
2018 Lombard St. (Webster St.), 415-929-8888
☑ "Check out the flamenco guitar" when dining at this "family-run" Union Street Iberian that provides "a touch of Spain without the slow service"; while the "paella is good", it's the "authentic tapas" that stir the most interest.

Alfred's Steak House L S M   21 | 19 | 21 | $40
659 Merchant St. (bet. Kearny & Montgomery Sts.), 415-781-7058
☑ Regulars may regret the move from North Beach, but this Downtown steakhouse is still "an SF classic", satisfying "that 'need meat' feeling" with "great Châteaubriand" and superb sides such as creamed spinach; hipper foodies think "nothing's remarkable" and are puzzled by the "older crowd's" penchant for the "gaudy red decor."

Alice's L S M   18 | 18 | 16 | $17
1599 Sanchez St. (29th St.), 415-282-8999
■ "The mango chicken sings" at this "lovely", reasonably priced Noe Valley venue where a "diverse crowd" enjoys "more-than-the-usual Chinese fare", even when "rushed" by the staff; with blown glass, orchids and "beautifully presented" plates, it's often compared to two similar competitors, so you decide whether Alice's "ain't Eliza's", seems like "an Eric's knock-off" or is "easier to get into" than either.

Alioto's L S M   14 | 14 | 15 | $29
8 Fisherman's Wharf (bet. Taylor St. & The Embarcadero), 415-673-0183
☑ This seafooder at Fisherman's Wharf is "mediocre" and "overpriced" in the opinion of many surveyors; still, "out-of-state guests always seem to enjoy it" and there are some "well-executed standards" on the menu, so just "don't order anything too fancy and keep your eyes on the view."

Allegro S M   20 | 17 | 20 | $32
1701 Jones St. (Broadway), 415-928-4002
☑ "Swaggering politicians" tend to gerrymander tables at this "upcoming, stylish" North Beach Italian, with an "intimate" ambiance, "friendly, patient staff" and food that runs the gamut from "average" to the "best gnocchi and brick chicken in the city."

Angkor Wat L S M   21 | 16 | 19 | $22
4217 Geary Blvd. (bet. 6th & 7th Aves.), 415-221-7887
■ Voters say Angkor yourself to this "authentic" Richmond District Cambodian, a "good place to take acquaintances when you want them to think you're cool"; the "solicitous" staff "falls all over each other" to serve you "aromatic", "excellent" dishes ("great soups and curries"); N.B. native dancers entertain on weekends.

Anjou **L**   22 | 18 | 21 | $33
44 Campton Pl. (bet. Post & Sutter Sts.), 415-392-5373
■ Recommended for lunch or a moderately priced pre-theater dinner, this "tiny", "unpretentious" French bistro off Union Square offers "attentive service" and "scrumptious entrees and desserts" ("great tarte tatin"); factor in lots of brass and it's clear this is about as "authentic" as it gets.

Antica Trattoria **S**   21 | 17 | 20 | $31
2400 Polk St. (Union St.), 415-928-5797
■ This Van Ness/Polk trattoria has "bare-bones decor", but wins over voters with its "tasty angle on Italian", including "exceptional pastas" and an "unforgettable buckwheat polenta starter"; throw in "warm", "chummy hospitality" and "valet parking a block away" and you've clearly got yourself "a winner."

Anzu **L S M**   – | – | – | E
(fka Cafe 222)
Hotel Nikko, 222 Mason St. (O'Farrell St.), 415-394-1100
Occupying the former Cafe 222 space Downtown in the Hotel Nikko is this "elegant" new East-meets-West hybrid where co-chef Kazuhito Takahashi crafts fine sushi and other Japanese fare while his partner Philippe Striffeler prepares American prime-cut beef; initial reports indicate that it's a "delicious", if pricey, combination.

Aperto **L S M**   20 | 14 | 19 | $25
1434 18th St. (Connecticut St.), 415-252-1625
■ Locals "return again and again" to this "simple and satisfying" Potrero Hill neighborhood Italian with "solid" dishes such as "perfect fish specials" off the chalkboard; it might be "small" and "a bit cramped", but all is forgiven after finishing the "lovingly presented Sunday brunch."

AQUA **L M**   27 | 26 | 24 | $57
252 California St. (bet. Battery & Front Sts.), 415-956-9662
■ Aqua-lytes gush that "everything is special" at this top-dollar Downtown New American, from the "very-glam" crowd to chef Michael Mina's "stunningly presented", "awesome" seafood ("I didn't know they could do that to a lobster!") to the "gorgeous" flowers; noise levels are high and there's minor carping about "cold-as-fish" service, but as the *Survey*'s second Most Popular restaurant, this is definitely a "jewel in SF's culinary crown."

Armani Cafe **L S M**   17 | 18 | 15 | $22
Emporio Armani, 1 Grant Ave. (O'Farrell St.), 415-677-9010
☑ "Designer eats" take on new meaning at this "stylish" Union Square Italian cafe in the Armani clothing boutique, where "it's fun to pretend you can afford the clothes" while people-watching and ciao-ing down on "great panini" and the "best cappuccino in town"; the unfashionably attired detect "attitude" from a staff of wanna-be models.

A. Sabella's 🅛🅢🅜　　17 | 16 | 18 | $31
2766 Taylor St. (Jefferson St.), 415-771-6775

▣ Venerable Fisherman's Wharf seafooder whose "kitschy" decor may be "30 years out of date", but gets some respect for its "decent" food and "wonderful waiters" who give you a "warm welcome."

AsiaSF 🅢🅜　　18 | 20 | 20 | $27
201 Ninth St. (Howard St.), 415-255-2742

■ "You go girl!" declare patrons of this "flamboyant" SoMa Asian-Eclectic where the staff and entertainers are "gender illusionists" and it's never boring taking in the drags; some even report that the "zingy", tapas-like dishes are "even sexier than the show", but most of the "tourists" and giggly "bachelorette parties from the suburbs" go for the scene not the cuisine.

Aux Delices 🅛🅢🅜　　16 | 9 | 16 | $18
2327 Polk St. (bet. Green & Union Sts.), 415-928-4977

■ There's "never a wait" at this "economical" Vietnamese in the Richmond, where the decor "could use a makeover" but the "consistently good" French-influenced cuisine is served by waiters who are "right on target" with recommendations.

Avenue 9 🅛🅢🅜　　19 | 13 | 17 | $25
1243 Ninth Ave. (bet. Irving St. & Lincoln Way), 415-664-6999

▣ Looking for "the great American bistro?"; this Inner Sunset New American could be it, with "well thought out", "boldly flavored" food served out of a counter-lined open kitchen (it's "hip to talk to the chefs"); the decor's "plain", the seating "congested", but "yummy sandwiches", the "best spinach salad" and homemade donuts come at a "fair price."

Backflip　　13 | 21 | 12 | $26
Phoenix Hotel, 601 Eddy St. (bet. Larkin & Polk Sts.), 415-771-3547

▣ "Shagadelic, baby" declare hipsters commenting on the "cool social scene" at this "funky", poolside Van Ness/Polk Cal-Mediterranean with aquatic-oriented, "tantalizingly tacky" decor; since it's "more of a nightclub than a restaurant", most prefer to "skip the food" and go "for drinks", especially the unusual cocktails.

Baker Street Bistro 🅛🅢　　19 | 14 | 18 | $25
2953 Baker St. (bet. Greenwich & Lombard Sts.), 415-931-1475

■ Reviewers say "oui" to this "affordable" Union Street bistro that "breaks the snotty French stereotype" while offering "astonishingly good" classic dishes such as duck confit and escargot; yes, it's "like eating in a closet" ("cramped"), but it's hard to resist a "neighborhood spot" where "even the dishwasher speaks French."

Balboa Cafe **L S M** 17 | 16 | 17 | $26 |
3199 Fillmore St. (Greenwich St.), 415-921-3944

◨ Partly owned by PlumpJack Cafe duo and men-about-town Billy Getty and Gavin Newsom, this Marina Traditional American cafe features what partisans think is the "best burger in town"; as at its sibling, there's a "fabulous wine list" and "beautiful people" working the bar's "intense singles scene"; but even for twentysomethings, the volume can be "way too loud."

Bam Restaurant Bar Cafe **L S M** – | – | – | I |
2301 Fillmore St. (Clay St.), 415-614-1111

More casual than its predecessor Alta Plaza, this new Pacific Heights Eclectic features an under-$10 menu of salads, small plates and noodles, ideal for either a quick fix or a leisurely meal, particularly when paired with one of the 24 inexpensive bottles of wine.

Bandol **L S M** – | – | – | M |
(fka U.S. Restaurant)
431 Columbus Ave. (Stockton St.), 415-362-6251

The owners of the venerable but less-than-hip U.S. Restaurant in North Beach bagged their Italian-American format and went to the South of France for inspiration, renaming their former spot after a town on the Riviera and filling their Provençal menu with such regional dishes as bouillabaisse and steamed mussels.

Baraonda **S M** 20 | 18 | 19 | $29 |
2162 Larkin St. (Green St.), 415-447-0441

◪ A "stark", "cosmopolitan", "Euro-chic" Van Ness/Polk Italian trattoria that can be "delicious" ("excellent veal chop", "interesting pastas") but is sometimes "hit-or-miss"; either way, the staff is "friendly, helpful and great to look at", as is the "beautiful crowd."

Barney's Gourmet 16 | 9 | 12 | $12 |
Hamburger **L S M**
4138 24th St. (Castro St.), 415-282-7770
3344 Steiner St. (Chestnut St.), 415-563-0307

◪ "Get your cholesterol hit" at these "unpretentious", "busy" Noe Valley and Marina hamburger joints with a "nice array" of "juicy" patties, "monster portions" of "wicked" curly fries and thick shakes; "plentiful" salads and deep-fried veggies make them popular with non–meat eaters too.

Basta Pasta **◐ S M** 13 | 13 | 13 | $22 |
1268 Grant Ave. (Vallejo St.), 415-434-2248

◼ Despite late hours and "better decor" (courtesy of a renovation), this North Beach Italian still "caters more to tourists", with critical locals calling the victuals "bland" and adding "there are better places in the area."

Beach Chalet Brewery L S M   12 | 19 | 13 | $23
1000 Great Hwy. (bet. Fulton St. & Lincoln Way), 415-386-8439
■ "Beautiful murals" and a "spectacular", "panoramic" Ocean Beach view bring hordes to this surfside American brasserie, a "swanky tourist spot" recommended for sipping homemade suds at sunset to live music; that said, "too bad" the food is "poor" and the service "mediocre."

Bella Trattoria S M   21 | 18 | 21 | $28
3854 Geary Blvd. (3rd Ave.), 415-221-0305
■ Comments such as "they know their veal" and "don't forget the polenta" suggest there's "not a bad choice on the menu" of this "excellent" Richmond District trattoria where every dish is "presented with skill and care" by a staff that's "eager to please" and "oozes Italian charm."

Belon ◑ L S M   – | – | – | M
Hotel Metropolis, 25 Mason St. (Turk St.), 415-776-9970
Paul Arenstam, a protégé of Joachim Splichal and former chef de cuisine at Rubicon, steps out on his own at this stylish new Downtown Californian in the hip Metropolis Hotel; as the name implies, the emphasis is on oysters and other shellfish from the raw bar, but the menu also includes a range of brasserie-style dishes based on local ingredients.

Benihana L S M   16 | 15 | 18 | $30
Japan Ctr., 1737 Post St. (bet. Laguna & Webster Sts.), 415-563-4844
☑ Groups of mesmerized surveyors say watching the chefs' "skilled", knife-wielding "performance cooking" at these Japan Center and Bay Area steakhouses is a form of "group therapy" and also keeps "wiggly" "kids entertained"; dissenters think "the act gets old" and the "bill seems high for the meal."

Betelnut Pejiu Wu L S M   22 | 22 | 17 | $30
2030 Union St. (Buchanan St.), 415-929-8855
☑ Stylish, "energetic" Union Street Pan-Asian beerhouse where a "see-and-be-seen" crowd enjoys "sitting at the counter and watching the chefs" prepare a "very creative selection" of "the city's tastiest finger food" ("love the anchovies" and "signature green beans"); only "annoying" waits and lots of "attitude" – "they still don't understand customer service" – prevent uniformly stellar scores.

Big Four L S M   21 | 25 | 23 | $44
Huntington Hotel, 1075 California St. (Taylor St.), 415-771-1140
☑ "Pretend you're a rich white male" at this "clubby", "comfortable" Nob Hill New American, which is "better than some museums" for a look into SF's past; before starting your "intimate conversation", take in the bar, "great piano player" and "beautiful paneled room", and don't be surprised if the "excellent" staff presents you with a dish that's more up to date than that "stuffy" guy at the next table.

Bill's Place 🄻🅂🄼   16 | 7 | 13 | $12
2315 Clement St. (bet. 24th & 25th Aves.), 415-221-5262

◪ This "old-fashioned", "working-class" "greasy spoon" in the Richmond features a variety of burgers (aka "stomach bombs"), "great onion rings", "out-of-this-world" milkshakes and other Americana; though Martha Stewart types suggest they "invest in a feather duster", there's always the "idyllic patio and fish pond" out back.

Biscuits & Blues 🅂🄼   13 | 13 | 14 | $20
401 Mason St. (Geary St.), 415-292-2583

◪ "Some great acts perform" at this "funky" Downtown club, but, with the exception of the namesake "killer biscuits" that alone are "worth a visit", critics think the "mediocre" Southern food generally "has the blues."

Bistro Aix 🅂🄼   20 | 16 | 18 | $28
3340 Steiner St. (bet. Chestnut & Lombard Sts.), 415-202-0100

▪ "Make sure to sit out back" on the "heavenly" outdoor patio of this "accommodating", "very reasonably priced" Marina Mediterranean, a "neighborhood favorite" with "awesome homemade breads", "simple, satisfying" bistro renditions and a "bargain" early bird.

Bistro Clovis 🄻🅂🄼   19 | 16 | 18 | $28
1596 Market St. (Franklin St.), 415-864-0231

▪ For a perfect "Parisian finish to making love", or just a pre-opera meal, consider this "rarely crowded", midrange Civic Center French bistro; it's a "sleeper" with a "charming" Left Bank atmosphere and "intriguing wine samplers."

Bistro Zaré 🅂🄼   – | – | – | M
1507 Polk St. (California St.), 415-775-4304

Hoss Zaré has opened this more casual, bistro-scale sibling to his popular Downtown Mediterranean on a busy intersection of Van Ness/Polk, and as former patrons of Aromi (the location's previous incarnation) can attest, the happening outdoor patio is an ideal spot for people-watching.

Bitterroot 🄻🅂🄼   – | – | – | M
3122 16th St. (bet. Mission & Valencia Sts.), 415-626-5523

Located on the hip 16th Street strip that hosts Ti Couz and Picaro is this Western-themed, three-meals-a-day American, which takes the comfort-food route, serving everything from "bitchin' omelets" and sassy salads (try the portobello) to chocolate cake that's "better than sex."

BIX 🄻🅂🄼   22 | 25 | 21 | $41
56 Gold St. (bet. Jackson & Pacific Sts.), 415-433-6300

◪ Relive the "roaring '20s" at this "classy" North Beach New American, a "snazzy supper club" in a Gold Rush–era building, where "glamorous" yuppies sip "perfect martinis", listen to "great jazz" and revel in the "electric atmosphere"; there's also "fine" food, which means that, overall, this place is "still terrific after all these years."

Bizou L M   23 | 19 | 20 | $36
598 Fourth St. (Brannan St.), 415-543-2222

☑ Many grateful reviewers first learned to "love beef cheeks" and batter-fried green beans at this SoMa Mediterranean-French featuring chef-owner Loretta Keller's "innovative, rustic" menu; set in a 1906 building, this "comfortable" cafe also appeals with its "cool" wood bar and proximity to "easy parking."

Black Cat ◑ L S M   17 | 19 | 17 | $37
501 Broadway (Kearny St.), 415-981-2233

☑ A "trendy" crowd tomcats late into the night at Reed Hearon's "loud" North Beach "hot spot", with red-leather seats, checkerboard-tile floors and a huge pan–San Francisco menu (Italian, Chinese, retro American and seafood); while phobes complain that the "pricey" victuals are "uneven" ("too many styles", "lacks focus"), the people-watching is undeniably top notch ("I saw the mayor"), as is the "great jazz" at the Blue Bar downstairs.

Blowfish, Sushi To Die For L S M   20 | 20 | 15 | $28
2170 Bryant St. (20th St.), 415-285-3848

☑ "It's the new millennium" declare hipsters explaining the appeal of this Gen X sushi bar in an industrial no-man's land of the South Mission, where loud "techno music" and Japanese animation provide the backdrop for "artsy appetizers", "creative" hand rolls and an "extensive sake list"; P.S. they don't actually serve blowfish, so "the fish won't kill you, but the slow service just might."

Blue Plate, The L   – | – | – | M
3218 Mission St. (29th St.), 415-282-6777

Set in a remote neighborhood bordering Bernal Heights, this Mission "hipster" stop is generating a quiet buzz thanks to solid Eclectic cuisine ("delicious fried polenta"), sane prices, a "funky", flea-market-kitsch setting and laid-back servers.

Blue Point S   20 | 17 | 19 | $25
2415 Clement St. (25th Ave.), 415-379-9726

☑ Locals feel "lucky to have" this "cozy" Cal-Mediterranean bistro that specializes in "elegantly" presented "simple but original" fish dishes in their Outer Richmond neighborhood; while it's a "real find" that "deserves a Downtown location", if it had one, it might not be such an "excellent value."

Bocca Rotis L S M   18 | 16 | 17 | $24
1 West Portal Ave. (Ulloa St.), 415-665-9900

☑ "Get a booth in back" and order the "juicy" rotisserie chicken with potatoes and some "awesome" desserts advise insiders at this "family-friendly" French-Italian located in a converted West Portal bank building; owned by the Aperto people, it's an equally "good value."

Bocce Cafe 🆛🆂🅼   12 17 13 $18
478 Green St. (Grant St.), 415-981-2044

◨ "Always fun but rarely delicious" sums up opinion on this North Beach Italian where a crowd of "stubbornly devoted patrons", mainly "large groups with small wallets", gathers "for drinks" and "cheap pasta" in a "beautiful courtyard" that – sorry, folks – no longer contains a bocce court (but, hey, they've got "plants!").

Bontà Ristorante 🆂   21 16 20 $28
2223 Union St. (bet. Fillmore & Steiner Sts.), 415-929-0407

■ This "quaint, romantic" Union Street Italian – "a personal favorite" of several of our reviewers – may still be "a secret, but not for long", what with a "simple" but "delicioso" menu (with vegetarian selections) and an "extra-friendly staff"; it's "tiny", but many say "small and cozy is what we like here"; P.S. "call ahead to see if the chef will do stuffed lamb."

BOULEVARD 🆛🆂🅼   27 26 24 $48
1 Mission St. (Steuart St.), 415-543-6084

■ "The girl can cook" declare reviewers blown away by chef Nancy Oakes' "always amazing" New American food at this Pat Kuleto–designed SoMa "art nouveau carnival", with "three distinctive rooms" and a "professional" staff that's "genuinely pleased to serve you"; so "get the company credit card and go" to what is once again the No. 1 Most Popular restaurant in this *Survey*.

Brandy Ho's 🆛🆂🅼   17 10 14 $18
217 Columbus Ave. (bet. Broadway & Pacific Ave.), 415-788-7527
450 Broadway (Kearny St.), 415-362-6268

◨ These North Beach Hunan venues may be "devoid of atmosphere", but their "spicy", "solid" food ("fantastic smoked dishes") represents "a change of pace from the standard Chinese fare"; P.S. while "heavy accents" refers to the staff's English, it could also apply to the cuisine.

Brasserie Savoy 🆂🅼   19 19 18 $36
Savoy Hotel, 580 Geary St. (Jones St.), 415-441-8080

◨ "Musical chefs" mean "inconsistent results" for patrons of this "expensive" Downtown New French outpost, convenient for pre-theater dinners; while it's clear regulars "will miss" former chef Fabrice Canelle, new kitchen maestro Paul Singhapong (from Dallas' highly acclaimed Mansion on Turtle Creek) intends to keep winners such as the "great beef cheeks" while adding an Asian influence.

Brazen Head ◑🆂🅼⇆   18 19 20 $27
3166 Buchanan St. (Greenwich St.), 415-921-7600

■ For "late-night comfort food", night owls (and chefs) frequent this signless American "insiders' hangout" "tucked away" in Cow Hollow; surveyors love the "dark", "wood-paneled" interior, "fabulous lamb chops" and thrill of wowing visitors with a "show-me-a- hidden-restaurant experience."

Bruno's   19 | 19 | 16 | $34
2389 Mission St. (bet. 19th & 20th Sts.), 415-550-7455

☑ Grab a "big, comfy red booth", order a couple of "great cocktails" then snuggle with your honey to live jazz music at this "self-consciously hip" Outer Mission supper club with a "retro-lounge" atmosphere that makes you "expect Frank Sinatra to walk by"; while a recent chef change makes it tough to gauge the Mediterranean fare, it's safe to say the food is more upscale than the "dubious" neighborhood.

Bubble Lounge ●⑤Ⓜ   13 | 22 | 13 | $31
714 Montgomery St. (bet. Jackson & Washington Sts.), 415-434-4204

☑ "Bring your cell phone", "score a big couch" and settle in for some "faux-NYC chic" at this "decadent" North Beach champagne bar where an "amazing selection" of by-the-glass bubbly quickly allows the "beautiful people" to "figure out who has the money"; critics say the limited Eclectic menu (caviar, pâté, cheese, sushi) is "not the focus" and dis the staff "attitude" and the "self-important yuppie" clientele – wait "'til the stock market tanks."

Buca Giovanni ⑤   20 | 18 | 19 | $31
800 Greenwich St. (bet. Columbus & Mason Sts.), 415-776-7766

☑ "A cozy, cool retreat from the bustle of North Beach" thanks to its cave-like subterranean setting, this "old" Italian "gem" recently brought in a new chef, but still offers its signature fettucine with house-smoked rabbit.

Buchanan Grill Ⓛ⑤Ⓜ   14 | 15 | 16 | $25
3653 Buchanan St. (bet. Bay & North Point Sts.), 415-346-8727

☑ Recommended "during football season", especially during Packers-Niners games, this "friendly" sports bar and grill is described as a "perfect neighborhood eatery" ("*Cheers* on the Marina"), even if the "huge helpings" of American fare are "uninspiring."

Cafe Akimbo Ⓛ Ⓜ   21 | 17 | 20 | $28
116 Maiden Ln. (bet. Grant & Stockton Sts.), 415-433-2288

☑ "Hard to find, easy to remember", this Downtown Eclectic is a "real sleeper" off busy Union Square that's "lovely for lunch" or for "a bite before the theater"; the "tight seating" has some reviewers' arms akimbo, but most everyone appreciates the smart service and "budget-gourmet" cuisine, including "divine desserts."

Cafe Bastille Ⓛ Ⓜ   16 | 16 | 15 | $22
22 Belden Pl. (bet. Bush & Pine Sts.), 415-986-5673

☑ "Real" accents help authenticate this "legitimate French hangout" in Downtown's Belden Alley (SF's answer to the Rive Gauche); it's recommended "after shopping" for a "people-watching" lunch on the sidewalk – try the crêpes or steak tartare (on Friday).

Café Claude 🅛🆂🅼   17 | 16 | 15 | $21
7 Claude Ln. (bet. Grant & Kearny Sts.), 415-392-3515
◪ Authentic '50s bistro decor (shipped over piece by piece from a restaurant the owner purchased in France) makes visitors to this Downtown spot feel as if they've been "beamed directly to Paris", which means this is naturally a "top spot for a café au lait" or "wonderful croque monsieur"; P.S. three nights a week you can "listen to cool jazz while you nibble the cheese on your onion soup."

Café de la Presse 🅛🆂🅼   13 | 13 | 12 | $20
352 Grant Ave. (Bush St.), 415-249-0900
◪ "Meet homesick Parisians", catch up on "foreign magazines" (the "connected newsstand is great"), or just "watch the world go by" at this Downtown French venue; P.S. while the cafe is "more of a hangout than a place to go for food", there is an adjacent formal dining room.

Cafe de Paris L'Entrecôte 🅛🆂🅼   18 | 17 | 19 | $33
2032 Union St. (bet. Buchanan & Webster Sts.), 415-931-5006
◪ "Fabulous french fries", "classic entrecôte" and other "stick-to-your-ribs" Gallic goodies taste best on the "enclosed sidewalk seating" of this Union Street bistro; while critics call the place a "blast from the past" that "needs a makeover", for others it's been a "favorite for years", especially because of the "charming" service.

Cafe Flore 🅛🆂🅼⊘   14 | 17 | 13 | $16
2298 Market St. (Noe St.), 415-621-8579
◪ "The place to perfect your sidelong glance" while pretending to use your laptop or cell phone ("a must"), this "fun" Castro-Noe cafe has a largely gay clientele that pays only perfunctory attention to the "decent" American menu, zeroing in instead on the real dish – the "beautiful boys ambling by" its coveted enclosed sidewalk tables.

Cafe For All Seasons 🅛🆂🅼   21 | 14 | 20 | $23
150 West Portal Ave. (bet. 14th Ave. & Vicente St.), 415-665-0900
◪ "Bright and cheery", with "tiled floors" that contribute to its "noisy" atmosphere, this "all-American" "neighborhood standby" in West Portal may be the "best reason to head southwest of Twin Peaks", thanks to "solicitous service", "consistently good" "comfort food" and a "great brunch"; N.B. salads, polenta and desserts are the specialties.

Cafe Jacqueline 🆂   24 | 19 | 20 | $36
1454 Grant Ave. (bet. Green & Union Sts.), 415-981-5565
■ "Impress your date" at this "quintessentially romantic", "unique" North Beach French where chef-owner Jacqueline Marguiles turns out an "exquisite" three-course, all-soufflé menu; since each "dreamy", "light" offering is made to order, "set the evening aside" and don't be surprised to pay (appropriately enough) a slightly "inflated" price.

CAFE KATI S
24 | 19 | 21 | $39

1963 Sutter St. (bet. Fillmore & Webster Sts.),
415-775-7313

■ "Towering" "skyscraper" presentations of "imaginative" New American cuisine ("almost too beautiful to eat") is the hallmark of this "compact", "classy" Pacific Heights favorite; quibblers find the seating "cramped" and the architectural arrangements "too precious", but most dub it "divine."

Cafe Majestic S M
21 | 22 | 21 | $37

Hotel Majestic, 1500 Sutter St. (Gough St.), 415-441-1100

☑ Called "a great spot for a tryst" because it's "never really crowded", has "courteous" discreet servers (wink, wink) and is set in the Hotel Majestic (if things really heat up), this "romantic", "old-fashioned" American in the Van Ness/Polk area might otherwise strike some as "staid"; while few comment on the Asian-influenced California cuisine, the food rating is up three points since our last *Survey*.

Cafe Marimba L S M
19 | 17 | 15 | $23

2317 Chestnut St. (bet. Divisadero & Scott Sts.),
415-776-1506

☑ Vibrant, colorful, "funky" decor that recreates a Mexican market draws a "boisterous" young crowd to this "dynamic" Marina hot spot, home to "magnificent moles" and other "authentic" "nontaqueria" offerings, including regional dishes from Oaxaca, Veracruz, Puebla and Merida; P.S. if you think you're walkin' in on Friday night without a reservation – "fuhgeddaboutit!"

Cafe Mozart S
19 | 20 | 20 | $39

708 Bush St. (Powell St.), 415-391-8480

☑ "As romantic as Mozart's" *The Marriage of Figaro*, this "intimate" Downtown French-Californian is a "reliable old friend" to couples looking for "fine" (but "not outstanding") fare in an antique-and-fireplace-filled setting.

Cafe Riggio S M
17 | 15 | 17 | $26

4112 Geary Blvd. (5th Ave.), 415-221-2114

☑ A "lively and unpretentious" Richmond District Italian with "cute" light fixtures ("upside-down flowerpots") and a "veteran staff" that "knows the regulars"; the calamari, veal piccata and other "basic" dishes are "dependable" and a "solid value."

Cafe Tiramisu L M
19 | 17 | 18 | $28

28 Belden Pl. (bet. Bush & Pine Sts.), 415-421-7044

☑ This mural-filled, "high-energy" midrange cafe on Belden Alley has "fresh, delicious" food that's as authentic as the staff ("Italian spoken here"); while that sounds tempting, some might be discouraged by the crowds in the dining room, which would be a shame since there's extra seating at sidewalk tables and in the wine cellar.

Caffe Centro 🄻🄼   ▽ 15 | 13 | 13 | $16
102 South Park (bet. 2nd & 3rd Sts.), 415-882-1500
☑ Looking for a "quick" SoMa lunch spot?; consider this South Park coffee shop, "perennially packed with net slaves" from nearby Multimedia Gulch grazing on "salads big enough for two" and picking at sandwiches while finishing up their latest website projects; though not a destination, it is a "convenient", interesting glimpse into SF's digital culture.

Caffe Delle Stelle 🄻🅂🄼   17 | 15 | 16 | $25
395 Hayes St. (Gough St.), 415-252-1110
☑ Loyalists "love the plates on the walls" of this "busy" Civic Center Italian, which most feel is a "reliable" pre-performance "value"; others think it's "slipped" a bit since the old days when it was located around the corner, but concede the "delicious" bread, tapenade and "all the sparkling water you can drink" is some consolation.

Caffe Greco ◑🄻🅂🄼⊄   16 | 15 | 14 | $14
423 Columbus Ave. (bet. Green & Vallejo Sts.), 415-397-6261
■ "Even the local police" recommend this North Beach coffeehouse for a cappuccino and tiramisu while "people-watching" at a sidewalk table; but they reserve their right to remain silent on the salads and sandwiches.

Caffe Macaroni 🄼⊄   20 | 14 | 18 | $24
59 Columbus Ave. (Jackson St.), 415-956-9737
☑ "Bring your own shoehorn to get in" to this "cramped" North Beach trattoria where chef "Mario takes care of you" with "garlicky" Southern Italian homestyle cooking and it's "worth the wait" for the upstairs mezzanine (if you're "five-foot six and under"); P.S. female diners note that the "waiters are flirts", which is fine as long as you're not the jealous type ("will hit on your date").

Caffe Proust 🄻🅂🄼   – | – | – | M
1801 McAllister St. (Baker St.), 415-345-9560
Named for the owner's favorite author, Marcel Proust, and designed with themes from the writer's work (look for the quotes on each table), this small, artsy Haight-Ashbury cafe also features an Italian-French menu that may make expensive meals seem like a remembrance of things past.

Caffe Sport 🄻⊄   17 | 15 | 11 | $29
574 Green St. (Columbus & Grant Aves.), 415-981-1251
☑ "Heaven help you if you don't like garlic" when dining at this Southern Italian "North Beach institution", with "fantastic" "tacky" decor and a famously "cranky" staff that's now admittedly "less brusque"; sure it's a "tourist attraction" with "heavy", "outdated" food, but the portions are "big" ("vats of sauce poured over piles of pasta") and they still make a "world-class pesto."

California Pizza Kitchen ⌶ ⌶ ⌶　14 | 10 | 13 | $17
438 Geary St. (bet. Mason & Taylor Sts.), 415-563-8911
◪ If you're looking for a "fast" salad and your kids like "odd", "multi-ethnic" combos on their pizza, then consider these "consistent" Downtown and Bay Area chain outposts; while critics carp about "cheesy" decor ("tiles, Formica", "lots of mirrors") and "pseudo" pies, they're ok "in a pinch."

Calzone's ◐⌶⌶⌶　13 | 14 | 13 | $21
430 Columbus Ave. (Vallejo St.), 415-397-3600
◪ "Streetside dining" for "people-watching" is the draw at this North Beach Italian that's an "easy place to meet" on busy Columbus Avenue; however, despite a recent remodel and some promising new dishes, the food is only "so-so."

CAMPTON PLACE ⌶⌶⌶　26 | 25 | 26 | $54
Campton Pl. Hotel, 340 Stockton St. (bet. Post & Sutter Sts.), 415-955-5555
■ This hotel-based Downtown "oasis of refinement" is a "quiet", "spacious" "grown-up place" with a polished staff and "excellent" food; while chef Todd Humphries has departed, Laurent Manrique (ex NYC's Gertrude's) and his new Southern French menu are expected to maintain the same high culinary standards.

Capp's Corner ⌶⌶⌶　15 | 12 | 16 | $21
1600 Powell St. (Green St.), 415-989-2589
◪ "Your immigrant parents would love" this "funky", "nostalgic" North Beach Italian where the "wine is served in water glasses" and the "hearty", "family-style" dishes are delivered by "entertaining" "grumpy old matrons"; even foes who find the victuals "mediocre" concede the place has a "big heart."

Caribbean Zone ⌶⌶　13 | 21 | 14 | $23
55 Natoma St. (bet. 1st & 2nd Sts.), 415-541-9465
◪ "Tourists" love to "have drinks in the fuselage" of the plane that doubles as the lounge at this "gimmicky" SoMa Caribbean with a "fantastic tropical setting", complete with waterfalls and jungle decor; you can have a "fun" time, as long as you remember that you're "not paying for the food or service."

CARNELIAN ROOM ⌶⌶　19 | 26 | 21 | $48
Bank of America Ctr., 555 California St., 52nd fl. (bet. Kearny & Montgomery Sts.), 415-433-7500
◪ At dusk "on a clear night", impress your visiting mother-in-law by taking her to the top of this 52nd-story Downtown New American where an "awesome 360-degree view of the city" is a feast for the eyes; while some feel the pricey edibles are "better than expected" – especially the "quality brunch" – others prefer to play it safe and "go for a drink"; N.B. jackets required.

Carta ●◗ⓁⓈⓂ   19 14 18 $31
1772 Market St. (bet. Gough & Octavia Sts.), 415-863-3516
◪ Bring your *carta* to this newly expanded Civic Center International because every two months the menu changes to reflect the cuisine of a different geographic region; it's an "interesting concept" that's "always worth checking out", though the formula naturally lends itself to "inconsistency."

Casa Aguila ⓁⓈⓂ   21 12 17 $20
1240 Noriega St. (bet. 19th & 20th Aves.), 415-661-5593
◼ A "fish out of water" in its remote Outer Sunset location, this "funky", "hole-in-the-wall" Mexican "with a twist" is known for its "free tamales", "tremendous" portions and "sophisticated", "stunning" presentations, many of which include "piles of fruit" as garnishes.

Cassis ⊘   21 18 22 $28
2120 Greenwich St. (Fillmore St.), 415-292-0770
◪ Union Street diners praise the "impossibly felicitous combination of good food, low prices and great ambiance" at this "sunny", "charming" bistro where the "traditional" Gallic victuals are highlighted by a winning onion tart and "don't-miss" chocolate crème brûlée; in addition, expect a "warm greeting" from the "very French" staff and don't be surprised if the owner "sits down at your table to chat."

Castagnola's ⓁⓈⓂ   14 16 14 $30
Fisherman's Wharf, 286 Jefferson St. (Jones St.), 415-776-5015
◪ This Fisherman's Wharf Italian seafooder can be a "fun place to eat" if you "go with lots of friends" who are tourists and concentrate on the "beautiful view"; but if you're a foodie, you might find the offerings "bland."

Cha Am Thai ⓁⓈⓂ   21 13 16 $18
701 Folsom St. (3rd St.), 415-546-9711
307 Kearny St. (Pine St.), 415-956-8241
4621 Lincoln Way (bet. 26th & 27th Aves.), 415-681-9333
◪ Diners insist "you can't go wrong" at any of these "cheap", "above-average" SF and East Bay Thais, especially if you choose such recommended dishes as steak salad, BBQ beef ribs, fresh noodles or pad Thai; N.B. the Lincoln Way location is the newest entry.

Cha Cha Cha ⓁⓈⓂ   19 17 13 $21
1801 Haight St. (Shrader St.), 415-386-5758
◼ "Dangerously subtle sangria" means many are bombed "by the time they get a table" at this youthful, "loud" "permanent party", a Haight Street Caribbean–Latin American where it helps to go off hours to avoid the "wait of the century"; P.S. if the menu starts to look blurry, just ask them to send out a selection of "yummy tapas."

Cha Cha Cha
at Original McCarthy's ⑤Ⓜ
– | – | – | M
2327 Mission St. (bet. 19th & 20th Sts.), 415-648-0504
A spin-off of the wild and festive Cha Cha Cha on Haight Street, this Caribbean–Latin American is set in a refurbished working-class Irish bar in the Mission; expect the same tapas-style menu and potent sangria, but a relatively more subdued environment.

CHAPEAU! ⑤
26 | 18 | 24 | $36
1408 Clement St. (15th Ave.), 415-750-9787
■ "The secret is out" about this "bright, lively" Richmond District French bistro that draws raves for its "superb" food ("delicious cassoulet"), "extraordinary wine list", "outstanding" staff and "gracious" owners Philippe and Ellen Gardelle, who "make every diner feel special"; P.S. the early-bird "prix fixe is the way to go."

Charanga
▽ 21 | 14 | 18 | $21
2351 Mission St. (bet. 19th & 20th Sts.), 415-282-1813
☑ Here's a new "sangria-sippin'", "tapas kind of place" in the Mission opened by a former chef from Cha Cha Cha; there are "low prices", plenty of "creative" Latin American–Caribbean dishes and, to help make up for the "sparse" interior, unusual "piercings" on the hip, "loud" clientele.

CHARLES NOB HILL ⑤
26 | 25 | 26 | $61
1250 Jones St. (Clay St.), 415-771-5400
■ "Solid gold" chef Ron Siegel – victorious on the Japanese cult TV cooking show *Iron Chef* – "deserves awards" for his "extraordinary" New French–Cal cuisine according to the "older crowd" that patronizes this "romantic" "hideaway" in a Nob Hill residential building; sure, there's also a "professional" staff that makes diners feel "taken care of", but "wow, I'm glad it was an expense-account meal."

Cheers Ⓛ⑤Ⓜ
16 | 14 | 16 | $20
127 Clement St. (bet. 2nd & 3rd Aves.), 415-387-6966
■ "French toast on the patio" is the way to go at this "bright, clean" Richmond District three-meal-a-day American cafe, which gets plenty of votes as the "best" breakfast place in the neighborhood.

Chevys Ⓛ⑤Ⓜ
12 | 12 | 13 | $18
590 Van Ness Ave. (Golden Gate Ave.), 415-621-8200
Stonestown Galleria, 3251 20th Ave. (Winston St.), 415-665-8705
2 Embarcadero Ctr. (bet. Front & Sacramento Sts.), 415-391-2323
☑ A "boisterous", "kid-friendly" Tex-Mex chain that gets some respect for its "good chips and salsa", but "after that" say critics "it's all downhill", with "bland", cheese-heavy offerings that are slightly "better than Taco Bell."

Chow 🇱🇸🇲　　　18 ‖ 14 ‖ 17 ‖ $19
215 Church St. (Market St.), 415-552-2469
◪ One of the best "bangs for the buck" in the Castro/Noe area is this "homey" Eclectic cafe, a "straight/gay gathering place" where there's "always something you feel like eating", whether it be a burger, vegetarian plate or Asian dish; even those who find the offerings "average" consider it a valid "default" choice.

Citizen Cake 🇱🇸🇲　　　24 ‖ 17 ‖ 16 ‖ $13
399 Grove St. (Gough St.), 415-861-2228
■ "Pure artistry" is how surveyors describe the "amazing breads", "creative" cakes, "magical" pastries, "incredible cookies" and "super-yummy" personal pizzas produced at this "chichi", "cutting-edge" Hayes Valley bakery-cafe, which is moving to new, expanded quarters at press time; bottom line: it's "expensive", but "these people love what they do, and you can taste it."

Clementine 🇸　　　20 ‖ 19 ‖ 19 ‖ $34
126 Clement St. (bet. 2nd & 3rd Aves.), 415-387-0408
◪ Situated in the former Alain Rondelli space, this Richmond District French bistro is "warmer" and "less pretentious" than its predecessor, but continues the location's Gallic tradition with hearty fare such as escargot, sweetbreads and "wonderful braised dishes"; despite some service "kinks", devotees declare that this "welcome addition" may one day be their darling Clementine.

Clement Street Bar & Grill 🇱🇸　　　17 ‖ 14 ‖ 17 ‖ $22
708 Clement St. (8th Ave.), 415-386-2200
■ "Meatloaf's a favorite" at this moderately priced American grill in the Richmond, a "safe" "neighborhood spot for fish, pasta and burgers"; "comfortable" booths add to its "kick-back"-and-relax atmosphere, which is just right for the older crowd that's not in any rush.

Cliff House 🇱🇸🇲　　　14 ‖ 21 ‖ 16 ‖ $29
1090 Point Lobos Ave. (Great Hwy.), 415-386-3330
◪ "It's all about the view" at this American above Ocean Beach, a place to "bring out-of-towners" to "watch the sun set over the Pacific"; while the "adequate", "uninspiring" food means many go just "for drinks", "brunch upstairs" ("hearty omelets") does get a few votes, especially if you follow it up with a walk along the water.

Columbus Ristorante 🇸　　　▽ 18 ‖ 15 ‖ 15 ‖ $27
3347 Fillmore St. (bet. Chestnut & Lombard Sts.), 415-474-4180
◪ Fans of garrulous chef-owner May Ditano's Marina Tuscan say it has an "excellent wine selection" and "great menu", including dishes from Florence, Pisa and her native Lucca; signature dishes include calamari, veal sweetbreads, polenta and homemade gnocchi.

Connecticut Yankee **L S M**   16 | 15 | 16 | $17 |
100 Connecticut St. (17th St.), 415-552-4440

■ "Bostonians feel at home" at this New England–themed Potrero Hill American grill, which has "some of the friendliest barkeeps in town", a "great outdoor patio", "fascinating sports memorabilia" and Patriots, Red Sox and Celtics games on the big-screen TVs; the "down-to-earth" crowd also likes the humorous menu ('The Larry Bird Burger'), "great salads" and brunch.

Cordon Bleu **L S ⊅**   ▽ 22 | 7 | 16 | $10 |
1574 California St. (Polk St.), 415-673-5637

■ "If you're on a small budget", "you can't beat" this "authentic" Van Ness/Polk Vietnamese serving "large portions" of "excellent BBQ"; while some "develop a life-long craving for the food", the setting is "plain" and you'll most likely be sitting at a counter facing a hot grill.

Crustacean **L S M**   22 | 17 | 18 | $36 |
1475 Polk St. (California St.), 415-776-2722

☑ "Garlic noodles I dream about" and "magical" roast crab that's "a sexual experience" (though "too messy for a first date") are the two "don't-miss" items at this Van Ness/Polk Vietnamese; phobes could do without the "commercialized" setting and say "bring your wallet."

Curbside Cafe **L S M**   17 | 13 | 17 | $21 |
2417 California St. (Fillmore St.), 415-929-9030
Curbside Too **S M**
2769 Lombard St. (Lyon St.), 415-921-4442

☑ While breakfast and brunch are the "strong points" of this "cute", moderately priced "shoebox-size" Pacific Heights American cafe, it's also a "nice destination for lunch", especially if you order the crab cakes, "yummy salads" or "great steak sandwich"; N.B. the new branch on Lombard is brunch and dinner only.

CYPRESS CLUB **S M**   21 | 26 | 20 | $48 |
500 Jackson St. (bet. Columbus Ave. & Montgomery St.), 415-296-8555

☑ Light fixtures shaped like breasts and other "voluptuous" oddities contribute to the "fantastic" surreal decor of this North Beach New American supper club that "still stuns"; yes, the food can be "sensual", but most find it "not as exciting" as the sizzling atmo, which includes "great jazz" and "outstanding people- watching" at the happening bar.

dalla Torre **S**   ▽ 16 | 24 | 17 | $38 |
1349 Montgomery St. (north of Union St.), 415-296-1111

■ The "romantic atmosphere" and "epic view upstairs" at this Northern Italian hidden on Telegraph Hill ("the fun is finding it") "almost make you fall in love all over again"; the food is only "ok", but a "wine list to die for" is a draw and helps make it a "great parent place."

dame, a restaurant S　　　19　15　20　$28
1815 Market St. (bet. Guerrero & Valencia Sts.), 415-255-8818
◪ Castro/Noe American boasting a "varied menu" and "home-cooked food with flair"; views on the service vary ("sincere" vs. "snooty"), but the "comfortable prices" make some wonder "why in the world is this place not crowded?"

Delancey Street L S　　　16　16　19　$23
600 The Embarcadero (Brannan St.), 415-512-5179
■ A "restaurant with a social conscience" is what surveyors say about this South Beach American where the "earnest", "committed staff" consists of ex-cons on the mend; the "average" food "tastes better" because of the "admirable cause" and comes with a "warm, easy" ambiance and a "sunny" Bayside terrace that provides appealing outdoor seating.

DELFINA S M　　　25　16　23　$33
3621 18th St. (Dolores St.), 415-552-4055
■ This year's talk of the town is Craig Stoll's "crowded, cramped" (but soon to expand) Mission "standout", serving an "adventurous menu" of "unusual Italian" and other "melt-in-your-mouth" Mediterranean dishes with "intense flavors"; the "superb" staff has "recovered the lost art of hospitality" ("like a big warm hug from your Jewish/Italian grandmother"), and despite rare dissenters who "don't understand what all the fuss is about", most agree it "lives up to its hype, and then some."

Doidge's Cafe L S M　　　20　13　16　$17
(aka Doidge's Kitchen)
2217 Union St. (bet. Fillmore & Steiner Sts.), 415-921-2149
◪ Pros praise the "best-way-to-start-the-day" breakfasts and brunches at this Union Street American that's so "packed" that you have to "make a reservation" or endure "long waits"; but Doidge-dodgers shrug "what's the big deal?" and dis the "overpriced" cooking and "ho-hum decor"; N.B. no dinner.

Dottie's True Blue Cafe L S M　　　22　13　17　$13
522 Jones St. (bet. Geary & O'Farrell Sts.), 415-885-2767
■ This "classic", on-the-cheap Downtown American coffee shop is "truly the way to break a fast" declare devotees who dote on Dottie and her "excellent homemade" fare that "tastes like Mom's"; despite the dumpy digs and "seedy" neighborhood, it's still "crowded."

Dragon Well L S M　　　20　16　19　$17
2142 Chestnut St. (bet. Pierce & Steiner Sts.), 415-474-6888
■ "A comer", this newish and "exceptionally pleasant" Marina "yuppie Chinese" offers "fresh, tasty" dishes and "lots of vegetarian choices" that lead loyalists to say they "love this healthy food"; a "wonderful staff" and "cheap" prices are additional pluses.

Dusit Thai 🄻🅂🄼 ▽ 21 | 11 | 19 | $19
3221 Mission St. (bet. Army & 29th Sts.), 415-826-4639
■ Longstanding Mission Thai whose "surprisingly good", "consistently flavorful" food ("wonderful lamb specials"), "attentive service" and "neighborhood rates" make our critics crow that Dusit really does it for them, despite its "tired decor"; no wonder "the same people always seem to be here."

E&O Trading Co. 🄻🅂🄼 18 | 21 | 17 | $31
314 Sutter St. (bet. Grant Ave. & Stockton St.), 415-693-0303
◪ This "pure melting pot" Downtown Asian-fusion brasserie with a "fabulous, exotic" atmosphere ("J. Peterman would feel right at home") offers lots of "intriguing" little dishes and "dynamite beer"; while it's "full of young Schwab trendoids" and "loud" ("can anyone hear in here?"), many maintain that the "bar food rocks" and call it "unique", especially for a group.

E'Angelo 🅂⌀ 19 | 11 | 18 | $21
2234 Chestnut St. (bet. Pierce & Scott Sts.), 415-567-6164
■ "Neighborhood eats as they should be" are found at this "old-time [Northern] Italian gem" in the Marina that "feels more like a restaurant in Italy than most" and is also a "price performer"; its fans flip for the "fresh pasta and flirty waiters", concluding that "proper recognition is overdue."

Eastside West 🄻🅂🄼 ▽ 20 | 21 | 22 | $35
3154 Fillmore St. (Greenwich St.), 415-885-4000
■ Some say this "upscale" Union Street American with an emphasis on East Coast seafood (Chesapeake Bay crab cakes, Maine lobster bisque) could be one of the "hottest new trendy joints" ("if you don't mind being surrounded by yuppies"); there's also live jazz, making it a "nice addition to the neighborhood."

Ebisu 🄻🅂🄼 24 | 13 | 17 | $28
1283 Ninth Ave. (Irving St.), 415-566-1770
■ If you can take the "brutally long wait" at this "always ebullient", highly rated Sunset Japanese, you'll get "fabulous, fresh and imaginative" sushi from "congenial chefs" who put on a "great performance", producing signature rolls like the Pink Cadillac and the Dragon; most overlook "so-so surroundings" that are as raw as the fish in order to get the "best sushi in town."

Eddie Rickenbacker's 🄻🄼 14 | 16 | 14 | $20
133 Second St. (bet. Howard & Mission Sts.), 415-543-3498
◪ Ricken-backers believe this "crowded" SoMa New American with Harley-Davidsons for decor is a "good place for happy hour"; however, detractors dub it a "sub-Bennigan's" and shrug "nice motorcycles – not much else."

Elan Vital Restaurant &   ▽ 26 22 24 $42
Wine Bar Ⓜ
1556 Hyde St. (bet. Jackson St. & Pacific Ave.),
415-929-7309
■ "Watch this one" – a small, "very sweet", "casually
elegant" and slightly pricey Van Ness/Polk French-
influenced New American with "incredible wines" and
"creative but not too far out" food on the "always exciting
menu"; "warm, intelligent service" is another asset that
helps make this "romantic" spot with cable car views
"one of SF's hidden gems."

El Balazo Ⓛ Ⓢ Ⓜ ⊅   19 13 12 $10
1654 Haight St. (bet. Belvedere & Clayton Sts.),
415-864-8608
■ "Fast, cheap and so good", this Haight-Ashbury Mexican
offers "interesting choices", including dishes named after
members of the Grateful Dead ("Jerry's burrito is a must",
especially if you've just driven in from Boulder in your VW
van); the "loud but cheerful" decor and "friendly" staff
make some say it "feels like Mexico", but the largely
tie-dyed crowd is pure SF.

Elite Cafe Ⓢ Ⓜ   19 18 17 $30
2049 Fillmore St. (California St.), 415-346-8668
■ "Nab a booth" underneath the turning ceiling fans and
settle into this "spicy, hip" Pacific Heights Cajun-Creole
with "solid" cookin' and a "good" Sunday brunch; its
"easygoing" atmosphere includes "lots of smiling patrons"
and a "nice old bar" that turns into "yuppie heaven" as
the weekend approaches.

Eliza's Ⓛ Ⓜ   23 18 17 $20
1457 18th St. (Connecticut St.), 415-648-9999 Ⓢ
205 Oak St. (Gough St.), 415-621-4819
■ What a concept: "a Chinese restaurant with atmosphere";
these "classy" Civic Center and Potrero Hill twins appointed
with orchids, "incredible glassware" and "gorgeous china"
definitely have "eye appeal", and "you can't go wrong"
with the food, either, when the chefs "consistently serve
aces" and offer "dishes you can't find elsewhere" with
"fresh, crisp" flavors at "reasonable prices."

Ella's Ⓛ Ⓢ Ⓜ   22 14 17 $20
500 Presidio Ave. (California St.), 415-441-5669
■ "All the world knows about Ella's brunch", so get to this
Pacific Heights New American early and prepare for a wait
that even fans call "ungodly" and phobes pronounce
"inexplicable" ("I don't get it, do you?"); it's "exceptionally
well-run" and "service is personal once you're a regular",
so "just bring a paper" and join the queue for some "good,
rich hangover food"; N.B. "dinners are fine" too.

ELROYS L S M
13 | 19 | 14 | $29

300 Beale St. (Folsom St.), 415-882-7989

This moderate SoMa New American "meat market" with the "George Jetson meets George Stephanopoulos" ambiance packs "more testosterone than a bottle of Viagra" (the limp staff, on the other hand, "lacks excitement" and "needs to warm up"); "it's cooler to be here than to eat here", but new chef Marc Valliani (ex LuLu) is reportedly "working wonders" with the formerly "blah" food.

Empress of China L S M
16 | 16 | 15 | $28

838 Grant Ave. (bet. Clay & Washington Sts.), 415-434-1345

The "elegant setting" at this Chinatown Chinese is "reminiscent of Hong Kong" and its window tables provide "one of the best views of the city"; but most maintain that this dowager has "gone downhill", even if she's still "holding on" to what's left of her empire by appealing to tourists.

Enrico's ● L S M
18 | 19 | 16 | $30

504 Broadway (Kearny St.), 415-982-6223

The "sparkly atmosphere" and "great mojitos" at this "noisy, hip, streetwise" North Beach Mediterranean make for "great people-watching from the patio", and the "competent" kitchen can put out some "good" food too; some say the "happening" jazz performances "outshine the cuisine" and service hits every note from "rude" to "exceptional", but all agree it's "very North Beach."

Entros ● S
▽ 14 | 18 | 16 | $28

270 Brannan St. (bet. 1st & 2nd Sts.), 415-495-5150

High-tech, interactive parlor "games for adult kids" are the draw at this SoMa entertainment center, which is "a lot of fun" "with a large group", even if the Eclectic fare is at best "hit-or-miss"; curmudgeonly critics call it just another "bread and (electronic) circus" show.

EOS RESTAURANT & WINE BAR S M
25 | 19 | 20 | $40

901 Cole St. (Carl St.), 415-566-3063

Boosters rave they're "always amazed" at Arnold Wong's "daring" Asian-fusion bistro in Cole Valley, where "gorgeously creative" cuisine comes with "provocative" selections from the "exceptional" wine bar next door, which also offers the same menu; it may be "a little precious" for some, but it's "a must for foodies and wine geeks"; N.B. take a cab, parking is awful.

Eric's L S M
21 | 15 | 15 | $19

1500 Church St. (27th St.), 415-282-0919

Noe Valley Chinese whose "tasty", "creative" cuisine is complemented by a "sunny, open dining room"; it's a "frantic scene most nights" with a "cell-phone crowd" jockeying for tables, but almost everyone agrees it's "worth the wait" for "unique dishes" and "damn good food at a super price."

Ernesto's S | 17 | 10 | 16 | $22 |
2311 Clement St. (bet. 24th & 25th Aves.), 415-386-1446
☑ This "old-fashioned" Richmond District Italian has pizzas, lasagna and other budget-friendly "comfort food", and insiders advise "head for the specials, which really are"; a few find "marginal, standard fare" and gripe it "would be better if they'd use less sauce", "but, hey, they still serve carafes of wine" and even have "waiters with memories."

Esperpento L S M | 17 | 15 | 13 | $20 |
3295 22nd St. (Valencia St.), 415-282-8867
☑ "Strolling mariachis" provide music at this affordable Mission Spanish "where tapas is spelled g-a-r-l-i-c" and the sangria is "great"; while the less enthused say the "food could come up a notch" and add the south-of-the-border service makes for "excruciating waits at peak hours", they're drowned out by those who cheer it's "cheap."

FARALLON L S M | 24 | 28 | 23 | $51 |
450 Post St. (bet. Mason & Powell Sts.), 415-956-6969
☑ Chef Mark Franz works "sheer magic with seafood" while Pat Kuleto's "dizzying", "drop-dead gorgeous" "underwater fantasy" decor is like "Captain Nemo on acid" at this "expense-account" Downtowner; while a disenchanted few say "attitude is an ingredient" here and claim they "need a microscope to find the appetizers", most advise "take the dive" for simply "sublime" coastal cuisine and "very smooth" service.

Faz L M | 18 | 18 | 18 | $28 |
Crocker Galleria, 161 Sutter St. (bet. Kearny & Montgomery Sts.), 415-362-0404
☑ Moderate Downtown Mediterranean–Middle Eastern with two other branches in the Bay Area offering "a solid meal" that's "just right for business lunches"; while a few are not Fazed by the experience ("didn't make a huge impression"), loyalists like the "inventive cuisine" and the "civilized but not stiff surroundings."

Fifth Floor S M | – | – | – | VE |
Palomar Hotel, 12 Fourth St. (Market St.), 415-348-1555
Acclaimed chef George Morrone left One Market to open this 75-seat newcomer in the urbane Palomar Hotel; expect an interior that's as up-to-date (zebra-print carpet, modern furniture) as the New French menu's take on classic dishes.

Fior d'Italia L S M | 17 | 17 | 18 | $33 |
601 Union St. (Stockton St.), 415-986-1886
☑ North Beach "relic" that bills itself as America's oldest Italian restaurant (1886), whose "typical" "old-world" cooking, Brando-sized portions and "*Godfather*-like aura" are attractions for some; but cynics snipe that the "fair" food and "mothball atmosphere" "don't make my heart skip a beat."

Firecracker L S
20 | 19 | 17 | $23

1007½ Valencia St. (21st St.), 415-642-3470
■ Pyrotechnists praise the "spirited, inventive Asian food" at this "upscale", "out-of-the-ordinary" Mission District Chinese, as well as the "great-looking room" with "groovy red curtains", the "hot crowd" and the "reasonable" prices; a few feel that this Firecracker fizzles with "fusion that just doesn't fuse", but most maintain "when it's good, it's very good" and say it gives them a real bang.

FIREFLY S M
22 | 18 | 20 | $34

4288 24th St. (bet. Diamond & Douglass Sts.), 415-821-7652
■ Reviewers light up and glow over the "fabulous, hearty" fare and "diverse menu options" ("no matter which food group you crave") at this Noe Valley Eclectic with a "charming, down-home atmosphere" and a staff that "takes good care of you"; it's "one of the few unique restaurants around – what a joy."

Firewood Cafe L S M
15 | 13 | 12 | $16

4248 18th St. (Diamond St.), 415-252-0999
Sony Metreon Ctr., 101 Fourth St. (Mission St.), 415-369-6199
◪ Cafeteria-style, "semi-fast food" like wood-oven pizzas and pastas are dished up at these rotisserie "joints"; some "don't like the self-service thing" and report "bland, generic" fare, but pragmatists point out that they're "there when you need them" and they're "cheap."

First Crush ◗ S M
– | – | – | M

101 Cyril Magnin St. (bet. Mason & Powell Sts.), 415-982-7874
Oenophile alert: this Downtown wine bar receives strong write-in votes for its mammoth, all-Californian vino list proffered by a staff that knows its cellar ("no one does it better"); since it also offers midpriced solid New American fare, make sure you "get there early" to "beat the crush."

FLEUR DE LYS M
27 | 27 | 26 | $68

777 Sutter St. (bet. Jones & Taylor Sts.), 415-673-7779
■ Hubert Keller's "flawless creations" ("if it weren't so classy you'd lick the plate") still stun reviewers at this "always superb" Downtown New French, which also offers an excellent vegetarian tasting menu; the "opulent" decor is "tops for elegance" and the service is "attentive", making it a "best splurge" for a "gala, romantic evening."

Florio S M
20 | 21 | 20 | $34

1915 Fillmore St. (bet. Bush & Pine Sts.), 415-775-4300
■ This "warm, appealing" Pacific Heights French newcomer (sibling to Bɪx) has the "feeling of a Parisian brasserie" and "delivers on the promise of straight-ahead bistro food" like "delicious roasted chicken and pommes frites"; the "pretty people" who patronize the place proclaim that "they seem to have it right."

Flying Saucer
23 | 17 | 16 | $40

1000 Guerrero St. (22nd St.), 415-641-9955

◪ "Fun", "funky", "eccentric" and "expensive" Mission French offering the "unexpected"; critics claim the cuisine "must be from another planet" ("what are they thinking?") and cite "rude service", but UFO believers boast about their close encounter with "enormous portions of architecturally constructed", "imaginative food."

Fly Trap ⬛Ⓢ Ⓜ
19 | 18 | 20 | $34

606 Folsom St. (2nd St.), 415-243-0580

◼ Critics who have buzzed by this SoMa American report it's "worth being caught" in this Trap with its "old San Francisco atmosphere" and "very prompt service"; "food from the turn of the century" doesn't refer to Y2K but to "good petrale" and other "solid" traditional dishes.

Fog City Diner ⬛Ⓢ Ⓜ
18 | 19 | 18 | $29

1300 Battery St. (bet. Greenwich & Lombard Sts.), 415-982-2000

◪ Opinion is divided on this Downtown American stalwart on The Embarcadero; loyalists like this "classic", "upscale diner" with "zippy" decor and food that's "more hip than expected" ("graze" on the "creative small plates"), and conclude it's still "fun" with that "special SF spirit"; but cynics cite "overpriced" portions and a "touristy" clientele.

Food Inc. ⬛Ⓜ
18 | 12 | 12 | $17

2800 California St. (Divisadero St.), 415-928-3728

◼ The "casual setup doesn't do justice to the food" at this "small" Pacific Heights Cal-Med cafe where "creative sandwiches" are "perfect for takeout"; an "exceptional" Saturday brunch is a draw, but a few note that they seem to be "always short on staff", which makes for "slow service."

Foreign Cinema Ⓢ Ⓜ
– | – | – | M

2534 Mission St. (bet. 21st & 22nd Sts.), 415-648-7600

For a taste of *La Dolce Vita,* consider this upscale, big-budget production in the Mission, which offers free shorts, foreign classics and independent features on its large courtyard screen, complemented by chef Laurent Katgely's ambitious French Bistro fare, which is served at both communal and traditional tables; moreover, if you don't like what's showing that night, stay tuned – an adjacent movie house is supposedly in the works.

42° ⬛Ⓜ
21 | 21 | 18 | $36

235 16th St. (3rd St.), 415-777-5559

◪ "Happening" SoMa Mediterranean set among the warehouses near China Basin, with "imaginative food" ("don't forget to check the specials!"), upscale, "industrial chic" decor and "hot jazz"; too bad the "customers may not be hip enough for the staff" ("there's attitude" at this latitude) and several report reservations problems, though a "very cool" bar scene eases waits.

Fountain Court ◖L S M   18 ⎵ 12 ⎵ 15 ⎵ $21 ⎵
354 Clement St. (5th Ave.), 415-668-1100
▨ "Affordable", "better-than-average" Richmond District
Chinese whose Shanghai-style cuisine (i.e. gentle
braising and slow stewing) includes "some real treats"
like caramelized eggplant and signature pork meat balls;
the decor may be "bland", but it's a rung or two up from
fluorescent and Formica.

Fournou's Ovens L S M   22 ⎵ 22 ⎵ 22 ⎵ $46 ⎵
Renaissance Stanford Ct., 905 California St. (Powell St.),
415-989-1910
▨ Pricey Nob Hill Continental-Mediterranean stalwart
in the Renaissance Stanford Court Hotel with a "toasty
environment" and some "memorable entrees" from the
eponymous ovens ("if you like lamb, this is the place");
but while loyalists like to think of it as "an old friend",
cynics sigh "lackluster."

Frascati S M   23 ⎵ 20 ⎵ 21 ⎵ $35 ⎵
1901 Hyde St. (Green St.), 415-928-1406
■ The "charming venue" with "romantic" cable car views is
only one reason our surveyors love this "still undiscovered
gem" in Van Ness/Polk (just down the street from sibling
Elan Vital); there's also "fresh", "rustic" and "beautifully"
presented Cal-Italian cooking, not to mention "heartfelt"
service from a well-coached staff; all in all, "a delight."

Fresca L S M   – ⎵ – ⎵ – ⎵ M ⎵
24 West Portal Ave. (Ulloa St.), 415-759-8087
West Portal Muni station commuters alerted us to this
"terrific" Peruvian outlet, the "first restaurant outside the
tunnel" (it's on the right-hand side) and a source for top-
notch rotisserie chicken at an "excellent" price.

FRINGALE L M   26 ⎵ 19 ⎵ 22 ⎵ $39 ⎵
570 Fourth St. (bet. Brannan & Bryant Sts.), 415-543-0573
■ "Like a sunny Cezanne still life" come alive, Gerald
Hirigoyen's highly rated and "charmingly petite" SoMa
French is "buoyant" and "so bistro-y" ("about as authentic
as you'll get"), with some "unparalleled" dishes and an
"interesting wine list that consistently delivers"; the place
is always "crowded", but "use your high-school French
and get a bump up in service" from the "flirtatious waiters."

Fuzio L S M   14 ⎵ 13 ⎵ 13 ⎵ $15 ⎵
469 Castro St. (bet. 18th & Market Sts.), 415-863-1400
2175 Chestnut St. (Pierce St.), 415-673-8804
1 Embarcadero Ctr. (bet. Clay & Front Sts.), 415-392-7995
▨ These on-the-cheap, on-the-run pasta joints offer a
"cultural mishmash of a menu" featuring "wanna-be fusion"
noodles from around the world; Fuziophobes call them "not
overly inspired", but others just shrug and say "wish there
was one in my neighborhood" (there probably will be).

GARDEN COURT 🅛🅢🅜 | 18 | 27 | 19 | $40 |

Palace Hotel, 2 New Montgomery St. (Market St.),
415-546-5010

◪ "Gloriously set" in the Palace Hotel Downtown in one of "the most beautiful rooms outside of Versailles", replete with a "lovely glass roof" and marble columns, this "SF landmark" is all "drama" and "romance"; alas, the Californian "food doesn't measure up" to the "spectacular" surroundings, though the "elegant" afternoon tea and "excellent Sunday brunch" are worthy bets.

Garibaldis on Presidio 🅛🅢🅜 | 21 | 19 | 20 | $34 |

347 Presidio Ave. (bet. Clay & Sacramento Sts.), 415-563-8841

■ A "superior neighborhood restaurant", this "convivial" (or is that "noisy"?) Pacific Heights Mediterranean "defines hospitality" and offers "sophisticated homey food" ("they do the best tricks with lamb") in a "comfortable setting"; even if the menu holds "no surprises" and the "service needs work", "happy" regulars vouch that it's "always dependable" for "a fine meal."

Gary Danko 🅢🅜 | – | – | – | VE |

800 North Point St. (Hyde St.), 415-749-2060

Bay Area super-chef Gary Danko left Viognier in San Mateo to open this eponymous French-influenced New American on the former Chez Michel site near Fisherman's Wharf, along with partner and maitre d' Nick Peyton (ex Ritz-Carlton Dining Room); with a large, seasonal menu available in a user-friendly, three-to-six-course format, a 600-bottle wine list and a sophisticated, contemporary art–filled setting, this is sure to be one of the hottest tickets for some time.

Gaylord India 🅛🅢🅜 | 17 | 16 | 16 | $28 |

Ghirardelli Sq., 900 North Point St. (Larkin St.), 415-771-8822
1 Embarcadero Ctr. (bet. Battery & Sacramento Sts.),
415-397-7775

◪ Providing "civilized dining in a homelike setting", the Ghirardelli Square link in this Indian chain features "great breads" and "well-prepared *samosas* and tandoori" dishes, accompanied by a "nice view"; detractors, however, cite "tired" "standards" and "service that can be improved"; N.B. there's also a branch in the Embarcadero Center.

Gira Polli 🅢🅜 | 21 | 13 | 16 | $22 |

659 Union St. (bet. Columbus Ave. & Powell St.),
415-434-4472

■ "Chicken lovers have never had it better" than at this "great-value" North Beach Italian rotisserie (with branches in Mill Valley and the East Bay) where the birds are "memorably" "succulent"; while it's a "no-frills" kind of joint with a "sterile lunchroom feel" that encourages patrons to opt for takeout, fans don't mind because it "does one thing and does it to perfection."

Globe ◑ 🇱 🇸 🇲   21 | 17 | 18 | $36
290 Pacific Ave. (bet. Battery & Front Sts.), 415-391-4132
▣ With a "post-industrial buzz" and "hip NYC feel", this "casually upscale" Downtown late night "scene" is where "chefs from around the city" and "foodies come to eat" Joseph Manzare's "innovative" New American cuisine in "a dark setting that feels so cool"; though some "don't get the attraction" and suggest the "uppity" staff "needs to smile", many feel it's "the only place to be at midnight."

Godzilla Sushi 🇸 🇲   18 | 9 | 12 | $21
1800 Divisadero St. (Bush St.), 415-931-1773
▣ "Patience always pays off" at this "bustling" Pacific Heights Japanese where rewards such as "unbeatable spicy tuna rolls" await; despite "lukewarm" service and so-called decor that's "as low-end as it gets", a "young" "who's who" crowd queues up for "fresh" and "affordable" sushi.

Golden Turtle 🇸   21 | 16 | 18 | $25
2211 Van Ness Ave. (bet. Broadway & Vallejo St.), 415-441-4419
▣ "Consistently delightful" Vietnamese fare that's "pleasing to the wallet and the palate" pulls in patrons at this Van Ness/Polk "haunt"; dissenters dis the "reliable but never exciting" food, but most praise its "delicious flavors."

Gordon Biersch Brewery 🇱 🇸 🇲   14 | 15 | 14 | $23
2 Harrison St. (The Embarcadero), 415-243-8246
See review in South of San Francisco Directory.

Gordon's House of Fine Eats 🇱 🇸 🇲   – | – | – | E
500 Florida St. (Mariposa St.), 415-861-8900
Former BIX chef Gordon Drysdale has opened this Potrero Flats Eclectic in an "exciting", two-story industrial-chic setting, complete with rotating art installations and live jazz; there's also a daily changing menu of "fine" eats divided into a "great range" of categories (comfort, healthful, SF regional), making this one very hot newcomer.

Gramercy Grill 🇸 🇲   – | – | – | M
1177 California St. (Jones St.), 415-885-3300
The new kid on tony Nob Hill, but not as pricey or as stiff as the neighborhood would suggest, this Eclectic has a lot going for it: chef Phillip Kaufman, who brings blue-chip credentials based on his stints at One Market and Lark Creek, as well as a view of soaring Grace Cathedral.

GRAND CAFE 🇱 🇸 🇲   21 | 26 | 20 | $37
Hotel Monaco, 501 Geary St. (Taylor St.), 415-292-0101
■ "Grand it is" – this "sophisticate's dream" Downtown is set in a "magnificently decadent" space with "fabulous high ceilings" and "beautiful art"; "the room is sheer heaven" and seems to "improve" the New Cal–French cuisine, which while "not up to the surroundings", is "commendable"; the staff is "knowledgeable", and the tabs "reasonable."

Grandeho's Kamekyo 🄻Ⓜ   23 | 18 | 21 | $26
943 Cole St. (Carl St.), 415-759-8428 🅂
2721 Hyde St. (bet. Beach & North Point Sts.), 415-673-6828
■ "The owners care" at this "small", "boisterous" Cole Valley Japanese, a "paradise" for "fresh and unique sushi, especially the dynamite rolls" ("the teriyaki and tempura are good" too); the surroundings are "plain" yet "pleasant" ("sit at the bar") and "it's always packed, but worth the wait"; N.B. the Hyde Street branch is new and unrated.

Great Eastern ●🄻🅂Ⓜ   ▽ 21 | 11 | 15 | $25
649 Jackson St. (bet. Grant Ave. & Kearny St.), 415-986-2500
■ "Another hole-in-the-wall with excellent food", this moderately priced Chinese is one of "the best in Chinatown"; even if the "servers could warm up a little", piscatorial pundits report that "fresher seafood cannot be found", particularly the "great crabs."

Greens 🄻🅂Ⓜ   22 | 23 | 20 | $33
Ft. Mason Ctr., Bldg. A (Buchanan St.), 415-771-6222
☑ Marking its 20th anniversary, this "elegant" Marina "vegetarian's dream" is "still a wonderful" choice for "inventive" and "nurturing" "healthy food" served alongside a "knockout view" of the Golden Gate Bridge; while critics sniff it's "not entirely up to its hype" and find the service "scanty", the "unbelievable wine list" ("reasonably" priced too) will help assuage those who ask "where's the beef?"

Hamano Sushi 🅂Ⓜ   24 | 16 | 15 | $29
1332 Castro St. (24th St.), 415-826-0825
■ "Considering how long it takes them to get it to you" ("couldn't they hire a host and a few more servers?"), the "huge pieces" of raw fish are still "amazingly fresh" at this Noe Valley "benchmark for great sushi"; there's a "guaranteed wait, but it's guaranteed good."

Hamburger Mary's ●🄻🅂   15 | 16 | 14 | $16
1582 Folsom St. (12th St.), 415-626-1985
☑ Setting "the standard for SoMa funk", this "cool" American "hangout" housed in junk store–inspired "kitschy digs" long ago became "a SF fixture" that locals consider "beyond criticism"; it's become somewhat of "a tourist scene", but regulars can deal with that because here, "pinball, burgers and beer equal sweet, heavenly bliss."

Harbor Village 🄻🅂Ⓜ   22 | 18 | 16 | $28
4 Embarcadero Ctr. (Drumm St.), 415-781-8833
☑ Though it's "a bit of a factory", down to the "stiff, mechanical" service, this colossal, "upscale" Downtown Chinese is "where the Asian elite go to eat"; "famous" for its "diverse" selection of dim sum, the kitchen also turns out "authentic" "Hong Kong–style food" such as "the best roast duck"; insiders suggest "go with someone who speaks Chinese" for best results.

Hard Rock Cafe ◑ L S M   10 17 12 $20
1699 Van Ness Ave. (Sacramento St.), 415-885-1699
☑ Cynics call this kid-friendly Van Ness/Polk chain American
with "deafening music" a "tourist holding pen" that's mainly
about displaying "neato rock 'n' roll artifacts" and hawking
T-shirts (they seem to "sell burgers as an afterthought");
the more diplomatic concede it's a "fun way to look at
history", even if the food is only "fair."

Harris' S M   23 21 22 $45
2100 Van Ness Ave. (Pacific Ave.), 415-673-1888
■ "You'll never be steered wrong" at this "traditional" Van
Ness/Polk steakhouse where the "quiet" "atmosphere
whispers class" and "well-dressed diners" are served
"velvety" "prime" cuts by a "knowledgeable" staff;
"hedonistic carnivores" rave it's the "finest red-meat
experience in SF", fortified by a "killer wine list" (and
"great martinis") to help wash down all that "guilt."

Harry Denton's   16 24 18 $38
Starlight Room S M
Sir Francis Drake Hotel, 450 Powell St. (Sutter St.), 415-395-8595
☑ Party boy Harry Denton's original American venue, this
"unique" Downtowner boasts perhaps the "best rooftop
bar in SF", with a "spectacular view"; eating is clearly not
the focus here, but it's "the place" to trip the light fantastic.

HAWTHORNE LANE L S M   26 25 24 $50
22 Hawthorne St. (bet. 2nd & 3rd Sts.), 415-777-9779
■ Anne and David Gingrass' "fancy" SoMa Californian
virtually "defines sophistication" and is "designed to
impress"; "swoon" over the "gorgeous", "artful decor"
while reveling in "superlative" cuisine turned out by a
kitchen that "knows how to respect good ingredients";
the staff is "attentive" to "every detail" and most rejoice
in an "incredible dining experience."

Hayes & Vine Wine Bar S M   17 21 18 $24
377 Hayes St. (bet. Franklin & Gough Sts.), 415-626-5301
■ "Go for the vino" and "try a flight to educate your palate"
at this "refreshingly different" Civic Center wine bar (offering
more than 850 "fab" selections) with "lovely decor" and
"informative" service; "don't plan on it for a meal" because
the "limited" menu of "small plates" are really only "nibbles",
but pros peg it the "perfect prelude to any evening."

Hayes Street Grill L S M   22 17 20 $36
320 Hayes St. (bet. Franklin & Gough Sts.), 415-863-5545
■ "Great doesn't have to be fancy", as this "tried-and-true"
Civic Center American seafooder has long proved; the
kitchen is "serious about fish", cooking "honest-to-
goodness preparations" completely devoid of "trendiness";
though it may be "predictable", traditionalists say that just
means it's "completely reliable."

Helmand, The 🆂🅜   24 | 17 | 21 | $29
430 Broadway (bet. Kearny & Montgomery Sts.), 415-362-0641
■ "Don't be fooled by the dowdy" exterior, because inside this "underappreciated" North Beach storefront in a "strip-club neighborhood" is a "diamond in the rough" featuring "delicious", "unique" but "accessible" Afghan classics – "amazing dumplings and pumpkin appetizers" and "luscious lamb"; despite "slightly unctuous service", it's a "best-value" "original" "treat."

Hong Kong Flower Lounge 🄻🆂🅜   21 | 15 | 15 | $27
5322 Geary Blvd. (bet. 17th & 18th Aves.), 415-668-8998
See review in South of San Francisco Directory.

Hotei 🄻🆂🅜   13 | 16 | 14 | $16
1290 Ninth Ave. (Irving St.), 415-753-6045
☑ "A cut above the usual *udon* places", this "economical" Sunset District Japanese newcomer (sib of nearby Ebisu) specializes in "big portions" of "warming noodles"; while foes feel the "bland" dishes "need a pep pill" and find the staff "distracted", many think it's "a nice addition to the nabe."

House 🄻   24 | 17 | 20 | $29
1230 Grant Ave. (bet. Columbus Ave. & Vallejo St.), 415-986-8612 🅜
1269 Ninth Ave. (bet. Irving St. & Lincoln Way), 415-682-3898 🆂
■ The cuisine at this pair of "hip" North Beach and Inner Sunset "treasure" with "catchy decor" may be "hard to classify" (we'll go with Asian-American) and "seem precious – but wait until you taste it"; chef Larry Tse's "innovations" are "inspired", particularly his "wonderful seafood"; though it's "ridiculously" noisy, the "orgasmic mango tapioca pudding" sweetly compensates.

House of Nanking 🄻🆂🅜⇔   19 | 4 | 7 | $14
919 Kearny St. (bet. Columbus Ave. & Jackson St.), 415-421-1429
☑ What with the noise, crowds, "grungy" atmo and "quick in-and-out" action, it's "like eating at an Indy pit stop" at this Chinatown "experience" where "having food thrown at you" is part of its peculiar charm; queuing up here for "delicious" Hunan fare is an "old SF tradition", but phobes warn "the rumors are true" and insist the "masochistic" service "deserves its own paragraph" – oops, we're out of space.

House of Prime Rib 🆂🅜   23 | 18 | 21 | $35
1906 Van Ness Ave. (Washington St.), 415-885-4605
☑ "No vegetarians need" enter this "no-nonsense" Van Ness/Polk beef "dream" where "you want meat, you get meat" has been the rule of the house for a half-century; the decor's "a bit down at the heels" and the menu has offered "the same great meal for years" – "prime rib that has no competition" – but that's just fine with loyal carnivores who also "love" the "best creamed spinach in town" and "the security of knowing it's there."

Houston's 🄻🅂🄼 | 18 | 16 | 19 | $27 |
1800 Montgomery St. (Bay St.), 415-392-9280

■ In a town adverse to franchises, many residents have to admit that this chain American Downtown "has its act together", serving "large portions" of "surprisingly good" "comfort food" (it'd be "a crime to not order the spinach-artichoke dip") at "moderate prices"; even if the menu is "a little boring", there are "lots of choices", plus the "staff is friendly and competent", making it a "solid standby."

Hunan 🄼 | 20 | 8 | 13 | $18 |
924 Sansome St. (Broadway), 415-956-7727 🄻🅂
674 Sacramento St. (bet. Kearny & Montgomery Sts.),
415-788-2234 🄻
1016 Bryant St. (8th St.), 415-861-5808 🅂

■ "Unless you have a mouth of steel, order mild" at these Hunan siblings where the "tasty" food is so "spicy", it could "set you on fire"; they're "famous for a reason" because "nowhere is hot so flavorful" (the "curried chicken is a favorite dish"); while there's "no atmosphere" and the "decor is less than appealing", this is "great stuff" that's "reliable" and affordable.

Hungarian Sausage   ▽ | 15 | 15 | 15 | $19 |
Factory & Bistro 🄻🅂
419 Cortland Ave. (bet. Bennington & Wool Sts.),
415-648-2847

☑ Goulash gurus appreciate that the "good but rich" "unique" dishes at this "fascinating" Hungarian bistro in Bernal Heights "add to SF's cultural and culinary tradition", though it seems to be too "out of the way" for many; as for service, a few patient souls say the "staff is super-friendly", but most find it frustratingly slow.

Hyde Street Bistro 🅂 | 21 | 17 | 20 | $32 |
1521 Hyde St. (bet. Jackson St. & Pacific Ave.),
415-292-4415

■"Simple but terrific fare" is the calling card of this "charming" French bistro on the Van Ness/Polk Hyde Street cable-car line, where "talented" chef Fabrice Marcon "works magic" ("delicious duck confit"); along with "eager-to-please service" and an "excellent-value" menu, it's no wonder this "treasure" is usually "tightly packed" with locals who hope it doesn't lose "that neighborhood feel."

I Fratelli 🅂🄼 | 19 | 17 | 18 | $28 |
1896 Hyde St. (Green St.), 415-474-8240

☑ Regulars gather at this "comfortable" Van Ness/Polk trattoria for big helpings of "real food", particularly "flavorful" pastas, at "reasonable" prices; critics, however, snort "they call themselves Italian? – phooey!" and also point to "confused service"; but many consider it a "great neighborhood joint" with a "pleasant" atmosphere.

Il Fornaio ●ⓁⓈⓂ　　　19 | 21 | 18 | $30 |
Levi's Plaza, 1265 Battery St. (bet. Greenwich & Union Sts.), 415-986-0100

◪ "Consistent but not very original", this Italian chainlet's (with branches around the Bay Area) "surprisingly strong kitchen" sends out "dynamite breads", "standards" such as "yummy pastas" and some "interesting regional dishes"; even if the food is "kind of generic" and the service "slow", it's a "good standby" in a "lovely setting" where there's "always a table" available.

Indian Oven ⓈⓂ　　　22 | 13 | 16 | $21 |
233 Fillmore St. (bet. Haight & Waller Sts.), 415-626-1628

■ "Bravo to the friendly host" at this "great" Lower Haight-Ashbury subcontinental "find" where the "accomplished dishes" will "take you from Kashmir to New Delhi"; even the "tough neighborhood" can't keep fans away from the "most dazzling Indian food" around; "these guys are good", so be sure to "bring an extra stomach and order everything."

Indigo Ⓢ　　　21 | 21 | 22 | $33 |
687 McAllister St. (bet. Franklin & Gough Sts.), 415-673-9353

■ Convenient to the Opera House and Symphony Hall, this "dark, cool and sexy" "culture-gulch option" is worth a trip in itself for the "dynamic" New American cuisine ("don't miss the BBQ pork tenderloin"); tended to by an "attentive" staff and "nice owners", "you won't be blue when you dine here", making admirers wonder why this "highly underrated" "jewel" is "still unknown."

Infusion Bar & Restaurant ⓁⓈⓂ　　17 | 17 | 16 | $28 |
555 Second St. (bet. Brannan & Bryant Sts.), 415-543-2282

◪ The "live jazz" and "fun-loving crowd" at this SoMa "hangout" make it "too loud to enjoy" for some, but the "fantastic" signature infused-vodka cocktails are "unlike anything else" and far more "creative" than the New American menu, which "sounds better" than it is; insiders suggest "have a martini, skip the meal" and "eavesdrop on the "twentysomethings."

Iroha ⓁⓈⓂ　　　▽ 19 | 13 | 15 | $16 |
1728 Buchanan St. (bet. Post & Sutter Sts.), 415-922-0321

■ While it's "not worth the trip" as a dining destination, if you're in the Japantown area and "want to enjoy good noodles", "one choice" is this "find" that prepares some of the "best ramen" and *soba* in town; it's "plain" but "cheap."

Iron Horse ⓁⓈⓂ　　　14 | 13 | 15 | $29 |
19 Maiden Ln. (bet. Geary & Post Sts.), 415-362-8133

◪ Even though the service is still "solid" as iron at this "kind of tacky", "old-fashioned" Downtown watering hole, the "ordinary" Northern Italian chow "exemplifies mediocrity"; nevertheless, for some nostalgists, the "dark bar" provides a "welcome escape from California trendiness."

Irrawaddy Burmese Cuisine S M ▽   16   15   17 $20
1769 Lombard St. (bet. Laguna & Octavia Sts.), 415-931-2830
☑ "They try hard" at this "relaxing" Union Street Burmese
with "friendly" service and an "extensive, exotic menu";
when the "inconsistently damn good" kitchen is on, the
"unusual food" is "wonderful" (mango chicken, smoky
eggplant), though the decor is always "confused."

Isobune Sushi L S M   16   14   14 $22
*Japan Ctr., 1737 Post St. (bet. Buchanan & Webster Sts.),
415-563-1030*
☑ Offering a "novel" approach, this "gimmicky" Japantown
Japanese serves sushi on toy boats that float around the
bar in a channel of water; while the "raw fish in a moat"
concept fails to appeal to purists who "have doubts about
the freshness" of the cargo, the less-choosy "love" the
flotilla, even if it carries merely "average sushi"; N.B.
there's also a branch in Burlingame.

Izzy's Steak & Chop House S M   21   17   19 $32
3345 Steiner St. (Lombard St.), 415-563-0487
☑ "You can go wearing anything" to this "dictionary
definition" of a "down-home" Traditional American
chophouse where the order of the day is "the works" –
"pretty good" steaks and "don't- miss creamed spinach";
though the Marina locale is "a bit dumpy" and they "charge
extra for everything but the silverware", sated carnivores
warn "don't plan on moving anytime soon after a meal here."

Jack's L M   17   22   17 $43
615 Sacramento St. (Montgomery St.), 415-421-7355
☑ "Beautifully restored", the second oldest restaurant in
SF (since 1864) is "back with a bang" after a two-year
renovation; to loyalists this Downtown landmark with an
"old-money" feeling is still "the one and only", even if the
"aimless" Continental kitchen is "out of touch with modern
times", but critics find it a "major disappointment."

Jackson Fillmore Trattoria S M   21   13   16 $29
2506 Fillmore St. (Jackson St.), 415-346-5288
■ Behind a "laundromat-esque facade" "in the middle of
trendyville" Pacific Heights, this "lively" Southern Italian
trattoria "delivers the tastiest meals; the "annoying wait"
and "tight seating" notwithstanding, locals "delight" in this
"absolute gem" and "could eat here seven nights a week."

Jakarta S   ▽   19   14   20 $21
615 Balboa St. (7th Ave.), 415-387-5225
■ A "great ethnic surprise" awaits at this "neat-as-a-pin"
Richmond District Indonesian; the "warm, sincere" "owners
make a real effort" to please, as does the "gracious,
thoughtful" staff that delivers "beautifully presented" dishes,
notably the traditional rijsttafel; N.B. temporarily closed at
press time due to a fire, but it's set to reopen soon.

JARDINIÈRE §Ⓜ 26 | 26 | 23 | $54 |
300 Grove St. (Franklin St.), 415-861-5555
■ "Incredible talent" Traci Des Jardins (ex Rubicon) is "in full bloom" in the kitchen of this "cosmopolitan" Civic Center New French, turning out "peerless" cuisine with "memorable flavors"; equally "dazzling" is the "opulent" room designed by Pat Kuleto, with a "way cool round bar" that affords "great people-watching"; despite "too-small portions", most feel this "magical place" is "as close to perfection as it gets" and applaud "bravo!", "certain it'll become a SF classic"; P.S. "a balcony table over the bar is the best seat in town."

Jasmine House ᴸ§Ⓜ ▽ 20 | 11 | 17 | $21 |
2301 Clement St. (bet. 24th & 25th Aves.), 415-668-3382
■ Devoted regulars have "always been pleased" with this "favorite neighborhood haunt" in the Outer Richmond, which offers "delicious" Vietnamese food at "incredible prices"; "feast" on the signature dish of roasted whole crab in garlic butter, served by a "friendly" staff that makes up for the "spare" room.

Jessie's Cajun/Creole § ▽ 17 | 12 | 14 | $26 |
1256 Folsom St. (bet. 8th & 9th Sts.), 415-437-2481
☑ "The owner works hard and it shows in her great Cajun-Creole food" at this moderately priced SoMa joint that offers a "good variety" of regional specialties ("try the alligator", if you're adventurous, or the "tasty" crab cakes); despite "spotty service", some think it has "potential."

John's Grill ᴸ§Ⓜ 17 | 17 | 17 | $30 |
63 Ellis St. (bet. Powell & Stockton Sts.), 415-986-0069
☑ Sam Spade's favorite haunt, this "classic", "hard-boiled" Downtown Traditional American grill is "steady in its crusty way", still featuring "standards" such as steaks, chops and seafood, and live jazz nightly; even if the eats are only "so-so", those hungry to bite into SF's "literary history" will eat up the "terrific Dashiell Hammett display", which stars the original Maltese falcon from the film.

Juban ᴸ§Ⓜ 18 | 17 | 15 | $28 |
Japan Ctr., 1581 Webster St. (Post St.), 415-776-5822
See review in South of San Francisco Directory.

Julie's Supper Club §Ⓜ 15 | 17 | 15 | $28 |
1123 Folsom St. (bet. 7th & 8th Sts.), 415-861-0707
☑ A "hip, jumpin' crowd" who "likes to party" "goes for the vibe" at this "full-of-fun" SoMa Californian "with dim lighting and jazzy music"; judging from the "limited menu" of "unremarkable" food, it's clearly "more club here than supper", but it's a "great meeting spot" with "good people-watching" opportunities.

Julius' Castle 🆂Ⓜ | 17 | 24 | 20 | $46 |
1541 Montgomery St. (Union St.), 415-392-2222

◾ In an "unforgettable setting" with an "unsurpassed view" from high on Telegraph Hill, this Northern Italian is a favorite destination for "celebration-type dinners"; the menu is no more than "mediocre", so you can bet that you're overpaying for the "great location", but oh what a "very romantic place to take someone special."

Kabuto Sushi 🆂 | 23 | 11 | 16 | $32 |
5116 Geary Blvd. (15th Ave.), 415-752-5652

◾ Overcoming a "soul-less interior" that "needs a renovation", chef-owner and "SF personality" Sachio Kojima prepares a "large selection" of "excellent", "distinctive" sushi at this Richmond District Japanese mecca, which attracts an "enthusiastic crowd" of raw-fish worshippers ("long live Kabuto").

Kate's Kitchen Ⓛ🆂Ⓜ🍴 | 21 | 11 | 15 | $14 |
471 Haight St. (Fillmore St.), 415-626-3984

◼ A "bohemian chic" American cafe in the Lower Haight where the staff's so hip some "fantasize about working there" and the "unforgettable", "super-size" breakfasts mean "you'll be full all day"; even wits who wager it should be called "Waits Kitchen" (because of the lines) concede they now understand "what hush puppies are all about"; N.B. dinner is not served.

Katia's - A Russian Tea Room Ⓛ🆂 | 19 | 15 | 19 | $24 |
600 Fifth Ave. (Balboa St.), 415-668-9292

◾ This Richmond District Russian offers relatively "light", "subtle" fare with "lots of delicious tastes"; situated in a "small", "cute" storefront that will surprise those expecting a dreary set out of *Dr. Zhivago*, it also offers nightly music and the warmth of owner Katia Troosh and her "friendly" staff.

Kelly's Mission Rock Ⓛ🆂 | - | - | - | M |
817 China Basin St. (Mariposa St.), 415-626-5355

The hip, "modern-industrial" renovation of the old Mission Rock Resort, which was basically a funky, drinking hangout, has resulted in this bi-level SoMa newcomer; downstairs is a casual cafe with pool tables, bar and dockside patio, while upstairs the foodies congregate for chef Richard Crocker's (ex Boulevard) Californian cuisine; overall, one to watch.

Khan Toke Thai House 🆂Ⓜ | 21 | 23 | 19 | $23 |
5937 Geary Blvd. (bet. 23rd & 24th Aves.), 415-668-6654

◾ Diners sit shoeless on the "comfortable floor cushions" of this "gorgeous", "exotic" Richmond District Thai, which makes a "wonderful date place" assuming you "remember to wear socks" and find parking; with "well-prepared" food as well, it's one of the top overall places in its category.

KOKKARI ESTIATORIO 🖥Ⓜ　25 | 27 | 23 | $42

200 Jackson St. (Front St.), 415-981-0983

■ Receiving lots of votes for "best new restaurant" is this "high-end" Downtown Greek with a "superbly comfortable environment" that "looks like a million" ("dramatic fireplace") and "spectacular" cooking from chef Jean Alberti, including "wonderful spreads", "scrumptious moussaka" and "great fish"; authentic or not, "the food is never this good in Greece."

Korea House 🖥Ⓢ　21 | 12 | 16 | $23

1640 Post St. (Laguna St.), 415-563-1388

■ "Hidden away" in Japantown is this "great" source for "traditional Korean food", especially barbecue specialties that you grill yourself; while not well known by surveyors, it offers late hours and generally "polite" service.

Kuleto's 🖥ⓈⓂ　21 | 20 | 19 | $34

Villa Florence Hotel, 221 Powell St. (bet. Geary & O'Farrell Sts.), 415-397-7720

☑ For a real taste of "Downtown energy", "eat in the bar" of this "bustling", high-ceilinged trattoria off Union Square, which can be "somewhat touristy" due to its cable car proximity but remains an "old faithful" "for solid Northern Italian favorites" "before a show."

KYO-YA 🖥　26 | 21 | 22 | $49

Palace Hotel, 2 New Montgomery St. (Market St.), 415-546-5090

■ "Be prepared to spend" for some of the "best sushi in SF" at this "elegant", hotel-based Downtown Japanese, a "power"-dining spot for foreign businessmen with an "attentive" staff and "quiet", "calm" atmosphere; P.S. it's also "one of a select few" establishments to offer "refined *kaiseki* dinners."

La Bergerie 🖥Ⓜ　▽ 19 | 15 | 19 | $26

4221 Geary Blvd. (bet. 6th & 7th Aves.), 415-387-3573

■ "Bring a party of four to enjoy" the "'50s-era" Classic French cuisine prepared at this "tried-and-true" Richmond District "blast from the past", with a "cozy", "quaint" atmosphere and sane decibel level that allows you to "actually hear" conversation; P.S. the prix fixe dinner is an outright "steal."

La Cumbre Taqueria 🖥ⓈⓂ⊅　21 | 9 | 13 | $9

515 Valencia St. (bet. 16th & 17th Sts.), 415-863-8205

■ The No. 1 Bang for the Buck in the *Survey*, and "one of the top" burrito joints in SF, this Mission Mexican "institution" is a "must on moving day" when you just want to "double-park" and run in for the "best *carne asada*"; those who linger have varying reactions to the "campy" interior, especially the mural of the "buxom" 'soldier woman.'

La Felce █𝐒𝐌   20 | 14 | 21 | $28

1570 Stockton St. (Union St.), 415-392-8321

■ There's "no slick food" at this North Beach tribute to the red, white and green, just "reasonably priced" "old Italian classics" "served with love"; longtime patrons warn initiates: "don't judge the place by the decor", but do order the "best fried calamari" and veal dishes.

LA FOLIE 𝐌   27 | 23 | 25 | $65

2316 Polk St. (bet. Green & Union Sts.), 415-776-5577

■ Chef Roland Passot's "divine" culinary "artistry" at this Van Ness/Polk New French reminds reviewers "why we loved nouvelle in the first place"; there's "romantic" decor and "informal" service that "looks after every detail", but with "half the pretension of comparable restaurants"; the tab will be a "savings drainer", but this "favorite" "deserves its spot as one of SF's best."

Laghi 𝐒𝐌   21 | 16 | 20 | $30

2101 Sutter St. (Steiner St.), 415-931-3774

■ Despite a move to a new Lower Pacific Heights location, this midrange Northern Italian "hasn't lost a step" ("thank your Laghi stars") and is still "true to itself" with the "same great care" from a "friendly staff"; some think the new room "seems cold", but the "well-executed", daily changing menu still includes "savory homemade pastas" and rabbit that's "worth a detour."

La Méditerranée █𝐌   18 | 14 | 17 | $19

2210 Fillmore St. (bet. Clay & Sacramento Sts.), 415-921-2956
288 Noe St. (bet. Market & 16th Sts.), 415-431-7210

☑ They "really do a nice job" at these "cute", "little" Middle Eastern–Mediterraneans where meze mavens "live on the appetizers alone" and the "cheap" menu (despite "never changing") "satisfies all types from vegetarians to meat eaters"; N.B. there's an East Bay location too.

La Rondalla ◗█𝐒∅   12 | 15 | 13 | $17

901 Valencia St. (20th St.), 415-647-7474

■ "Year-round Christmas decor", mariachi music and "strong margaritas" that "make you want to dance on the table" fuel the "party atmosphere" at this Mission Mexican with "mediocre" grub that no one seems to notice ("it's the ambiance", "who goes for the food?").

La Scene Cafe 𝐒𝐌   20 | 19 | 21 | $34

Warwick Regis, 490 Geary St. (Taylor St.), 415-292-6430

■ Reports on this "blissfully quiet" Downtown French-Mediterranean bistro indicate that it's a "perfect pre-theater" choice with "affordable", "tasty" vittles and a "very good" staff that "gets you" to the theater on time; factor in valet parking and this just may be a "hidden jewel."

La Taqueria ⬛🅢🅜⊘　　23　10　13　$11
2889 Mission St. (25th St.), 415-285-7117

■ Surveyors say that this Mission District Mexican "master of flavor" turns out "killer soft-shell tacos" and carnitas to crow about, as well as what is "unquestionably the best burrito" in town for many ("accept no substitutes"), all at unbelievably cheap prices; bottom line: this is "another of SF's ethnic treasures."

La Traviata 🅢　　▽　22　20　21　$28
2854 Mission St. (bet. 24th & 25th Sts.), 415-282-0500

■ There's "opera paraphernalia everywhere" and Caruso in the air at this Mission District Italian where food divas are indulged with the "best gnocchi" and "attentive, European-style service"; despite being a "great neighborhood restaurant", some feel that it's "underpatronized" because of its "crummy" locale, but don't let that stop you.

La Vie ⬛🅢🅜　　21　12　19　$22
5830 Geary Blvd. (bet. 22nd & 23rd Aves.), 415-668-8080

■ "Messy but delicious" roasted crab and flaming beef with prawns are two of the must-try signature dishes at this "excellent", "creative" Richmond District Vietnamese with a "ho-hum setting" but "extremely friendly" waiters that don't mind if you "press them for suggestions"; in sum, an "enormous", "undiscovered" value.

Le Central Bistro ⬛🅜　　21　18　20　$35
453 Bush St. (bet. Grant Ave. & Kearny St.), 415-391-2233

■ Some suspect that the cook "sold his soul for the recipe" to the "dream" chicken at this "dependable" Downtown French bistro where there's "no fancy-pants stuff", just the "best onion soup in SF", fantastic cassoulet and "especially good steak tartare"; P.S. while you're there "say hello to mayor Willie Brown."

Le Charm French Bistro ⬛🅜　　23　17　21　$29
315 Fifth St. (bet. Folsom & Harrison Sts.), 415-546-6128

■ "On a warm night", consider sitting on the "relaxing" patio of this "aptly named" SoMa French bistro with "deftly done, delectable dishes" ("great mussels"), a "congenial" staff and "reasonable prices", including a prix fixe that "can't be beat."

LE COLONIAL ⬛🅢🅜　　21　26　20　$43
20 Cosmo Pl. (bet. Post & Taylor Sts.), 415-931-3600

◪ "Bamboo and ceiling fans reminiscent" of "Hanoi circa 1905" project "power brokers" and a "society crowd" into the colonial era at this "beautiful" Downtown Vietnamese; even those who think the "light, flavorful" food "doesn't live up to the expensive prices" concede that the "gorgeous bar" is ideal for "great cocktails."

Le Cyrano ⑤　　17 | 16 | 18 | $29
4134 Geary Blvd. (bet. 5th & 6th Aves.), 415-387-1090
☑ "Cream, comfort and complacency" sums up this Cyrano de Bergerac–themed Richmond District French, which has "been there forever", serving "inexpensive", "dependable" classic dishes to an appreciative "older" clientele ("thank goodness SF still has one like this"); while detractors think the menu "needs to get into the '90s", there are, in fact, some low-fat options.

Left at Albuquerque ⓁⓈⓂ　　13 | 15 | 14 | $21
2140 Union St. (bet. Fillmore & Webster Sts.), 415-749-6700
See review in South of San Francisco Directory.

Le Soleil ⓁⓈⓂ　　20 | 13 | 17 | $22
133 Clement St. (bet. 2nd & 3rd Aves.), 415-668-4848
☑ "Must-try" imperial rolls and five-spice chicken that "rocks" are the stars at this "affordable" Richmond District Vietnamese, a "tremendous" lunchtime value and an overall "tasty" "jewel amidst" crowded Clement Street.

Leticia's ⓁⓈⓂ　　12 | 13 | 15 | $23
2247 Market St. (bet. Sanchez & 16th Sts.), 415-621-0442
☑ An "aging" "disappointment" to finicky foodies, this Castro/Noe Mexican still appeals to those who value "large portions" and potent drinks over extraordinary flavors ("who cares after a couple of margaritas?").

Lhasa Moon ⓁⓈ　　15 | 14 | 17 | $20
2420 Lombard St. (bet. Divisadero & Scott Sts.), 415-674-9898
☑ While undeniably "different", since it's ostensibly the only Tibetan venue in the city, this "peaceful" Union Street ethnic receives middling food ratings and comments ("bland", "stick with the dumplings"); nonetheless, the staff is "cheerful" and the philosophical say they "go for the idea more than the eats" anyway.

Liberty Cafe & Bakery ⓁⓈ　　23 | 17 | 20 | $27
410 Cortland Ave. (bet. Bennington & Wool Sts.), 415-695-8777
■ This Bernal Heights New American is called a "dream neighborhood restaurant" where chef Randy Windham works wonders with salads and "anything with a crust", the "friendly staff" coddles the constant crowds and the adjacent wine bar (a bakery by day) handles the overflow; "the only flaw, their no-reservations policy."

Lichee Garden ⓁⓈⓂ　　19 | 8 | 12 | $19
1416 Powell St. (bet. Broadway & Vallejo St.), 415-397-2290
■ "Chinatown locals" bring "large parties" to this "upscale" parlor primarily for "quality" dim sum and "very good" Cantonese dishes ("especially the minced squab"), even though tabs are "slightly higher" than more touristy places.

Little City Antipasti Bar 🅛🅢🅜 17 | 15 | 15 | $29
673 Union St. (Powell St.), 415-434-2900

☑ It's "fun to people-watch" at the "cute alfresco tables" of this North Beach Italian, which is a "reliable place to bring timid out-of-towners" "for drinks and appetizers"; they recently hired a new chef, but you can still get the "great" roasted garlic and baked Brie dish.

Little Italy Ristorante 🅢🅜 19 | 16 | 19 | $23
4109 24th St. (bet. Castro & Diamond Sts.), 415-821-1515

☑ "Large portions" of garlic-heavy Southern Italian fare pull patrons into this "busy" Noe Valley veteran, which "feels like a real restaurant", especially since the staff makes you feel like "part of the family."

Little Joe's 🅛🅢🅜 16 | 10 | 14 | $20
523 Broadway (bet. Columbus Ave. & Kearny St.), 415-433-4343

☑ Be sure to "have a bowl of garlic cloves" when dining at this "casual" North Beach Italian "throwback", which overcomes its "bland" setting with "cheap", "hearty" "standards", highlighted by calamari, cioppino and mussels.

Liverpool Lil's 🅓🅛🅢🅜 16 | 16 | 17 | $24
2942 Lyon St. (Lombard St.), 415-921-6664

■ For some commuters, the "last stop before the Golden Gate Bridge" is this "late-night" Union Street "haunt" with English pub atmosphere and food, "more sophisticated" American grill offerings and "great black and tans"; P.S. the colorful clientele used to include Joe DiMaggio (his "favorite former hiding spot").

L'Olivier 🅛🅜 21 | 21 | 22 | $38
465 Davis Ct. (Jackson St.), 415-981-7824

■ "Fabulous" prix fixe deals at lunch and dinner mean "you're not cheated" at this "charming" Downtown Classic Gallic "place for conversation", with "pleasant servers" and an "elegant" "country French setting"; quibblers concede that it's "appealing", but say the victuals "fail to excite."

London Wine Bar 🅛🅜 13 | 14 | 16 | $23
415 Sansome St. (bet. Clay & Sacramento Sts.), 415-788-4811

☑ "Knowledgeable" oenologists, otherwise known as "awesome characters behind the bar", preside over an "excellent wine list" (40 by the glass), making this Downtown bar a "crowded" after-work favorite; the American menu elicits few comments, but you "don't go for the food" anyway.

Long Life Noodle Co. 🅛🅜 14 | 14 | 12 | $16
139 Steuart St. (bet. Howard & Mission Sts.), 415-281-3818
Sony Metreon Ctr., 101 Fourth St. (bet. Howard & Mission Sts.),
415-369-6188 🅢

☑ "There's a style of noodle for everyone" at these Chinese "carbo-loading" stops with two SoMa locations ("for a Financial District lunch" "on a cold day"); the unimpressed insist "go to Chinatown for the real thing at half the price."

L'Osteria Del Forno ⬛Ⓢ🅼⊘   22 | 13 | 16 | $23
519 Columbus Ave. (bet. Green & Union Sts.),
415-982-1124
■ "Try to get one of the cozy window seats" when eating
at this "laid-back" North Beach Italian, which is a favorite
"hole-in-the-wall" thanks to "the best roast pork", nifty,
thin-crust pizzas and focaccia sandwiches many would
"request as a last meal"; a "little more variety would be
nice", but why quibble when you get so much "more than
you pay for in taste?"

LuLu ⬛Ⓢ🅼   21 | 20 | 17 | $36
816 Folsom St. (bet. 4th & 5th Sts.), 415-495-5775
☑ "Bring a group" to this "cavernous" "SoMa classic" to
share "family-style" portions of "excellent" rustic French
food ("don't miss the mussels"), which rely heavily on a
large, open rotisserie that "will do justice to just about
anything"; serious "attitude" and a "deafeningly noisy"
atmosphere detract, but this remains a "happening" place;
N.B. 70 wines by the glass.

Macaroni Sciue Sciue ⬛🅼   – | – | – | M
124 Columbus Ave. (bet. Jackson & Kearny Sts.),
415-217-8400
Sciue sciue is Neapolitan slang for "make it snappy", and
this across-the-street Italian sibling to Caffe Macaroni does
its best, serving pastas and daily specials pronto, and at
reasonable prices; but even if your meal arrives quickly,
don't eat too fast because the sidewalk seating is great
for people-watching on busy Columbus Avenue.

MacArthur Park ⬛Ⓢ🅼   17 | 18 | 18 | $30
607 Front St. (Jackson St.), 415-398-5700
☑ Barbecue items like "great" "smoky ribs for serious
gnawing", plus a "huge" Cobb salad, keep families "coming
back" to these long-standing Downtown and Palo Alto
Americans; however, other items are called "average"
and some think the "formula" "needs updating."

Magnolia Pub & Brewery ⬛Ⓢ🅼   15 | 14 | 16 | $18
1398 Haight St. (Masonic Ave.), 415-864-7468
☑ For a "taste of the Haight", head to this "warm, mellow
and eager-to-please" American pub on the former site of
Magnolia Thunderpussy's famous hippie-era cafe, with
"great" cask-conditioned ales and "good" food, highlighted
by mussels, soups and gourmet sandwiches.

Maharani ⬛Ⓢ🅼   18 | 15 | 16 | $26
1122 Post St. (bet. Polk St. & Van Ness Ave.), 415-775-1988
☑ If you're planning a "romantic date", "book a booth in
the 'Fantasy Room'" of this "funky" Van Ness/Polk Indian
with a "moderately priced" menu, which includes monthly
changing regional dishes.

Maki ⬛L⬛S ▽ 26 | 17 | 21 | $38

Japan Ctr., 1825 Post St. (Webster St.), 415-921-5215

■ It may be "the smallest restaurant" in town, but this Japantown Japanese "jewel" still tastes big, turning out top-notch standards, as well as less common fare like "great" *wapa meshi* (ask the "knowledgeable" staff to explain).

Mama's on 22 | 14 | 15 | $19
Washington Square ⬛L⬛S⬛

1701 Stockton St. (Filbert St.), 415-362-6421

■ "One of the best breakfasts around" ("a Sunday morning tradition for San Franciscans who don't mind waiting in line for an hour") is what this wallet-friendly North Beach American cafe with its own in-house bakery excels at; N.B. dinner is not served.

Mandalay ⬛L⬛S⬛M 20 | 12 | 17 | $19

4348 California St. (6th Ave.), 415-386-3895

◪ Regulars at this Richmond District Burmese call it "a refreshing change from more typical Asian food", and suggest you "bring a group, get a big table" and "let them order you a feast", so long as it includes the "excellent mango chicken"; aesthetes assert "given the atmosphere" ("needs better lighting"), "perhaps takeout is best."

Mandarin, The ⬛L⬛S⬛M 20 | 22 | 19 | $37

Ghirardelli Sq., 900 North Point St. (bet. Larkin & Polk Sts.), 415-673-8812

◪ "When visitors insist on dining at the Wharf", consider this "elegant" Ghirardelli Square Chinese, a "good-view restaurant" with food that can be a "real winner if you order correctly", specifically the "must-try minced squab" and Peking duck (order five hours in advance).

Mangiafuoco ⬛S⬛M 19 | 16 | 18 | $30

1001 Guerrero St. (22nd St.), 415-206-9881

■ "Even though no one can pronounce the name", this "energetic" Mission District Tuscan trattoria is still a "perennial favorite" with young people for its "gorgeous", "sweet waiters" "who make everything sound delicious", including "perfect" homemade pastas and solid meat dishes.

Manora's Thai Cuisine ⬛L⬛M 21 | 14 | 17 | $21

1600 Folsom St. (12th St.), 415-861-6224

■ In spite of the crowds, this "lively" SoMa Thai manages to remain "competent all-around", with a "grace-under-pressure staff" and "excellent", "reasonably priced" food; several even vote it "best in the city" for its category.

Maria Therese ⬛S⬛M ▽ 19 | 15 | 20 | $34

2034 Chestnut St. (bet. Fillmore & Steiner Sts.), 415-567-8124

◪ While all but unknown to most surveyors, due to its "out-of-the-way location" in the Marina, this New French has "above-average" victuals, highlighted by such signature dishes as lamb tenderloin and blueberry duck.

Mario's Bohemian Cigar Store Cafe 🄻🅂🄼   17 | 15 | 14 | $16
566 Columbus Ave. (Union St.), 415-362-0536 ◑⊄
2209 Polk St. (bet. Green & Vallejo Sts.), 415-776-8226
■ Once the domain of the Beats, but still a "quintessential North Beach hangout", this "easy-going" Italian coffee shop is now more famous for its trademark focaccia sandwiches ("amazing eggplant", "extraordinary meatballs") and "best cappuccino"; the newer, "upscale" Van Ness/Polk spin-off has a larger menu, beer on tap and live jazz some nights.

Marnee Thai 🄻🅂🄼   23 | 13 | 15 | $20
2225 Irving St. (bet. 23rd & 24th Aves.), 415-665-9500
☑ Controversial owner May is a "free spirit" to some, "overbearing" to others, but either way don't be surprised if she "orders for you", "tells your fortune" and otherwise "keeps you entertained" at this "exciting", "always packed" Sunset District Thai; favorites include the "best spicy wings" and a "wonderful mango dessert."

MASA'S   28 | 25 | 26 | $75
Hotel Vintage Court, 648 Bush St. (bet. Powell & Stockton Sts.), 415-989-7154
☑ "All superlatives seem inadequate" when it comes to this "quiet", "very formal" Downtown Contemporary French shrine that "hasn't skipped a beat" since former chef Julian Serrano left, and continues to produce "unbelievable magic" courtesy of Chad Callahan's "imaginative" "works of art"; "flawless service" also makes it easier to swallow the prix fixe menu's "stratospheric" prices.

Massawa 🄻🅂   20 | 10 | 16 | $17
1538 Haight St. (Ashbury St.), 415-621-4129
■ You can "forget the annoyance of cutlery" at this budget-wise Haight-Ashbury Ethiopian where everything is "eaten with fingers" and scooped up with homemade *injera* (flatbread); the "knowledgeable and friendly staff" is happy to spend time guiding you through the unfamiliar cuisine, to the point where you may not even notice the "zilch decor."

Ma Tante Sumi 🅂🄼   24 | 19 | 22 | $35
4243 18th St. (bet. Castro & Diamond Sts.), 415-626-7864
■ "Sumi and her staff do an excellent job" at this Castro/Noe Californian, "one of the least pretentious" spots in town; "tasteful" surroundings and a "romantic" atmosphere provide "some serenity" in the busy nexus of 18th and Castro, making it a "neighborhood jewel."

Matterhorn Swiss Restaurant 🅂   18 | 17 | 18 | $31
2323 Van Ness Ave. (bet. Green & Vallejo Sts.), 415-885-6116
☑ "Not for the lactose intolerant", but perfect "if you like to play with your food", this Van Ness/Polk Swiss fondue specialist offers a "change of pace", especially if you like the challenge of eating your "weight in meat and cheese."

Max's Diner 🄻🅂🄼   16   14   15 $19
311 Third St. (Folsom St.), 415-546-0168

☑ "Be still, my tummy!" declare patrons anticipating this '50s-style SoMa deli's "massive" quantities of "golden-age" comfort food, including the "best corned beef west of Times Square"; detractors say it's "nothing special beyond large portions", but admit that it's "the right setting for a shake."

Max's on the Square 🄻🅂🄼   16   15   17 $22
Maxwell Hotel, 398 Geary St. (Mason St.), 415-646-8600

☑ This new Downtown relative to Max's Diner and Max's Opera Cafe offers the same "wide variety" and "ample servings" ("one will do for two") as its siblings; nonetheless, matzoh-ball mavens insist "SF still needs a good deli."

Max's Opera Café 🄻🅂🄼   17   14   16 $22
Opera Plaza, 601 Van Ness Ave. (Golden Gate Ave.), 415-771-7300

☑ "Eat, eat, eat" is what advocates advise when patronizing this Civic Center deli-cafe where "you gotta love the singing staff" and "super-sized" sandwiches and desserts; NYC expats gripe that "it ain't the Carnegie Deli" ("but what is?") and suggest "smaller portions, smaller prices."

Maya 🄻🅂🄼   22   22   22 $37
303 Second St. (bet. Folsom & Harrison Sts.), 415-543-2928

☑ This "lovely", new "high-end" SoMa Mexican (the sib to NYC's Maya) is a "much-needed alternative to burritos and tacos", with a "well-executed" menu of "refined" regional cuisine relying on "exotic ingredients"; "the fact that it's noisy does not deter", and neither does the price.

Maye's Oyster House 🄻🄼   16   13   16 $29
1233 Polk St. (bet. Bush & Sutter Sts.), 415-474-7674

☑ While cynics claim this Van Ness/Polk Italian-seafooder "may be older than SF" and "needs to be renovated", defenders say it has "character", with historic photographs and fish hanging from the ceiling; most are mum on the cuisine, but loyalists like the signature sand dabs.

Mayflower 🄻🅂🄼   20   11   14 $22
6255 Geary Blvd. (27th Ave.), 415-387-8338

☑ For "beautiful banquets", a dim sum lunch, or just "a Chinese meal in an upscale environment", consider this Richmond Districter where they serve "well-executed" dishes that are a grade "higher" than competitors.

McCormick & Kuleto's 🄻🅂🄼   18   22   18 $34
Ghirardelli Sq., 900 North Point St. (bet. Larkin & Polk Sts.), 415-929-1730

☑ "Guests from the Midwest" say this mammoth Ghirardelli Square seafooder "fulfills their expectations of a nice place at the Wharf", with "stunning views" and a menu filled with a "broad selection" of "classics"; locals simply sigh "oh, those poor tourists" paying "uptown prices."

mc² 🔲Ⓜ 21 | 23 | 20 | $44
470 Pacific Ave. (Montgomery St.), 415-956-0666

☑ "Stunning" is how many describe the "stark", "spacious", "industrial-elegant" interior ("warm wood ceiling, cold columns") of this Downtown Californian-French where the "interesting combos" can be "exciting" but, relatively speaking, "don't quite rise to the level of the decor"; nevertheless, it's a real "up-and-comer" on the SF scene.

Mecca ⓈⓂ 20 | 24 | 18 | $38
2029 Market St. (bet. Dolores & 14th Sts.), 415-621-7000

☑ The "21st-century" interior of this Castro/Noe New American supper club attracts a raffish, "Fellini-movie" crowd of "wanna-be celebrities" ("gay, straight, young and old") to its "wonderful", "sleek" bar; so despite a solid food score and "artful presentations", rubberneckers feel the "wild people-watching" overwhelms culinary considerations.

MEETINGHOUSE, THE ⓈⓂ 25 | 21 | 24 | $37
1701 Octavia St. (Bush St.), 415-922-6733

■ "A perfect match of food and decor" characterizes this Pacific Heights New American with "upscale", but "straightforward" cooking and a "homey", yet "elegant", "Shaker-inspired" interior; factor in "personal attention" from an "excellent" staff and you have a place that's "just like going home . . . only much better."

Mel's Drive-In ◑🔲ⓈⓂ⇦ 12 | 14 | 13 | $15
2165 Lombard St. (Steiner St.), 415-921-2867
3355 Geary Blvd. (bet. Parker & Stanyan Sts.), 415-387-2255
1050 Van Ness Ave. (Geary St.), 415-292-6357

☑ "Teenyboppers and tourists" love this American chain where you don't get actual car service but you do get a "flashback of Americana" ("'50s decor") with your "greasy" burger and fries; even townies who find the food "mediocre" concede that all-night hours make them "perfect for a 2 AM feeding frenzy" but, hey, "where's the Fonz?"

Mescolanza ⓈⓂ 19 | 15 | 20 | $24
2221 Clement St. (bet. 23rd & 24th Aves.), 415-668-2221

■ Now under the new ownership of its chef, who did a "nice redecorating job" to boot, this "cozy" Richmond District Northern Italian continues to be "another very good neighborhood place" for a winning Caesar salad, popular pizzettas or homemade pasta.

Michelangelo Cafe 🔲ⓈⓂ⇦ 18 | 17 | 18 | $21
579 Columbus Ave. (Union St.), 415-986-4058

■ "Lots of lovely oil paintings cover the walls" of this "tightly packed" North Beach trattoria where diners down "delicious Italian seafood" dishes with "goblets of red wine"; you can "expect to wait", and some "wish they took reservations", but the tab is modest and you'll "dig the Gummi Bears with the check."

Mifune ⌊⌋⑤Ⓜ　　　19｜ 11｜ 13｜ $15｜
Japan Ctr., 1737 Post St. (bet. Buchanan & Webster Sts.), 415-922-0337

■ To "combat the fog" on "a cold, rainy" day, savvy slurpers stroll over to this "tiny" Japantown noodle shop where "udon galore" and super soba come at "rock-bottom prices"; the decor may be "pseudo-Japanese" and the service not as hot as your steaming "big bowl", but otherwise this is a "dependable" choice for "comfort food."

Millennium ⑤Ⓜ　　　22｜ 19｜ 20｜ $32｜
Abigail Hotel, 246 McAllister St. (bet. Hyde & Larkin Sts.), 415-487-9800

■ "Who needs meat?" when you've got this "upscale", Civic Center "haute" Vegetarian whose "inventive" cuisine is served by "helpful servers" in a "charming atmosphere"; N.B. sybarites say that those staying at the Abigail Hotel should ask about the Full Moon Aphrodisiac Night package.

Miss Millie's ⌊⌋⑤　　　19｜ 18｜ 18｜ $19｜
4123 24th St. (bet. Castro & Diamond Sts.), 415-285-5598

■ "Orgasmic breakfasts" and brunches, consisting of "carefully crafted homey fare" such as "wonderful" lemon ricotta pancakes and cinnamon rolls, are the draw at this "cutesy" Noe Valley American with a retro look that "transports you back to the '40s"; dinner is served, but it's Millie's morning meal that draws the lines.

Mom is Cooking ⌊⌋⑤Ⓜ∅　　　19｜ 9｜ 14｜ $15｜
1166 Geneva Ave. (bet. Edinburgh & Naples Sts.), 415-586-7000

☑ "Big, messy plates" of "cheap", "super tamales" and "melt-in-your-mouth carnitas", washed down with "great margaritas", offset an atmosphere that "leaves much to be desired" at this "funky" Outer Mission Mexican.

MoMo's ⌊⌋⑤Ⓜ　　　20｜ 21｜ 19｜ $35｜
760 Second St. (The Embarcadero), 415-227-8660

☑ "It's a hit!" declare fans of this "attractive", new South Beach Traditional American in a "great location" across from Pac Bell Park, the future home of the Giants; with "flavorful", hearty dishes, a "comfortable room", "nice patios", an "action-packed bar" and "friendly, snappy service", it's best to "go now" because once the baseball season starts "you'll need to be Barry Bonds to get in."

Montage ⌊⌋⑤Ⓜ　　　–｜–｜–｜ E｜
Sony Metreon Ctr., 101 Fourth St. (Mission St.), 415-369-6111

Hungry culture vultures take note: this dazzling newcomer in the Sony Metreon Center has a speckled-blue marble bar and comfy booths that are ideal for watching large video screens that display a montage of art on exhibit at the nearby SFMOMA; the kitchen's pretty artistic too, putting out a creative menu of Cal-influenced New American cuisine.

Moonshine 🆂Ⓜ   – | – | – | E
498 Broadway (Kearny St.), 415-982-6666
On the North Beach site that once housed the venerable
Vanessi's comes this new Southern supper club featuring
BBQ from an in-house smoker and a "unique", high budget
film–quality, Prohibition-era interior designed by co-owner
Don DeFina, a former set designer; the "fun", speakeasy
ambiance (including dancing) is further fueled by a massive
selection of bourbons.

Moose's 🄻🆂Ⓜ   22 | 21 | 21 | $38
1652 Stockton St. (bet. Filbert & Union Sts.), 415-989-7800
◪ Host extraordinaire Ed Moose's eponymous North Beach
Cal-Mediterranean bistro is a "hub" for a "social-column"
crowd attracted to the "lively bar", "convivial" "people-
watching" and nightly jazz; rounding out "the warm SF
environment" is a "strong new chef's" "terrific" food
("better than it needs to be"), which is complemented by
an "awesome wine list."

Morton's of Chicago 🆂Ⓜ   22 | 21 | 22 | $52
400 Post St. (bet. Mason & Powell Sts.), 415-986-5830
◪ Truly a "man's" "expense-account" spot "for showing
off", this Downtown steakhouse may be a chain, but they
provide "classy" service and serve "gargantuan portions"
of "excellent" beef; that said, those not taking clients are
"surprised they don't charge for parsley garnish."

Mo's Burgers 🄻🆂Ⓜ   22 | 9 | 13 | $13
1322 Grant Ave. (bet. Green & Vallejo Sts.), 415-788-3779
Yerba Buena Gardens, 772 Folsom St. (bet. 3rd & 4th Sts.),
415-957-3779
■ "They know what medium rare means" at this cheap
North Beach patty joint where the "big, lusty burgers" are
"the standard by which all others are judged" and the
"excellent" shakes are "wonderfully thick"; N.B. there's
now a new branch in SoMa's Yerba Buena Gardens.

Mozzarella Di Bufala 🄻🆂Ⓜ   17 | 9 | 13 | $16
1529 Fillmore St. (bet. Geary Blvd. & O'Farrell St.), 415-346-9888 ◐
2114 Fillmore St. (California St.), 415-346-9928
69 West Portal Ave. (Vicente St.), 415-661-8900
■ Though this chain "isn't just a pizza place", and
offers Italian-Brazilian fare too, it's the "pretty good" pies,
particularly the cornmeal-crust version, that get the most
kudos ("hard to go there for anything else").

Narai 🄻🆂   ▽ 20 | 14 | 19 | $22
2229 Clement St. (bet. 23rd & 24th Aves.), 415-751-6363
■ For many residents of the Richmond District, this "family-
run" Thai "favorite" has virtually become "our second
dining room", serving "delicious", "top-quality" fare such as
"great curries and satays"; despite plain-Jane surroundings,
this "nice neighborhood place" is "always a pleasure."

Neecha Thai Cuisine 🄻🅂🄼   19 │ 14 │ 17 │ $20

2100 Sutter St. (Steiner St.), 415-922-9419

■ "Awesome Thai food for not a lot of money" is the appeal of this "cozy", "underrated" Van Ness/Polk eatery that specializes in vegetable dishes (more than 40 choices), as well as "tasty" pad Thai and "shockingly good tofu"; though "the decor is nothing special", a "sweet atmosphere" persuades and "prices are affordable."

New Joe's 🄻🅂🄼   15 │ 13 │ 15 │ $24

347 Geary St. (bet. Mason & Powell Sts.), 415-989-6666

■ Get a "great cooking show" thrown in for the modest price of your meal by sitting at the counter at this Downtown Italian and watching the chefs whip up "satisfying" dishes like "good pastas" tossed with "excellent sauces."

New Pisa 🄻🅂🄼   15 │ 15 │ 19 │ $23

550 Green St. (bet. Columbus & Grant Aves.), 415-989-2289

☑ Expect "plenty of hearty food at reasonable prices" at this "friendly" North Beach Italian "landmark"; even if the room "isn't elegant" and the "so-so" eats not really authentic, loyalists swear it's "plain old fun" anyway and the owner will throw in a few "good baseball stories" (he used to "play ball in the streets with Joe DiMaggio") – so "you won't leave hungry or unhappy."

Nippon Sushi 🄻🄼⊄   ∇ 18 │ 7 │ 13 │ $18

314 Church St. (15th St.), no phone

■ Also known as "No Name Sushi" because there's no sign out front (as well as no phone, no reservations and no credit cards), this tiny cult Japanese in the Castro does have "cheap, good and plentiful" sushi and there's "a line every night" to prove it; prepare for "sketchy service", but at these prices, don't complain.

Nob Hill Cafe 🄻🅂🄼   20 │ 16 │ 18 │ $26

1152 Taylor St. (bet. Clay & Sacramento Sts.), 415-776-6500

■ "If you want to eat, not dine" on tony Nob Hill, then this "quaint" Italian with a "small menu" of "solid-value" food "can't be beat"; with its "friendly, bustling" ambiance and "eager service", it makes for a popular "neighborhood spot", which means "the wait can be a problem" ("no reservations" accepted).

North Beach Restaurant ◐🄻🅂🄼   19 │ 18 │ 18 │ $33

1512 Stockton St. (bet. Green & Union Sts.), 415-392-1700

☑ "If you know what to order", this North Beach spot that prepares "rich, old-fashioned pastas" and other "mainstays" can be "a solid Italian experience"; while detractors consider it "stuffy" and "tired" and say the "food needs a lift", veterans defend the art-filled room as "an institution, for good reason."

North India 🄻🅂🄼   20 | 15 | 17 | $28
3131 Webster St. (bet. Greenwich & Lombard Sts.), 415-931-1556
◪ Despite a "drab interior", "lack of atmosphere" and "lackluster service", this Union Street standby is considered one of "our best Indian" options, featuring "spicy and pungent" homestyle cooking ("fantastic breads" and "consistently delicious tandoori" specialties); some gripe that it's "a tad pricey", but the fare is "true" and "reliable."

Northstar &   – | – | – | M
Little Dipper Bakery 🄻🅂
288 Connecticut St. (18th St.), 415-551-9840
The owners of popular Firefly have created this "very cute new place in Potrero Hill" with their first restaurant in mind: there's solid, home-style American-Eclectic fare (try the ahi tuna tempura maki), a "charming neighborhood" atmosphere ("warm, yellow walls") and fair prices; N.B. check out their Little Dipper Bakery around the corner, which provides the restaurant's desserts.

Oberon 🅂🄼   20 | 16 | 21 | $34
1450 Lombard St. (bet. Franklin St. & Van Ness Ave.), 415-885-6555
■ "A surprising find on motel row", this "quirky and great" Marina Mediterranean (with gypsy music on weekends) is lamb heaven, turning out "amazing" recipes in an "old-fashioned setting"; the staff is "friendly" and "attentive" too, making this an insider's "favorite for a restful, relaxing meal" and "a great joint" that "deserves to be discovered."

Occidental Grill 🄻🄼   17 | 16 | 18 | $31
453 Pine St. (bet. Kearny & Montgomery Sts.), 415-834-0484
■ Recently reopened after a kitchen fire, this "great", "old SF bar with a lot of class" is once again a happening scene Downtown; "too bad cigars are no longer" welcome (due to the state smoking ban), but tipplers can still sip the definitive martini; food is not really the point here, but some say the New American fare is "reliable."

One Market 🄻🄼   22 | 20 | 20 | $42
1 Market St. (Steuart St.), 415-777-5577
◪ After a recent chef change at Bradley Odgen's SoMa New American, some loyalists say the fare remains "delicious"; a larger contingent, however, are "disappointed" in "skimpy portions" from a "limited menu" of "uneven" dishes; admirers only hope it'll soon start to "live up to what it could be."

Oodles 🄼   21 | 16 | 19 | $37
900 Bush St. (Taylor St.), 415-928-1888
◪ Devotees of Elka Gilmore's "avant-garde" Nob Hill bistro laud her "cute and clever" Euro-Asian "fusion cuisine", particularly the "interesting tasting menus" with "unusual combos" (even if the "quality varies"); critics, though, dismiss the "bizarre" dishes that amount to a "mishmash of ideas."

O'Reilly's Irish Pub & Restaurant L S M   16 | 17 | 15 | $22
622 Green St. (bet. Columbus Ave. & Powell St.), 415-989-6222
■ You'll get "Irish delights from the great lads" at this "popular" North Beach pub; fans "love" "the finest Guinness in SF", which can't help but improve the "hearty", if "ordinary", grub; now, "where are the step dancers?"

Original Joe's ◐ L S M   18 | 13 | 17 | $24
144 Taylor St. (bet. Eddy & Turk Sts.), 415-775-4877
■ "How can you resist such a gamy spot" as this "old-style" Italian-American "landmark", which boasts a founder (aged 86) who still shows up for work every day, keeps on a staff that's "been there since the earth cooled" and has "character to spare"; the "scary" Tenderloin location is part of the experience, but otherwise it's comforting to know some things "stay the same, no matter what."

Original Old Clam House L S M   16 | 13 | 15 | $23
299 Bayshore Blvd. (Oakdale St.), 415-826-4880
☑ SF's oldest restaurant (since 1861), this "great old fish house" in a "horrible, out-of-the-way neighborhood" in the Mission attracts blue-collar types who "know a good cioppino when they taste it" (it's one of the few things not deep-fried here); while it's "not worth a special trip", try this "funky place if it's on your route."

Oritalia S M   24 | 23 | 22 | $41
Juliana Hotel, 586 Bush St. (Stockton St.), 415-782-8122
■ Since its move Downtown to "larger", "sophisticated" digs in the Juliana Hotel, this "superb" Asian-Mediterranean is even better across the board; Brenda Buenviaje's "seductive" cooking virtually "defines fusion cuisine" with "original", "incredible flavors"; though a few "preferred the intimate size of the old location" and bemoan that "it's lost some of its luster", most rate this destination "a must" and swear "the next day it's all you'll think of."

Osaka Grill L S M   ▽ 22 | 19 | 22 | $29
1217 Sutter St. (bet. Polk St. & Van Ness Ave.), 415-440-8838
■ For an "entertaining and delicious" meal, visit this Van Ness/Polk "local resource", which many consider the "best Japanese grill in SF"; "all the fun of flying knives" is paired with "quality ingredients" (which now includes Kobe beef and foie gras) cooked tableside on hibachis in "bright, pleasant" surroundings; the service is "friendly" too.

Osome S M   18 | 12 | 16 | $25
3145 Fillmore St. (bet. Filbert & Greenwich Sts.), 415-931-8898
■ "If an hour wait is too long at nearby Ace Wasabi's", this Union Street Japanese "isn't a bad alternative", offering "above-average sushi" and sashimi; fans claim it "never disappoints", but also concede that "it's hard to be negative" because it's staffed by such "nice" people.

Osteria S 21 | 18 | 21 | $28 |
3277 Sacramento St. (Presidio Ave.), 415-771-5030
☑ "One of our favorite places for Caesar salad", this "cozy" Pacific Heights Northern Italian caters to "neighborhood regulars" who are "a little geriatric"; detractors quip that "the place is getting as tired" as the crowd, with "food that seems ordinary"; still, even if it "isn't memorable", many feel it's a "good, much needed" trattoria in these parts.

OVATION S M 21 | 27 | 22 | $47 |
Inn at the Opera, 333 Fulton St. (bet. Franklin & Gough Sts.), 415-553-8100
☑ The "spectacular" setting of this Civic Center French-Continental makes it an "elegant" destination for "quiet celebrations", with live music and "plush" appointments; garnering more mixed reviews than the "smashing" room is the cuisine ("superb" vs. "so-so"), but in any case, it's "superconvenient to the Opera House."

PACIFIC L S M 26 | 23 | 24 | $46 |
Pan Pacific Hotel, 500 Post St. (Mason St.), 415-929-2087
■ "Still one of the city's best-kept secrets", this "quiet" Downtown Pacific Rim–Californian "oasis" tucked away in the Pan Pacific Hotel shines with "terrific" cuisine proffered in a "gorgeous room" by a cadre of "smart waiters"; it all adds up to "one class restaurant", a "real sleeper" where it shouldn't be this "easy to get a reservation."

Pacific Cafe S M 22 | 16 | 21 | $25 |
7000 Geary Blvd. (34th Ave.), 415-387-7091
■ "Omnipresent lines" attest to the popularity of this "wonderful" Outer Richmond seafooder where "they respect what they cook" in the kitchen; while a few dissenters yawn "run of the mill", most appreciate the "simply prepared fresh fish" offered at "bargain" prices and the "free-wine-while-you-wait policy."

Palio d'Asti L M 21 | 20 | 20 | $36 |
640 Sacramento St. (bet. Kearny & Montgomery Sts.), 415-395-9800
■ After a "wonderful greeting" from the "friendly hosts", "the whole meal follows through" "pleasantly" at this "high-buzz" Downtown Italian with colorful, "post-modern decor"; on the premises is the Enoteca della Douja wine bar, which offers a nifty variety of vini by the glass.

Palomino L S M 19 | 22 | 18 | $33 |
345 Spear St. (bet. Folsom St. & The Embarcadero), 415-512-7400
■ SoMa Mediterranean thoroughbred with "impressive views" and "awesome ambiance"; the "Friday night pickup" "scene" can turn it into "yuppie purgatory", but just dig into the "spectacular" Gorgonzola fries and you might find you "love this place."

Pancho Villa Taqueria ◐ⓁⓈⓂ   22 | 8 | 12 | $10
3071 16th St. (bet. Mission & Valencia Sts.), 415-864-8840
■ Despite the "sleazy locale", Mexican aficionados rave about this cafeteria-style Mission taqueria's "taste explosions in a tortilla", found in the "best burritos in the city" and other "honest", "beautifully fresh" eats; "another of SF's ethnic treasures", it's "always great and cheap."

Pane e Vino ⓁⓈⓂ   24 | 19 | 20 | $34
3011 Steiner St. (Union St.), 415-346-2111
■ For a "breath of Italy", book a table – if you can – at this "sunny", "lively" Union Street trattoria that celebrates "real, gutsy flavors" in such "scrumptious" dishes as "sensational pastas" and "sublime" risottos; the "charming" waiters deserve "Mr. Personality" awards and help make this "inviting" spot "an always happy experience"; most everyone agrees it's entirely "delightful" but just "wish it were easier to get in."

Park Chow ⓁⓈⓂ   19 | 15 | 18 | $19
1240 Ninth Ave. (Irving St.), 415-665-9912
■ There are "absolutely no pretensions" at this "cheap, bustling and yummy" Inner Sunset cafe with a "diverse" menu of "appealing" "down-home" chow (with Asian, American and Italian influences), "friendly service" and a "great beer selection"; in sum, this may be the "best deal in the city" for a "fun, tasty and easy" meal.

Park Grill ◐ⓁⓈⓂ   22 | 21 | 21 | $40
Park Hyatt Hotel, 333 Battery St. (Clay St.), 415-296-2933
■ Tucked away in the Park Hyatt Downtown, this "classy oasis" is set in a "tasteful, quiet" room where "conversation is actually possible", making it a prime choice for a "business breakfast" or "power lunch"; while the "corporate" atmosphere turns off some, bigwigs commend this "unsuspectedly super place" for its "fine" New American menu and "excellent service."

Parma ⓁⓂ   20 | 15 | 19 | $25
3314 Steiner St. (bet. Chestnut & Lombard Sts.), 415-567-0500
■ "Watch out for the garlic" at this "tiny and plain but wonderful" Marina Italian where "you can tell that the people who serve you love food"; the "homey" eats, such as "excellent eggplant parmigiana", come in "mammoth portions" at "reasonable" prices, prompting legions of fans to plead "don't change a thing!"

Pasta Pomodoro ⓁⓈⓂ   14 | 11 | 14 | $15
2027 Chestnut St. (Fillmore St.), 415-474-3400
655 Union St. (Columbus Ave.), 415-399-0300
1865 Post St. (Fillmore St.), 415-674-1826
1875 Union St. (Laguna St.), 415-771-7900
2304 Market St. (Castro St.), 415-558-8123

Pasta Pomodoro (Cont.)
816 Irving St. (9th Ave.), 415-566-0900
🔲 Respondents will have to agree to disagree on these "quick-fix Italian" pasta houses with "rubber-stamp" decor and a "formulaic" menu of "unbelievably consistent food"; cynics pan "boring", "chain pasta", but many supporters feel it's "excellent for the price" and wonder "how can they do it so cheaply?"

Pastis 🔲🅼　　　23 | 20 | 22 | $37
1015 Battery St. (Green St.), 415-391-2555
■ Executive chef Gerald "Hirigoyen has the touch", proven both at Fringale and here at his "intimate", "blessedly quiet" Downtown bistro that showcases a "deliciously different" menu of New French and Basque-influenced creations; the "impeccable service" takes just the right tone in the "inviting" room, leading devotees to proclaim "SF needs more restaurants like this."

Pauline's Pizza　　　21 | 13 | 16 | $20
260 Valencia St. (bet. Duboce & 14th Sts.), 415-552-2050
■ "NYC–style" "pizza par excellence" with "wild combos", along with "incredible salads", draw boosters to this "hip" Mission "joint"; "in a mediocre pizza town, these are unusually good", especially the "best pesto" pie, and make it "worth the trip" to this "dodgy" neighborhood.

Pauli's Cafe 🔲🆂🅼　　　15 | 12 | 16 | $22
2500 Washington St. (Fillmore St.), 415-921-5159
■ "Popular" Pacific Heights New American cafe featuring "yummy pancakes" and "eggs Benedict to die for" ("dinner's ok too, and you can always get a table"); a few cite "uneven" food, but many find it a "reliable spot" that "serves the neighborhood well."

Pazzia Caffe & Pizzeria 🔲🅼　∇ 22 | 14 | 20 | $22
337 Third St. (bet. Folsom & Harrison Sts.), 415-512-1693
■ "Superior thin-crust pizza" is the house specialty at this SoMa Italian, "a real charmer" with an "exceptionally warm neighborhood" feel; set in a "convenient location" near the Moscone Center and SFMOMA, it's a favorite lunch spot with "good people-watching."

Perry's 🔲🆂🅼　　　14 | 15 | 16 | $24
1944 Union St. (bet. Buchanan & Laguna Sts.), 415-922-9022
Perry's Downtown 🔲🆂🅼
Galleria Park Hotel, 185 Sutter St. (bet. Kearny & Montgomery Sts.), 415-989-6895
🔲 "Men in midlife crisis" frequent these twin Traditional American "hangouts" with a "sports bar feel"; aside from the occasional "excellent daily special", the eats are "standard", though "when you need to belong somewhere", these grills might do; still, skeptics can't help but quip "the '80s called – they want their look back."

Piaf's S　　　18 | 21 | 19 | $37
1686 Market St. (Gough St.), 415-864-3700

☑ The "clubby, hazy" ambiance at this "intimate" Civic Center New French brasserie is a fitting backdrop for the live cabaret performances; while the food is "quite good, if not outstanding", it's the "unusual entertainment" and "romantic and magical" ambiance that make a visit a "pleasant evening out."

Picaro L S M⇗　　　▽ 16 | 12 | 13 | $19
3120 16th St. (bet. Guerrero & Valencia Sts.),
415-431-4089

☑ Fine "for a quick meal before a show at the Roxie", this Mission District Spanish cafe specializes in tapas that aficionados say are "delish" and "cheap", while critics find them "overly greasy"; either way, it's an option "if you don't have a reservation" elsewhere in the area.

Pier 23 Cafe L S M　　　12 | 15 | 12 | $21
Pier 23, The Embarcadero (Greenwich St.),
415-362-5125

☑ "On a sunny day the place to be" is the "perfect outdoor patio" at this "casual" Traditional American cafe with enormous "waterfront appeal" and a "fantastic view" that "makes it irresistible", despite "mediocre" grub; otherwise, it's a "fun" "dive" that functions as a "meet market", where "you're certainly paying for the location."

Pintxos L S　　　– | – | – | M
557 Valencia St. (bet. 16th & 17th Sts.), 415-565-0207

The name may mean tapas in Basque, but the focus is on full dinners at this upscale, new Spaniard located on an up-and-coming strip of Valencia, which has become the Restaurant Row of the Mission; expect an exuberant crowd and a beautiful interior featuring Iberian-themed paintings, photographs and a centerpiece mural.

PJ's Oyster Bed L S M　　　20 | 14 | 17 | $27
737 Irving St. (bet. 8th & 9th Aves.), 415-566-7775

☑ "Be adventurous – try the alligator" at this "jovial" Inner Sunset Cajun seafood "delight" where diners "feast" on "large portions" of "fresh", "yummy" dishes filled with "Crescent City flavors"; regulars "let the good times roll" here, even though a few detractors quip "this oyster bed has lost its pearls."

Planet Hollywood L S M　　　7 | 15 | 9 | $22
2 Stockton St. (Market St.), 415-421-7827

☑ "If you're 12 or 13", you might be "dazzled" by the "cool paraphernalia" on display at this Downtown salute to Hollywood, but discerning palates will be offended by the "limp" cooking at this chain American "tourist trap"; while it may be "fun" enough for "movie buffs", most decree this "rip-off" "doesn't belong on my planet."

Plouf 🅛Ⓜ

| 22 | 18 | 19 | $31 |

40 Belden Pl. (bet. Bush & Pine Sts.), 415-986-6491
■ The notoriously "charming, flirty waiters" at this Downtown New French seafooder seem "straight from central casting" and surveyors find the signature mussels and frites equally "irresistible"; though the decor's "a little austere", the room is warmed by a lively clientele enjoying the "wonderful muscles" – er, we mean mussels.

PLUMPJACK CAFE 🅛Ⓜ

| 24 | 22 | 23 | $44 |

3127 Fillmore St. (bet. Filbert & Greenwich Sts.), 415-563-4755
■ Oozing "star quality", this "stylish", "clubby" Union Street Med entices with an "always changing, always great" menu, paired with a "tantalizing" retail-priced wine list (thanks to the owners' nearby spirits shop); a few sniff "how good can hype really taste?", but most praise an "upscale dining" experience enhanced by "professional service"; N.B. there's also a branch in Olympic Valley.

Pluto's 🅛🆂Ⓜ

| 18 | 11 | 12 | $13 |

3258 Scott St. (Chestnut St.), 415-775-8867
627 Irving St. (8th Ave.), 415-753-8867
■ "Who needs to cook" if this cafeteria-style American chainlet is nearby, heaping on "massive quantities of mom's home cooking"; despite a "byzantine" ordering system, most "love" this "terrific idea" – "eat cheap, get full."

POSTRIO 🅛🆂Ⓜ

| 26 | 26 | 24 | $52 |

Prescott Hotel, 545 Post St. (bet. Mason & Taylor Sts.), 415-776-7825
■ Prepare to be thoroughly "dazzled" by this "striking" Wolfgang Puck creation Downtown – sip a cocktail at the "energized" bar, "make your grand entrance" down the "fabulous" stairway, ease into the "plush" dining room, bask in the "star-studded scene", and revel in chefs Steven and Mitchell Rosenthal's "sensational" Cal cuisine (with Med and Asian accents); "they hit all the marks" and "get everything right from A to Z."

Prego Ristorante ●🅛🆂Ⓜ

| 17 | 17 | 17 | $31 |

2000 Union St. (Buchanan St.), 415-563-3305
■ A "solid standby", this Union Street Italian with a "European ambiance" is "not great but it's always good"; even if it's been "outclassed by newer, trendier restaurants" in the area, it remains a "neighborhood favorite" for many, with a bonus: "you can get in" easily.

Presidio Cafe 🅛🆂Ⓜ

| – | – | – | M |

300 Finley Rd. (Arguello Blvd.), 415-561-4661
Designed largely to appeal to golfers at the adjacent Presidio Clubhouse, this three-meals-a-day Californian cafe teed off in mid '99 with an unassuming menu of sandwiches, burgers and pastas, plus a few ambitious choices for those feeling giddy after breaking par; fore!

Primo Patio Cafe 🇱 Ⓜ⊄   ▽ 20 | 11 | 11 | $15 |
214 Townsend St. (bet. 3rd & 4th Sts.), 415-957-1129
■ For a "Caribbean experience", check out this "low-key" breakfast-and-lunch SoMa cafe; though the service operates at its own "rhythm" (read "slow"), it's a "cute place for good, cheap food" and the patio is "neatly" "funky."

Puccini & Pinetti 🇱 Ⓢ Ⓜ   16 | 17 | 17 | $27 |
Monticello Inn, 129 Ellis St. (bet. Mason & Powell Sts.), 415-392-5500
☑ "Fine for a pre-theater or shopping stop", this "casual" Downtown trattoria dishes up fare that "sometimes works and sometimes doesn't", although when the kitchen is on, the results can be "surprisingly good"; but critics warn about "unfriendly service", adding "don't be fooled by the name – the Italian connections are pretty tenuous."

Radicchio Trattoria Ⓢ   ▽ 19 | 17 | 18 | $28 |
1809 Union St. (bet. Laguna & Octavia Sts.), 415-346-7373
■ Naturally, there's always at least one dish with radicchio on the Northern Italian menu of this Union Street trattoria with a "romantic", fresco-filled dining room; since the kitchen's handiwork scores well, this "never-crowded" venue deserves to be less of a "secret."

Rasselas Ethiopian Ⓢ Ⓜ   ▽ 17 | 14 | 15 | $22 |
2801 California St. (Divisadero St.), 415-567-5010
■ An "unusual" combination of nightly live jazz and Ethiopian fare attracts a diverse crowd to this Pacific Heights hybrid, which works best "for large groups so that everyone can share."

Raw Ⓢ   14 | 11 | 15 | $20 |
1224 Ninth Ave. (Lincoln Way), 415-665-6519
☑ The name has changed a number of times, but the concept remains the same at this "unusual" Inner Sunset spot where all the food is organic, vegan and (yes) raw; it's "wonderful for the adventurous", even if the less enthused politely demure – "well, it was an experience."

Red Herring 🇱 Ⓢ Ⓜ   – | – | – | E |
(fka Roti)
Hotel Griffon, 155 Steuart St. (bet. Howard & Mission Sts.), 415-495-6500
Surfacing in the Hotel Griffon, on the site of the former Roti, is this newcomer that's reeling them in with chef James Ormsby's (ex Bruno's) adventurous American seafood with Asian accents; the fishing-themed decor and open, airy ambiance with striking Bay view are also part of the lure.

Redwood Room ◑🇱 Ⓢ Ⓜ   – | – | – | E |
Clift Hotel, 495 Geary Blvd. (Taylor St.), 415-775-4700
Supplanting the closed French Room as the main restaurant at the Clift is this art deco stunner, which has long been one of SF's most elegant bars, and now offers a Cal-Med menu.

Restaurant Marais 🔲Ⓜ — — — E
662 Mission St. (3rd St.), 415-538-1840
This new SoMa venture from chef Alan McLennan (ex Cypress Club) offers Classic and Contemporary French fare, plus modern 'régime cuisine', meaning no-salt, no-sugar, low-fat, high-flavor food; the restaurant is named after the hip Marais district in Paris – what more could a card-carrying trendy want?

Rick's ⓈⓂ 19 16 19 $25
1940 Taraval St. (30th Ave.), 415-731-8900
☑ This offbeat Outer Sunset venue features chef Rick Oku's Eclectic "comfort food", ranging from "superior pot roast" to kalua pork at the luau dinners on the first Monday of the month; nautical decor, a "big" bar scene and live Hawaiian bands on Saturday night should help draw the curious.

Ricochet Restaurant & Bar Ⓢ — — — M
215 West Portal Ave. (bet. 14th Ave. & Vicente St.), 415-566-5700
"At last, a place worth going to" in West Portal declare write-in comments for this newcomer that turns out "adept" New American "comfort" fare and "good martinis", including a nifty lobster version that's actually an appetizer.

Ristorante Bacco ⓈⓂ 21 18 22 $31
737 Diamond St. (bet. Elizabeth & 24th Sts.), 415-282-4969
■ "Killer" made-to-order risotto, unusual Roman dishes ("a welcome change") and "fabulous tiramisu" are a few of the many recommended choices on the "simple" but "wonderful" menu of this "small" Noe Valley trattoria serviced by "expert" "real Italian waiters."

Ristorante Ecco 🔲Ⓜ 22 22 21 $36
101 South Park (bet. 2nd & 3rd Sts.), 415-495-3291
■ Appreciative surveyors "always feel welcome" at this "stylish", "airy" SoMa "modern" Italian on trendy South Park ("great view"), "an adult restaurant where you can hear each other" while eating "deeply satisfying" fare or sipping Chianti from a "nice wine list"; a "terrific" staff and "easy parking" in the evening round out the experience.

Ristorante Ideale Ⓢ 21 16 21 $29
1309 Grant Ave. (bet. Green & Vallejo Sts.), 415-391-4129
☑ "Get a window table for people-watching" at this "ideal North Beach trattoria", which is "still a find" thanks to "Northern Italian tastes" served "with a Southern welcome"; insiders add that the "great ravioli" is the way to go.

Ristorante Milano Ⓢ 21 15 21 $31
1448 Pacific Ave. (bet. Hyde & Larkin Sts.), 415-673-2961
■ Another contender for serving the "best gnocchi" in the city, this Russian Hill hideaway is known for its "well-prepared" Northern Italian cuisine and devoted co-owners Aldo Blasi and Nicola Viti; N.B. since parking is tough, use the validated lot a block away or take public transportation.

RITZ-CARLTON DINING ROOM Ⓜ   28 | 28 | 28 | $68
Ritz-Carlton Hotel, 600 Stockton St. (bet. California & Pine Sts.), 415-773-6198

■ "Treat yourself to the good life" at this Nob Hill New French wallet-wrencher where "talented" Sylvain Portay always produces something "incredible" and "elegance takes on new meaning" after spending an evening in the "rarefied" room; a harpist in the background and a "pampering" staff (rated No. 1 in the *SF Survey* for service) round out the "seldom-less-than-extraordinary" experience.

Ritz-Carlton Terrace Ⓛ Ⓢ Ⓜ   25 | 25 | 26 | $47
Ritz-Carlton Hotel, 600 Stockton St. (bet. California & Pine Sts.), 415-773-6198

■ "It's pleasant to eat outside" on the "pretty patio" of this Nob Hill Mediterranean, which, despite living in the shadow of The Dining Room, is still "an amazing experience unto itself", with the "best Sunday brunch" and a snazzy seafood buffet on Friday evening; as befits a Ritz, there's also "impeccable" service and a pricey tab.

Rocco's Seafood Grill Ⓢ Ⓜ   21 | 20 | 20 | $31
2080 Van Ness Ave. (Pacific Ave.), 415-567-7606

■ "Finally, a winner!" exclaim reviewers excited by the possibility that this Van Ness/Polk Continental-seafooder will end the restaurant jinx at this location; their optimism is based on the "fun bistro atmosphere" and "helpful" staff that brings out "good prime rib" and "perfectly fresh" fish.

Roosevelt Tamale Parlor Ⓛ Ⓢ ⊭   19 | 7 | 13 | $14
2817 24th St. (bet. Bryant & York Sts.), 415-550-9213

☑ "Go ahead, take a chance" urge intrepid reviewers who've ventured to this "super cheap" deep–Mission District Mexican for "hearty plates of tamales" and holy mole; despite being "pretty old and decrepit", sentimental types hope that it will "survive forever."

Rooster, The Ⓢ Ⓜ   19 | 18 | 18 | $29
1101 Valencia St. (22nd St.), 415-824-1222

☑ "High-end comfort food" from various ethnic cuisines is the "hip" concept behind this "dark", rustic Mission District Eclectic; while the "experience varies" ("nothing to crow about" vs. "all the kudos are true"), there is agreement on the "thoughtful wine list" and moderate prices.

ROSE PISTOLA ◖ Ⓛ Ⓢ Ⓜ   21 | 20 | 18 | $38
532 Columbus Ave. (bet. Green & Union Sts.), 415-399-0499

☑ Reed Hearon's "trendy" North Beach Italian-seafooder attracts a "diverse crowd" ("big blondes, yuppies, gay couples") and generates an equally wide range of responses: boosters love the "hip" atmosphere and "family-style" portions of "excellent" Ligurian dishes; naysayers find it "overhyped" with a "brutal noise level" and a staff that's generous with the "attitude."

Rose's Cafe 🅛🅢🅜   18 15 15 $22
2298 Union St. (Steiner St.), 415-775-2200
■ On sunny weekend mornings, "yuppies" like to "grab"
a sidewalk table at this Union Street Italian, a sibling to
Rose Pistola with "occasionally inspired" omelets, salads
and sandwiches; "shaky", "Euro-paced" service detracts,
but "if you're too lazy to go to North Beach, this will do."

Rosti 🅛🅢   16 14 15 $25
2060 Chestnut St. (bet. Fillmore & Steiner Sts.), 415-929-9300
☑ This Marina spin-off of an LA-based Italian chain is
appreciated by some for its "reasonable prices" on
"yummy" rotisserie chicken, pizza and pasta, even if
foodies think there are "better places."

Rotunda 🅛🅢🅜   19 25 20 $30
Neiman Marcus, 150 Stockton St. (Geary St.), 415-362-4777
☑ After an exhausting morning trying on clothing, Union
Square shoppers make stop-overs for popovers at this
lunch-only New American cafe in Neiman Marcus; with
"luxurious" decor and a "fussy", "intimate" ambiance, it's
also a perfect "place to bring mother" for tea (2:30–5:00 PM).

Royal Thai 🅛🅢🅜   22 15 18 $24
951 Clement St. (11th Ave.), 415-386-1795
See review in North of San Francisco Directory.

Rubicon 🅛🅜   24 21 22 $49
558 Sacramento St. (bet. Montgomery & Sansome Sts.),
415-434-4100
☑ An "attractive crowd" of "business diners" packs this
celebrity-backed Downtown New French–Californian for the
dynamic combination of chef Scott Newman's "exceptional"
food and super sommelier Larry Stone's "spectacular wine
list"; quibblers find the "understated" setting "slightly stuffy"
and "corporate", but concede the place "still has the buzz."

Rumpus 🅛🅢🅜   19 18 19 $34
1 Tillman Pl. (bet. Post & Sutter Sts.), 415-421-2300
■ Set to reopen in fall '99 after being closed due to a flood,
this "stylish" Downtown New American should continue to
be a "wonderful hideaway" for lunch; menu highlights
include the pan-roasted chicken that's the "best thing I
ever tasted" and an "incredible" warm chocolate brioche.

Sam's Grill &   21 17 18 $32
Seafood Restaurant 🅛🅜
374 Bush St. (bet. Kearny & Montgomery Sts.), 415-421-0594
■ "For a true SF experience without the tourists", "look no
further" than this Downtown American-seafood landmark
(1867) where "old-boy customers" get comfortable in "cool,
curtained booths" and "seasoned", "curmudgeonly" waiters
serve "fab bread", creamed spinach and "reliable" classics,
such as sand dabs and petrale ("still gets fish right");
"fortunately, some things never change."

Sanppo ●⓵⓶⓷   ▽ 17 | 13 | 15 | $19 |
1702 Post St. (Buchanan St.), 415-346-3486
☑ While "not much for atmosphere", this Japantown
Japanese is a smart choice when looking for all the
standards (sushi, tempura, teriyaki) at "affordable" prices.

Sanraku Four Seasons ⓵⓶⓷   ▽ 24 | 13 | 18 | $28 |
704 Sutter St. (Taylor St.), 415-771-0803
Sony Metreon Ctr., 101 Fourth St. (Mission St.),
415-369-6166
■ "Sit at the sushi bar" and indulge in a "wide variety" of
"premium sakes" is the advice given by the small coterie
of voters familiar with this Downtown Japanese; ambiance
may be "lacking", but the "fresh and beautifully" prepared
offerings compensate; N.B. the Sony Metreon Center
branch is new and unrated.

Savor ⓵⓶⓷   17 | 17 | 15 | $18 |
3913 24th St. (Sanchez St.), 415-282-0344
☑ "Unusual crêpe combos", "both savory and sweet",
are the draw at this affordable Noe Valley Eclectic with a
pleasant, Taos-like ambiance and a "lovely patio in back",
which is an ideal setting for a lunchtime salad or "good
brunch"; the unimpressed say it's fine for the area, but
otherwise "nothing special."

Scala's Bistro ●⓵⓶⓷   23 | 22 | 20 | $36 |
Sir Francis Drake Hotel, 432 Powell St. (bet. Post & Sutter Sts.),
415-395-8555
■ This late-night Downtown French-Italian is a real people-
watching and "eavesdropping" scene, with popular pre-
and post-theater meals ("the best portobellos", "try the
Bostini"), a "well-trained", "gracious" staff and a "warm"
bistro ambiance; despite being "loud" and "a little tourist-
worn", it remains a "best bet in Union Square."

Schroeder's ⓵⓶   14 | 15 | 15 | $25 |
240 Front St. (bet. California & Sacramento Sts.),
415-421-4778
☑ "Best for men", this "dark", "old-style" Downtown
German has been serving "authentic", "heavy" sauerbraten,
Wiener schnitzel and potato pancakes since 1893; while
detractors call the place "way past its prime" with a "tired",
"impatient" staff, they still make a point of returning when
the Bavarian polka band plays.

Scoma's ⓵⓶⓷   19 | 17 | 18 | $33 |
Pier 47 (bet. Jefferson & Jones Sts.), 415-771-4383
☑ "Stick with the simple stuff" such as "worthwhile
cioppino" and you'll do fine, say advocates for this "festive",
"touristy" Fisherman's Wharf seafooder; the less impressed
appreciate the "large portions", but find the food "bland
for the price."

Scott's L S M
17 | 17 | 17 | $32
3 Embarcadero Ctr., promenade level (Drumm St.), 415-981-0622
◾ While its Lombard Street outpost has closed, this "touristy" Downtown Embarcadero Center location still offers "fresh", "consistently good" (if "not imaginative") seafood; for those who can't get enough of Scott's fish, there are also branches south and east of SF, though the aforementioned are under different ownership.

Sears Fine Food L S M ⊘
16 | 10 | 15 | $16
439 Powell St. (bet. Post & Sutter Sts.), 415-986-1160
◾ Out-of-towners "stand in line" to sample this Downtown retro coffee shop's "best silver-dollar pancakes" and strawberry waffles, but that doesn't stop some locals from rolling their eyes and saying "please tell the tourists that there are lots of better breakfast spots."

Seoul Garden ◖ L S M
▽ 22 | 14 | 16 | $22
Japan Ctr., 22 Peace Plaza (bet. Laguna & Webster Sts.), 415-563-7664
◼ Bargain-hunters note that "you get so much food for your money" at this Japantown Korean with an authentically clad staff and a menu that "focuses on rustic country" dishes and barbecued meats and vegetables.

Shanghai 1930 L S M
20 | 23 | 18 | $40
133 Steuart St. (bet. Howard & Mission Sts.), 415-896-5600
◾ "Exotic elegance" best describes the decor of George Chen's "sophisticated" SoMa Chinese supper club, a "classy" celebrity hangout with a "super bar", "great jazz" and "some novel, excellent dishes" ("go with a mouth ready to experiment"); foes bemoan occasionally "spotty service", "small portions" and "expensive" prices.

Silks L S M
24 | 25 | 24 | $53
Mandarin Oriental Hotel, 222 Sansome St. (California St.), 415-986-2020
◾ "If you're on a business trip" to SF, consider a visit to this Downtown Cal-Asian, which soothes with its "imaginative presentation" of "superb", "complicated" dishes, "solicitous service" and "excellent wine list"; P.S. the "gorgeous" dining room, which is "quiet" and sometimes "surprisingly empty", is scheduled to be remodeled in early 2000.

SLANTED DOOR L S
25 | 17 | 19 | $31
584 Valencia St. (17th St.), 415-861-8032
◼ This "outstanding", "unique twist on" Vietnamese (tops in its category) in the Mission District has "cool", "spartan" decor, "waiters who stay on their toes" and some of the "most exciting", "creative" cuisine in town ("I'll never forget the clay-pot chicken") that's "pure flavors and textures"; "unreal" wines only add to the misery of those who find it "impossible to get in"; N.B. there's now valet parking.

Slow Club ⬛🅛🅢🅜   20 | 18 | 16 | $26
2501 Mariposa St. (Hampshire St.), 415-241-9390
🔳 A "trendy", black-clad crowd says take a good look at the person you're dining with before entering this "industrial" Potrero Hill New American, because "it's so dark" "you won't see them once inside"; no matter, because the "excellent, innovative dishes" can be "quite a surprise", even if the place "must have been named for the waiters."

Socca ⬛🅛🅢   21 | 19 | 20 | $34
5800 Geary Blvd. (22nd Ave.), 415-379-6720
◼ For a "joyful surprise in the hinterlands" of the Outer Richmond, stop by this "romantic" Mediterranean with an "eager-to-please staff", a "fairly priced wine list" and "interesting, delicious food", even though much-loved chef John Caputo has departed.

South Park Cafe ⬛🅛🅜   21 | 19 | 19 | $31
108 South Park (bet. 2nd & 3rd Sts.), 415-495-7275
◼ Sorry, kids, there are "no cartoon chefs" at this "unpretentious" SoMa French bistro on South Park, just "terrific" "comfort food" and a "sixth-arrondissement" ambiance that's "so romantic it will make your date look better" (proof: "witnessed two proposals"); easy "Citroën parking" adds to its appeal with Francophiles.

Splendido ⬛🅛🅢🅜   21 | 22 | 19 | $36
4 Embarcadero Ctr. (Drumm St.), 415-986-3222
🔳 The combination of chef Giovanni Perticone's "splendid" contemporary Italian cuisine ("gorge yourself on the appetizers") and Pat Kuleto's whimsical country-village setting prompts first-time visitors to this Downtown high-achiever to ask: "what's a restaurant like you doing in a mall like this?"; to get over the shock, they might order a bottle from the "incredible wine list."

Stars ⬛🅛🅢🅜   – | – | – | E
555 Golden Gate Ave. (Van Ness Ave.), 415-861-7827
Big changes are afoot in the foodie firmament with the completion of Jeremiah Tower's sale of his legendary SF icon in the Civic Center; as we go to press, new owner Andrew Yap is closing the restaurant briefly for an overhaul; when it reopens (in early fall), new chef Christopher Fernandez (a Paul Bertolli protégé) is scheduled to oversee a menu of rustic Italian cuisine; the redone space will have a clubbier feel and there will be expanded dining at the famous bar.

Stelline ⬛🅛🅢🅜   13 | 13 | 16 | $23
429 Gough St. (bet. Hayes & Ivy Sts.), 415-626-4292
🔳 "Cheap" and "upbeat", this "homey" Civic Center Italian works for a "friendly" pre-performance meal when sibling Caffe Delle Stelle "is full"; otherwise, finicky foodies find the edibles "unimaginative" and "nothing too special."

Stinking Rose ●ⓁⓈⓂ   14   14   14 $25
325 Columbus Ave. (Broadway), 415-781-7673

◪ "Expect no vampires after eating" at this garlic-themed
North Beach Italian, which might be an amusing "place for
your friends from out-of-town who won't be dissuaded",
but is, otherwise, a "tourist trap" and "sad gimmick", right
down to its retail shop selling garlic-flavored condoms.

Straits Cafe ⓁⓈⓂ   22   18   18 $29
3300 Geary Blvd. (Parker St.), 415-668-1783

■ This Richmond District Singaporean features "exotic
cocktails", chef-owner Chris Yeo's "mouthwatering" flavors
from a "very different" menu, "clever decor" that recreates
a country village and "knowledgeable servers" ("ask for
suggestions"); in sum, a "unique spot" that's "strongly
recommended"; N.B. there's another location in Palo Alto.

Sukhothai ⓁⓈⓂ   ▽ 17   14   18 $17
1319 Ninth Ave. (Irving St.), 415-564-7722

◪ "If you can get over the name", some say you'll find
"bright flavors" at this affordable Inner Sunset Thai, while
the unexcited counter that it's just "another decent place" in
its category; to find out for yourself, consider ordering the
signature spicy string beans with chicken or sizzling duck.

Suppenküche ⓈⓂ   21   16   17 $24
601 Hayes St. (Laguna St.), 415-252-9289

■ Young groups of sudsophiles love tapping into the
"unbelievable selection" of "fantastic" Deutsch brews at
this "stark", "modern" Civic Center beerhall where "lighter"
but still "satisfying" German food ("great venison", "terrific
sauerbraten") is brought to communal plank tables by a
"friendly" staff; while it's "crowded" and "too noisy", at
least "you don't leave needing a bypass."

Sushi Groove ⓈⓂ   22   20   15 $28
1916 Hyde St. (Union St.), 415-440-1905

■ "Beautiful people" and hipsters ("many nightclub
owners") flock to this "trendy", midrange Van Ness/Polk
Japanese for the "best spicy tuna roll in the city" and
other "groovy sushi" from a chef who "takes pride in his
creations"; while the "teenybopper" staff may dish out
"attitude" and the setting is "cramped", this is undeniably
a "cool place."

Swan Oyster Depot ⓁⓂ⌀   25   12   21 $24
1517 Polk St. (bet. California & Sacramento Sts.), 415-673-1101

■ "Darling countermen" shuck "flawless oysters", dish out
"the best clam chowder" and plate up "yummy cracked
crab" at this legendary Van Ness/Polk seafood bar with an
"old-fashioned" counter and tile decor that haven't changed
since it opened it 1912; "so what if it's chaotic", and a
"bit expensive", this is an old SF tradition that retains its
"personal touch"; N.B. 5:30 PM is closing time.

Sweet Heat ⬛🅛🅢🅜   17 | 11 | 14 | $14
3324 Steiner St. (bet. Chestnut & Lombard Sts.), 415-474-9191
1725 Haight St. (bet. Cole & Shrader Sts.), 415-387-8845
2141 Polk St. (bet. Broadway & Vallejo St.), 415-775-1055
◪ These "cheap", "child-friendly" Marina, Haight-Ashbury and Van Ness/Polk sibs are "not your average Mexicans", thanks to "healthy", "interesting seafood and vegetarian offerings" and an "amazing array of tequilas"; there may be some "rather strange combos" ("love the ice cream burrito for dessert"), but they're part of the reason these are some of "the better gringo taquerias in town."

Tadich Grill ⬛🅛🅜   20 | 18 | 18 | $31
240 California St. (bet. Battery & Front Sts.), 415-391-1849
◪ "Everyone should go once" to this Downtown seafooder, reputedly SF's oldest restaurant (1849) and decidedly a piece of "cultural bedrock", where an "interesting" crowd, ranging from businesspeople to tourists, is "captivated by the "bygone-era" decor and "gruff" waiters; so "get a curtained booth", "stick with the grilled items", and presto, "you're back in the 19th century."

Taiwan ⬛🅛🅢🅜   18 | 7 | 12 | $15
445 Clement St. (6th Ave.), 415-387-1789
289 Columbus Ave. (Broadway), 415-989-6789
■ "All sorts" of "fine potstickers" headline the menu at these "bargain" Richmond District and North Beach Taiwanese spots; however, "at these prices don't expect great service" or elaborate decor.

Tanuki ⬛🅛🅢🅜   ▽ 21 | 13 | 16 | $23
4419 California St. (bet. 6th & 7th Aves.), 415-752-5740
◪ "Underrated" in the opinion of Richmond Japanese buffs, perhaps because its "location could be better", this "tiny, neighborhood treat" has a "relaxed mood" ("good place for a beer") and a "very friendly", "alert" sushi chef who prepares a "creative selection of rolls."

Tavolino ⬛🅛🅢🅜   21 | 20 | 18 | $33
401 Columbus Ave. (Vallejo St.), 415-392-1472
◪ North Beach residents love to "sit outside", soak up the "good people-watching" and "nibble" on the more than 25 kinds of Venetian-style tapas, or *cichetti*, served at this "wonderful new addition"; while many are "anxious to return" to make a larger dent in the menu and "eclectic wine list", they warn that "the check adds up."

Terra Brazilis 🅢   – | – | – | M
602 Hayes St. (Laguna St.), 415-241-1900
Cal-influenced Brazilian fare is the concept behind this "nice", hip addition to the Civic Center area; its "sweet service", "pretty" setting, generally "yummy food", "complementary wine list" and fair prices are fueling a buzz.

Thanh Long ⑤   – | – | – | M |
4101 Judah St. (46th Ave.), 415-665-1146
"Beautifully remodeled with a spiffy bar", this French-
influenced Vietnamese sister to Crustacean continues to
serve "excellent seafood", including a "great roasted
crab" and "to-die-for garlic noodles"; it's a Long way to
its Outer Sunset location, but "go early" because the
distance doesn't deter folks ("long lines").

THEP PHANOM THAI CUISINE ⑤Ⓜ   25 | 16 | 19 | $22 |
400 Waller St. (Fillmore St.), 415-431-2526
■ "Phanomenal" Thai can be had at this top-rated, "always
packed" Lower Haight venue, a source of continuing
"innovation" with an "endless menu of amazing dishes",
a "gracious" staff that "makes you feel at home" and
affordable prices; recommended choices include "great
BBQ chicken" and "fabulous seafood."

Thirsty Bear Brewing Co. ⓁⓈⓂ   17 | 14 | 14 | $24 |
661 Howard St. (bet. Hawthorne & 3rd Sts.), 415-974-0905
■ An "unusual selection" of "zesty" tapas ("you must try
the fish cheeks"), washed down with "original" suds, is
the concept behind this SoMa Spanish brewpub, a "good
postwork meeting place" for "yup hordes", despite a
"deafening" "industrial setting."

Ti Couz ⓁⓈⓂ   21 | 15 | 16 | $19 |
3108 16th St. (bet. Guerrero & Valencia Sts.), 415-252-7373
■ Hordes of surveyors say they'd gladly "wait in line" for
the "never-ending combinations" of "excellent" sweet or
savory Breton-style crêpes, washed down with hard cider
or "fabulous" lemonade, served at this wallet-friendly "taste
of France in the Mission"; it's also an "awesome brunch
spot" where it's always smart to "save room for dessert."

Timo's ◐ⓈⓂ   19 | 13 | 14 | $25 |
842 Valencia St. (bet. 19th & 20th Sts.), 415-647-0558
■ Sangria-savvy surveyors sing the praises of this "loud",
"lively" Mission Spaniard, a "good tapas option" that's
"perfect for a group" or parties; P.S. there's a "tremendous
variety" of "tasty tidbits" on the menu, but the "to-die-for"
Catalan-style spinach is a favorite.

Tin-Pan Asian Bistro ⓁⓈⓂ   19 | 18 | 17 | $24 |
2251 Market St. (bet. Noe & Sanchez Sts.), 415-565-0733
◪ Boosters of this Castro/Noe bistro with "modern Oriental
decor" describe it as "a sort of greatest hits" of Pan-Asian
food, where "dynamic combinations" produce "unusual
flavors"; critics think the "inconsistent" offerings "look
and sound better" than they taste; nonetheless, a "good
location" means on a busy night "this place sizzles" like
won tons on a wok.

Tita's 🄻🅂🄼⇗ ▽ 15 | 10 | 16 | $18 |
3870 17th St. (bet. Noe & Sanchez Sts.), 415-626-2477
▣ "Authentic Hawaiian fare with a hearty portion of aloha spirit" is the word on this unusual, little-known Castro/Noe outpost; it's also a "good brunch place" (try the French toast), "especially since there's never a wait."

Tokyo Go Go 🅂 22 | 22 | 18 | $28 |
3174 16th St. (bet. Guerrero & Valencia Sts.), 415-864-2288
▣ "Sit at the sushi bar" and watch the chefs concoct "interesting combos" at this Mission Japanese, a "quieter" sibling to Ace Wasabi with a "cute", '60s retro look that shouldn't distract from the fact that the kitchen "can cook well too" ("miso-marinated sea bass = heaven"); sake cocktails and a full wine list round out this newcomer.

Tommaso's 🅂 22 | 16 | 19 | $25 |
1042 Kearny St. (bet. Broadway & Pacific Ave.), 415-398-9696
■ "Truly nice owners" run this North Beach Italian that makes classic calzone, "melt-in-your-mouth lasagna" and "legendary", thin-crust pies that are "by far the best in the city"; diners can "expect long waits" and a "tiny" setting that's "like being in a cocoon", but they're small prices to pay considering that they "make you feel like family."

Tommy's Joynt ◐🄻🅂🄼⇗ 14 | 13 | 11 | $15 |
1101 Geary Blvd. (Van Ness Ave.), 415-775-4216
▣ "Neon signs" lure in SF's "most blue-collar" "good ol' boys" to this "cheap", cafeteria-style Van Ness/Polk American hofbrau, a "funky" "late-night" "joint" where the "hearty feed" of meats, such as oxtail, brisket and signature buffalo stew, is washed down with "lots o' beers."

Tommy Toy's
Cuisine Chinoise 🄻🅂🄼 25 | 24 | 24 | $50 |
655 Montgomery St. (Washington St.), 415-397-4888
■ With "silk-boudoir" decor, a "seductive", attractively lit atmosphere that makes "everyone look good", a staff that "treats guests like kings and queens", "exceptional" French-influenced Chinese fare and an "excellent wine list", this Downtown Chinese is clearly operating "on another level"; so even if it's "expensive", and the jacket-and-tie-required policy (at dinner) and other "pretentious" touches turn off a few, the majority calls this a "favorite place to take visitors."

Tonga Restaurant
& Hurricane Bar ◐🅂🄼 11 | 24 | 13 | $31 |
Fairmont Hotel, 950 Mason St. (California St.), 415-772-5278
▣ "It doesn't get any kitschier" than this Nob Hill, pseudo–South Seas spot where artificial rainstorms punctuate the festivities and live Polynesian bands strike up what one critic suspects are actually "covers of Spice Girls'" songs; "the novelty wears off quickly", as does tolerance for the "mediocre" Chinese food, but that doesn't mean it isn't "fun."

Ton Kiang Restaurant L S M　　25 | 13 | 16 | $23

5821 Geary Blvd. (bet. 22nd & 23rd Aves.), 415-387-8273

■ In the eternal SF dim-sum wars, this "clean", "bright" Richmond District Chinese takes no prisoners and is proclaimed the "best in town" thanks to a "dizzying assortment" of offerings, including dumplings so light "they can be inhaled"; but save some room, because there's also "excellent Hakka cuisine" such as "marvelous clay-pot casseroles."

TOP OF THE MARK S　　18 | 26 | 20 | $42

Mark Hopkins Hotel, 1 Nob Hill (bet. California & Mason Sts.), 415-616-6916

◩ A "still magical" view and a room that "embodies the history, beauty and sophistication" of SF are the two main attractions at this tourist-oriented Nob Hill Californian, a "romantic place for drinks" and dancing, with a "quality", if "expensive", Sunday brunch; N.B. a three-course, prix fixe dinner is available on Friday and Saturday nights, otherwise the menu is limited to appetizers.

Tortola L　　17 | 13 | 16 | $20

3640 Sacramento St. (bet. Locust & Spruce Sts.), 415-929-8181 S
Stonestown Galleria, 3251 20th Ave. (Winston St.), 415-566-4336 S M 🍽
Crocker Galleria, 50 Post St., 3rd. fl. (bet. Kearny & Montgomery Sts.), 415-986-8678 M 🍽
UCSF Medical Ctr., 500 Parnassus Ave., Millberry Union Bldg. (2nd Ave.), 415-731-8670 M 🍽

◩ Fresh, "healthy" Cal-Mex food is the concept behind this "casual" local chain that does a "welcome variation" on burritos, tacos and enchiladas; N.B. while the other locations are basically for takeout, the full-service Sacramento Street branch has some "nice specialties" like signature tamales.

Town's End
Restaurant & Bakery L S　　21 | 17 | 19 | $24

2 Townsend St. (The Embarcadero), 415-512-0749

◩ With the new Giants stadium opening two blocks away, this "friendly" SoMa New American restaurant/bakery will be even more "busy" because of its "wonderful breakfasts" and "perfect brunches" that are "worth the wait for the bread basket alone"; surveyors seem to pay scant attention to dinner ("uninspired"), but those "baked goods are yum."

Trattoria Contadina S M　　21 | 17 | 20 | $27

1800 Mason St. (Union St.), 415-982-5728

◩ "Exactly what one expects in North Beach", this "cute" bistro offers a "straightforward menu" of "family-style" dishes ("excellent pasta"), "good service" and decor "flavor" in the form of photographs of Italian-American sports heroes; "weekend waits are a killer sometimes", but that's because everyone knows this a "great place for a Friday night dinner with friends."

Tu Lan ⃝L⃝M⃝⌐
8 Sixth St. (Market St.), 415-626-0927

20 | 4 | 9 | $12

◪ Set in a "dicey" Downtown neighborhood that's ideal for "buying stolen stuff", this "seedy" Vietnamese's "third-world atmosphere" prompts diners to "close everything but their mouths" while chowing down on "cheap", "terrific food", including "the best" imperial rolls.

2223 Restaurant ⃝S⃝M
2223 Market St. (bet. Noe & Sanchez Sts.), 415-431-0692

22 | 19 | 19 | $34

■ "The best option for a nice meal" and "even better people-watching" in the Castro, this American bistro is now "back in the groove" under its original chef (and now co-owner) Melinda Randolph, who works wonders with "upscale" comfort food such as "excellent" roast chicken and the "best mashed potatoes."

Universal Cafe ⃝L⃝S
2814 19th St. (bet. Bryant & Harrison Sts.), 415-821-4608

23 | 18 | 19 | $31

■ In a "cool" "industrial-looking" space with "lots of energy", this Mission New American "winner" is "worth the trek" for "delicious, serious food made with care"; its "off-the-beaten-track" location is considered "a good thing" by the "oh-so-trendy clientele" that puts up with "uncomfortable seating" and "arrogant service" because "each dish is interesting and tasty."

Valentine's Cafe ⃝S
1793 Church St. (30th St.), 415-285-2257

19 | 14 | 18 | $23

■ "Cozy and sweet", this Noe Valley Vegetarian "find" serves an "excellent, inventive" menu of Indian-inspired, mostly vegan fare that's so "incredibly good", some think it "rivals" that of the legendary Greens; you've never truly eaten a portobello mushroom until you try the "perfect piccata" here, so forgive the "cramped quarters."

Venticello ⃝S⃝M
1257 Taylor St. (Washington St.), 415-922-2545

22 | 23 | 21 | $34

■ "What a find on Nob Hill" enthuse admirers of this "intimate" Northern Italian "hideaway" that "hands down is one of the most romantic restaurants in SF"; nearly as "wonderful" as the "beautiful" room is the "mouthwatering" fare, prepared with "flair" and first-rate service; the smitten predict "you'll come back."

Via Vai ⃝L⃝S⃝M
1715 Union St. (bet. Gough & Octavia Sts.), 415-441-2111

19 | 16 | 17 | $28

■ "Chic" "customers that look like stars" constellate at this "friendly" Union Street Italian (a "more relaxed" spin-off of nearby Pane e Vino) for "awesome" pizzas from the wood-burning oven, "tasty" pastas and other "amazing food for the price"; repeat customers agree it's "worth going to again" and again, but "please do something about the noise!"

Vicolo L S M | 20 | 11 | 13 | $18 |
201 Ivy St. (bet. Franklin & Gough Sts.), 415-863-2382
■ "Though there's not much atmosphere" at this Civic Center Italian, it "takes pizza to a different place" with "superb cornmeal crusts" and "creative" "yuppie toppings like wild mushrooms"; convenient to Davies Symphony Hall, it's a "pre-opera perennial" "for a quick and affordable" "light meal", but "good luck finding it in the *vicolo* (alley)."

Vineria S | 21 | 16 | 19 | $26 |
3228 16th St. (bet. Dolores & Guerrero Sts.), 415-552-3889
◪ "The price is right" at this "no-frills" Mission Northern Italian (from the owners of L'Osteria Del Forno) that dishes up "straightforward" food, including "the best gnocchi in sage-butter sauce"; cynics cite "uninteresting" stuff, but others "knew after the first time that we'd be back again."

Vinga L S M | 19 | 19 | 19 | $31 |
320 Third St. (Folsom St.), 415-546-3131
◪ "If you want paella", head over to this "intriguing" yet "undiscovered" SoMa Spaniard that specializes in "unusual Catalan dishes"; though the "food is uneven", much of it is "tasty and worth trying"; thus, despite its "misses", it "has possibilities", leading many to "hope this place makes it."

Vivande Porta Via L S M | 22 | 16 | 18 | $31 |
2125 Fillmore St. (bet. California & Sacramento Sts.),
415-346-4430
■ Find "stellar preparations" of Italian dishes (particularly Sicilian specialties) at Carlo Middione's Pacific Heights trattoria, "a restaurant disguised as an Italian deli" where you can dine in or get the "appealing" fixings to go; while it may be "a bit pricey" considering "the deli atmosphere", most maintain "I've loved this place for years."

Vivande Ristorante L S M | 21 | 22 | 20 | $41 |
Opera Plaza, 670 Golden Gate Ave. (bet. Franklin St. &
Van Ness Ave.), 415-673-9245
◪ "Near the opera house", this "fancy" Civic Center Italian (another Carlo Middione venue) turns out "reliably delicious" fare, notably the "best fresh pasta" in SF, in an "elegant" room; partisans "can't figure out why this place isn't packed", but perhaps it's because so many gripe that it "should be even better" for the "upscale" price.

Wa-Ha-Ka
Oaxaca Mexican L S M⊐ | 15 | 10 | 12 | $13 |
1489 Folsom St. (11th St.), 415-861-1410
1980 Union St. (Buchanan St.), 415-775-4145
◪ "Tacos, booze and noise" sums up these "no-frills" Mexicans "with all the charm of a cafeteria"; aficionados say the grub is "fresh and cheap", but critics pass on "Americanized" eats that "need work"; still, night owls depend on them "for a quick bite" before hitting the clubs.

Washington Square Bar & Grill L S M
17 | 18 | 18 | $33

1707 Powell St. (Union St.), 415-982-8123

■ Endearingly referred to as "the Washbag" by its "politico" clientele, this "convivial hangout" in North Beach is "an all-around SF tradition", serving American "comfort food in comfortable surroundings" with "old-world charm"; even if some detect "shrinking menu, creeping prices", it's a "mainstay" for its loyalists.

Waterfront Cafe L S M
22 | 24 | 19 | $44

Pier 7 (Broadway & The Embarcadero), 415-391-2696
Waterfront Restaurant
Pier 7 (Broadway & The Embarcadero), 415-391-2696

■ The "breathtaking Bay view" is a major lure at this pier-side Californian seafood house on The Embarcadero, but the "innovative" cuisine "happens to be wonderful" too; "truly gourmet" courses are "prepared with care", and despite "phantom waiters", the "fantastic setting" promises "a night to remember"; the casual cafe downstairs is more of "a deal", but the "delightful" restaurant "upstairs is closer to heaven."

Watergate S M
23 | 19 | 20 | $37

1152 Valencia St. (bet. 22nd & 23rd Sts.), 415-648-6000

■ Well, this Mission Franco-Asian newcomer is certainly "different for the area"; gourmands rave about "exquisite" fusion cuisine "that works" – "interesting combinations" based on "generous ingredients"; dissenters, however, deem the "stuffy decor" "just too precious" and hint the service "needs work."

WOODWARD'S GARDEN S
26 | 15 | 21 | $37

1700 Mission St. (Duboce St.), 415-621-7122

■ A "real miracle" in a "lousy" "under-the-freeway" Mission District location, this "extremely cozy" (only 31 seats) New American "treasure" somehow "feels like a secret though everyone knows it's so good"; the "gem of a menu" is "unique" yet accessible, offering "some of the best food in SF", and it's served by an "endearing" staff that ensures it's "always a treat" – "even with a view of the exit ramp."

World Wrapps L S M ⊉
13 | 8 | 11 | $10

2257 Chestnut St. (bet. Pierce & Scott Sts.), 415-563-9727
2227 Polk St. (bet. Green & Vallejo Sts.), 415-931-9727
Safeway Ctr., 2012 Market St. (Church St.), 415-487-7300

■ "They'll wrap anything" but "the kitchen sink" at this International chain of "yuppie burrito" joints; some like the "oversized" bundles stuffed with "savory combinations of tastes", especially the "samurai salmon" concoction, but most yawn it's "a concept that's been worked to death"; still, it's an "affordable", "filling" "alternative to fast food."

Xyz L S M | – | – | – | E |
W Hotel, 181 Third St. (Howard St.), 415-817-7836
Universal Cafe owners Gail Defferari and Bob Voorhees
teamed up with Starwood Hotels to create this Cal-French
restaurant and wine bar in SoMa's tony new Hotel W; with
chef Alison Richman (ex Rubicon) behind the stove, the
cuisine should be as cutting-edge as the decor.

Yabbies Coastal Kitchen S M | 24 | 19 | 20 | $36 |
2237 Polk St. (bet. Green & Vallejo Sts.), 415-474-4088
■ Though Mark Lusardi has stepped down from day-to-day
kitchen duties, this "underrated" Van Ness/Polk seafood
house still "makes a fish lover's heart go pitter- patter" over
its "amazing" dishes and an "excellent raw bar"; a "smiling"
staff and "great ambiance" throughout the "cool, modern"
room add to the lure of this piscatory "heaven."

Yank Sing L S M | 24 | 15 | 18 | $26 |
49 Stevenson St. (bet. 1st & 2nd Sts.), 415-541-4949
427 Battery St. (bet. Clay & Washington Sts.), 415-781-1111
■ "Eat yourself silly" on "dim sum at its best" at this pair of
Downtown Chinese "mob scenes" where grateful grazers
appreciate that "the pushcart ladies speak English"; be
warned that it's "really easy to go overboard" because
every morsel is "incomparable" and "who could say no to
anything on those small plates?"; N.B. no dinner.

Ya-Ya Cuisine L M | 21 | 16 | 18 | $27 |
663 Clay St. (bet. Kearny & Montgomery Sts.), 415-434-3567
■ "Warm and cozy" Downtown Middle Eastern whose loyal
following "loves everything about it" – the "distinctive" Fertile
Crescent cuisine that's "unusually tasty", the "charming"
owner and the "nice, quiet ambiance"; it's "reasonably
priced" too, making puzzled partisans wonder "why don't
more people go here?"

Yet Wah L S M | 14 | 10 | 13 | $20 |
Pier 39, Fisherman's Wharf (The Embarcadero), 415-434-4430
*Diamond Hts., 5238 Diamond Hts. Blvd. (Duncan St.),
415-282-0788*
2140 Clement St. (23rd Ave.), 415-387-8040
☑ All the "old-time favorites, like pressed duck and egg
foo young", can be found at these "busy" Chinese spots;
pros say they're "still good after all these years", providing
"fine, fast" meals at "reasonable prices", but many critics
dismiss the "inconsistent", "too-greasy" standard chow.

Yoshida-Ya L S M | 18 | 18 | 17 | $29 |
2909 Webster St. (Union St.), 415-346-3431
☑ In "tasteful surroundings", this Union Street Japanese
specializes in the "best variety of yakitori in SF" – skewered
meats, seafood and vegetables grilled on tabletop hibachis –
as well as "always-fresh" sushi; even if detractors find it
"overrated", families say it's "great fun with our kids."

Yoyo Bistro ⑤Ⓜ   ▽ 19 | 14 | 18 | $29
Miyako Hotel, 1611 Post St. (Laguna St.), 415-922-7788
■ Apparently too "out-of-the-way" for many diners, this "small", "undiscovered" Cal-Asian bistro in Japantown's Miyako Hotel rewards those who seek it out with "inventive East-West combos"; order lots of the "great appetizers" to best experience the "unique" tastes.

Yuet Lee Ⓛ⑤Ⓜ   19 | 5 | 10 | $18
1300 Stockton St. (Broadway), 415-982-6020 ●≠
3601 26th St. (bet. Guerrero & Valencia Sts.), 415-550-8998
■ "Don't be scared" of the "bizarre decor" at this garish Chinatown Cantonese seafood house where a "stubborn avoidance of charm" seems to be part of the "interesting experience"; the "wonderful menu" offers "superb" dishes, and as it's open till 3AM, "there's no better spot for late-night grubbing"; N.B. there's a Mission District branch too.

Yukol Place Thai Cuisine ⑤Ⓜ   ▽ 22 | 12 | 19 | $22
2380 Lombard St. (bet. Pierce & Scott Sts.), 415-922-1599
■ While there's next to "no ambiance" at this neighborhood Marina spot, it's "one of the best places for Thai food" in SF, turning out "delicious preparations" at palatable prices; the staff is "charming" and "friendly", making this definitely worth a visit.

Zaré on Sacramento Ⓛ Ⓜ   25 | 21 | 23 | $36
568 Sacramento St. (bet. Montgomery & Sansome Sts.), 415-291-9145
■ "The secret is leaking out" about Hoss Zaré's charming Med, which offers "a breath of fresh air Downtown"; the executive chef–owner "couldn't be more hospitable" and his "huge portions" of "robust cooking" are as "genuine, warm and focused" as he is; best of all, "you can always get a table – whoops, not anymore!"; P.S. the "cave-like" room is "a good place to seek shelter in the event of a nuclear war."

Zarzuela   21 | 17 | 20 | $28
2000 Hyde St. (Union St.), 415-346-0800
■ "We love the waiters, who add zip" to this "friendly, accommodating" Van Ness/Polk Spaniard that "sets the standard for tapas in SF", presenting an "endless variety" of "awesome" bites that are "impossible to pass" up; there's also "excellent paella" and "great sangria", making "it hard to go wrong here", but aficionados advise "take a taxi or ride your bike", because "parking is the only downside here."

Zax   24 | 19 | 23 | $37
2330 Taylor St. (Columbus Ave.), 415-563-6266
■ A "sweet little romantic spot" "hidden away" in North Beach, this Mediterranean "gem" enchants with a "superb" menu that may be limited "but everything on it is wonderful"; though it's "out of the way", the "friendly folks" who run it will make a meal here "a treat."

Zazie ⬛🅂🅜 20 17 18 $23
941 Cole St. (bet. Carl St. & Parnassus Ave.), 415-564-5332
■ Devotees head straight for the "lovely little patio" at this "casual" Upper Haight French bistro to delight in the "ooh-la-la" "wonderful" weekday breakfasts and weekend brunches; "warm, welcoming" and "unpretentious", it's a très "pleasant" "hangout", but locals plead "stop telling people about our secret."

Zinzino 🅂🅜 18 17 17 $26
2355 Chestnut St. (bet. Divisadero & Scott Sts.), 415-346-6623
■ A "young, local", devoted crowd has helped this "zany, modern" Marina Italian "evolve" into a "wonderful neighborhood" "favorite", with an "original, well-executed menu" that includes "excellent pizzas" and "delicious brick-oven entrees"; "no pomp or ceremony" here, just a "fun atmosphere" amplified by "colorful decor" and a "cute outdoor dining area" that affords "great people-watching."

Zodiac Club, The ◑🅂🅜 – – – M
718 14th St. (Market St.), 415-626-7827
Astrologically inclined reviewers thank their lucky stars for this "hip new spot in the Castro", a "dark", "kinda-clubby" Mediterranean where the entrees change according to the zodiac sign and all 12 constellations get their own cocktail; so check your horoscope then head on over; N.B. large parties should try to snare the circular, curtained Lion's Den table.

ZUNI CAFE ◑🅛🅂 23 20 19 $37
1658 Market St. (bet. Franklin & Gough Sts.), 415-552-2522
◪ "Joy radiates from the kitchen", an "artistic clientele" swarms the "hippest zinc bar in the city" and there's a "never-ending celebration" in the "cool" dining room of this Civic Center Mediterranean "scene"; from the "steadily brilliant menu", the famous and the famished feast on the "best roasted chicken on the planet"; even if it's "a little too-too", baby, "you're nobody in this town if you haven't been seen here."

East of San Francisco

Ajanta 🇱🇸🇲
23 | 17 | 19 | $24

1888 Solano Ave. (bet. Alameda & Colusa Aves.), Berkeley, 510-526-4373

☑ Yes, this "upscale" Berkeley Indian's reproduction Ajanta-cave "murals are mesmerizing", but patrons are also entranced by the "unconventional" menu, which features a different regional cuisine every month, meaning lots of "dishes you can't get anywhere else"; "reasonable prices" and an "attentive" staff and owner ("takes great pride") help offset quibbles about "skimpy" portions.

Autumn Moon Cafe 🇱🇸🇲
18 | 14 | 17 | $24

3909 Grand Ave. (Sunny Slope St.), Oakland, 510-595-3200

☑ "Terrific burgers" and "interesting chicken hash" are "attentively served" at this "unpretentious", movie poster–filled Oakland American cafe, which is "needed in the 'hood" and consequently gets "lines out the door for brunch."

Battambang 🇱🇸🇲
▽ 19 | 11 | 17 | $19

850 Broadway (9th St.), Oakland, 510-839-8815

■ Cambodian cuisine connoisseurs appreciate this "inexpensive" Oakland ethnic for its "good", "authentic flavors" and service that "exceeds expectations" for such a modest spot; N.B. don't leave without trying the desserts.

Bay Wolf 🇱🇸🇲
24 | 20 | 23 | $39

3853 Piedmont Ave. (Rio Vista), Oakland, 510-655-6004

☑ "It may not be flashy", but owner Michael Wild's Oakland Cal-Med is still a "classic" that "never disappoints" thanks to "awesome" preparations using "fresh ingredients", a "great wine list" and a "sincere" staff that gives a "friendly welcome at the door"; and as those who've "loved this place for 24 years" already know, "always bet on the duck dishes."

Benihana 🇱🇸🇲
16 | 15 | 18 | $30

Willow Shopping Ctr., 1989 Diamond Blvd. (Willow Pass Rd.), Concord, 925-827-4226

See review in San Francisco Directory.

Bette's Oceanview Diner 🇱🇸🇲
20 | 15 | 17 | $17

1807 Fourth St. (Hearst Ave.), Berkeley, 510-644-3230

■ "Long waits" for "the world's greatest breakfast" served at this Berkeley diner mean that you'll probably have to "leave your name and go window-shopping" on trendy Fourth Street before you can chow down on "dynamite souffléd pancakes"; N.B. tourists should leave the binoculars at home because there's no ocean view.

Bighorn Grill L S M ▽ | 16 | 17 | 17 | $29 |
2410 San Ramon Valley Blvd. (Crow Canyon Rd.), San Ramon, 925-838-5678
☑ While this San Ramon steakhouse features a Pat Kuleto–designed "hunting-lodge" interior that puts carnivores in the mood for meat, reactions to the kitchen's handiwork are lukewarm ("average"); nonetheless, it's "a nice choice if you're at the cinema" – just "don't go out of your way."

Bistro Viola L S M | – | – | – | M |
1428 San Pablo Ave. (2 blocks south of Gilman St.), Berkeley, 510-528-5030
This small, art-filled French-Californian bistro is a new addition to Berkeley's up-and-coming San Pablo corridor scene, serving gourmet hipsters all the essentials, such as frogs' legs, foie gras and fresh cheese.

Blackhawk Grille L S M | 22 | 22 | 20 | $36 |
Blackhawk Plaza, 3540 Blackhawk Plaza Circle (bet. Camino Tassajara & Crow Canyon Rd.), Danville, 925-736-4295
■ After examining the grilles on the vintage cars at the nearby Behring Auto Museum, consider "lunch on the patio" "by the pond" of this Cal-Med culinary version, a "local favorite" for Sunday brunch in "chichi" Danville.

Blue Nile L S | 18 | 15 | 16 | $16 |
2525 Telegraph Ave. (Dwight Way), Berkeley, 510-540-6777
☑ Maybe a "somewhat dark" place with "beaded booths" and no utensils (you eat with your fingers) is "not a good choice for the in-laws from the Midwest", but Berkeley residents have long viewed this Ethiopian as a convenient, "affordable" way to have an "interesting" ethnic experience.

Brazio L S M ▽ | 19 | 22 | 19 | $40 |
Blackhawk Plaza, 3421 Blackhawk Plaza Circle (Camino Tassajara), Danville, 925-736-3000
■ Fred Halpert, of St. Helena's Brava Terrace, recently opened this Italian-Mediterranean in Danville, and it's already being hailed as a smart addition; highlights include "beautiful decor" (tiled walls, elegant columns), two terraces overlooking a man-made waterfall and an exhibition kitchen serving "some interesting first choices" such as smoked salmon with mascarpone.

Breads of India L S M ▽ | 24 | 8 | 19 | $15 |
2448 Sacramento St. (Dwight Way), Berkeley, 510-848-7684
■ There are "lines out the door every night" for the daily changing menu of "excellent" "light, fresh" Indian cuisine, including winning breads ("best naan I ever tasted"), served at this "tiny" Berkeley newcomer; even those who find the setting "cramped" concede that for its category this is one of the "best in the East Bay."

Bridges Restaurant L S M 24 | 23 | 22 | $41
44 Church St. (Hartz Ave.), Danville, 925-820-7200
◪ "Where gorgeous people eat gorgeous" Pacific Rim–
Californian food in a truly "elegant" Danville setting ("even
the bathroom is exquisite"), this long-standing high-achiever
was "put on the map" when it was featured in *Mrs.
Doubtfire,* even if locals insist that they "appreciated it
much earlier"; bragging rights aside, a few critics find the
food "underportioned" and "pricey."

Bucci's L M 20 | 19 | 19 | $27
6121 Hollis St. (bet. 59th & 61st Sts.), Emeryville, 510-547-4725
■ Set in an "airy", "tasteful industrial" room with "good
art" and "amusing quotes" on the walls, this "popular"
Emeryville Mediterranean gets lots of huzzahs for its
"pleasing informality", "great pizza" and daily changing
menu that usually features a few "excellent" appetizers.

Cafe 817 L M ▽ 20 | 18 | 18 | $17
817 Washington St. (bet. 8th & 9th Sts.), Oakland, 510-271-7965
■ Oakland goes Tuscan with this Downtown cafe's Italian-
style breakfasts, where dishes such as polenta with
Taleggio and poached egg are "a morning revelation";
it's "an island of good food" in the middle of dullsville and
"every town should have one", so "how do we get" the
"delightfully attentive owner" "to open for dinner?"

Cafe Fanny L S M 22 | 12 | 13 | $15
1603 San Pablo Ave. (Cedar St.), Berkeley, 510-524-5447
■ Alice Waters' "trendy" breakfast/lunch counter New
French attracts an "artsy crowd" that tolerates the
"discomfort" of "practically nonexistent seating" because
they "love her buckwheat crêpes" and "to-die-for granola",
washed down with great, "big bowls of" "café au lait for
the gods"; comfort creatures crab – it's "nice food, if you
don't mind eating in a parking lot."

Cafe Rouge L S M 19 | 18 | 17 | $33
1782 Fourth St. (Delaware St.), Berkeley, 510-525-1440
◪ The "uplifting" atmosphere of this "large, airy" Berkeley
French bistro makes it "fun" for unrepentant carnivores
to indulge in a menu that's "heavy" with red meat dishes;
there's also what some call "the best roast chicken" and
"great oysters" too, but that doesn't stop critics from saying
the "inconsistent" kitchen "never lives up to its promise."

California Cafe L S M 18 | 18 | 18 | $31
*1540 N. California Blvd. (bet. Bonanza St. & Civic Dr.),
Walnut Creek, 925-938-9977*
See review in North of San Francisco Directory.

California Pizza Kitchen L S M 14 | 10 | 13 | $17
*Broadway Plaza, 1120 Broadway Plaza (Main St.), Walnut
Creek, 925-938-0720*
See review in San Francisco Directory.

César ⑤Ⓜ   22 | 20 | 19 | $25
1515 Shattuck Ave. (bet. Cedar & Vine Sts.), Berkeley, 510-883-0222
■ For the "ultimate" in Berkeley "cool", try to "make the scene" at this "late-night" Spanish tapas bar whose principals formerly worked at Chez Panisse; there's a "small menu" of "delicious" finger food backed by a "stunning spirits list", but brace yourself for the "noise" and "waits."

Cha Am Thai Ⓛ⑤Ⓜ   21 | 13 | 16 | $18
1543 Shattuck Ave. (Cedar St.), Berkeley, 510-848-9664
See review in San Francisco Directory.

Chevys Ⓛ⑤Ⓜ   12 | 12 | 13 | $18
650 Ellinwood Way (Contra Costa Blvd.), Pleasant Hill, 925-685-6651
See review in San Francisco Directory.

CHEZ PANISSE Ⓜ   27 | 23 | 25 | $64
1517 Shattuck Ave. (bet. Cedar & Vine Sts.), Berkeley, 510-548-5525
■ Culinary "goddess" Alice Waters' Berkeley Cal-Med "mother church" continues to draw raves ("a national treasure") for its "harmonious" use of the "freshest" ingredients in "barely embellished dishes"; since everyone goes in "expecting perfection", naturally a few "fail to understand" the "unadulterated" "magic" of the cuisine, but the overwhelming majority says it's definitely worth the "difficult reservations."

CHEZ PANISSE CAFE ⓁⓂ   27 | 22 | 24 | $39
1517 Shattuck Ave. (bet. Cedar & Vine Sts.), Berkeley, 510-548-5049
■ This Berkeley Cal-Med cafe upstairs from Chez Panisse is called a "better value" than its parent, with a "more flexible" menu and equally "wonderful" food using "high-quality ingredients"; an "unexpectedly informal" setting adds to its appeal as a "gem" that's "guaranteed to impress" – "if ya can get in" (same-day reservations only).

Citron ⑤Ⓜ   24 | 19 | 22 | $39
5484 College Ave. (bet. Lawton & Taft Sts.), Oakland, 510-653-5484
■ "Another Oakland star", this recently expanded, "cute" French-Med serves a limited menu that changes every three weeks, but always contains "top-notch" dishes with "big" flavors; the "great patio" and "welcoming" staff also explain why this stalwart is another "reason not to" dine in SF.

FatApple's Ⓛ⑤Ⓜ   16 | 12 | 16 | $15
7525 Fairmount Ave. (Colusa Ave.), El Cerrito, 510-528-3433
1346 Martin Luther King Way (Rose St.), Berkeley, 510-526-2260
■ "Terrific burgers", "fabulous olallieberry milk shakes" and pies worth a "pilgrimage" are the stars at these "wholesome" Americans that attract "long lines" for their "great breakfasts."

Faz L S M   18 | 18 | 18 | $29 |

600 Hartz Ave. (School St.), Danville, 925-838-1320
5121 Hopyard Rd. (bet. Gibraltar & Owens Drs.),
Pleasanton, 510-460-0444
See review in San Francisco Directory.

Garibaldis on College L S M   23 | 22 | 21 | $37 |

5356 College Ave. (bet. Bryant St. & Manila Ave.),
Oakland, 510-595-4000
■ The noise level at times may "prohibit conversation beyond sign language", but this "bustling", "airy" Oakland Cal-Mediterranean impressively combines "industrial-Renaissance decor" with "snappy" food (try a risotto), a "strong wine list" and "professional service" to produce an overall "winner"; in fact, some think this higher-rated outpost is even "better than" its city sibling – take that SF!

Ginger Island L S M   17 | 18 | 17 | $26 |

1820 Fourth St. (Hearst St.), Berkeley, 510-644-0444
◪ Surveyors have divergent reactions to this Berkeley New American "yuppie hangout": while boosters concede that "you need to know what to order", they insist you can't go wrong if you choose the tri-color fries, "to-die-for" baby-back ribs and homemade ginger ale; dissenters call the place a "gimmicky concept" that's "nothing special."

Gira Polli   21 | 13 | 16 | $22 |

1616 N. Main St. (Civic Way), Walnut Creek,
925-945-1616
See review in San Francisco Directory.

Hotel Mac L M   – | – | – | M |

Hotel Mac, 50 Washington Ave. (Park Pl.), Point Richmond,
510-233-0576
Set in a hotel oozing lots of "historic charm", this Point Richmond Continental maintains a "strong local following" thanks to "the best rack of lamb", "creamed spinach that's worth the trip alone", a "great wine list" and a staff that "tries hard and succeeds."

Il Fornaio L S M   19 | 21 | 18 | $30 |

Broadway Pointe, 1430 Mt. Diablo Blvd. (Broadway),
Walnut Creek, 925-296-0100
See review in San Francisco Directory.

Jade Villa L S M   17 | 10 | 12 | $19 |

800 Broadway (8th St.), Oakland, 510-839-1688
◪ Regulars note that "if you have questions" about the menu at this "no-frills" Oakland Chinese, it's best to first "learn Cantonese"; language issues aside, there's a large variety of "excellent dim sum" "not found elsewhere"; P.S. unless you want the full "bustling" effect, you may want to avoid it on weekends, when it becomes a "zoo."

Jordan's ◑ L S M   ▽ 22 | 25 | 22 | $44
The Claremont Resort, 41 Tunnel Rd. (bet. Ashby & Domingo Aves.), Berkeley, 510-549-8510
■ This Pacific Rim–influenced Californian, in Berkeley's "grande-dame" hotel, is "where we take my mother" when she visits, a "quiet", "lovely place" with a "spectacular view", "fine" (if expensive) cuisine and "careful" service.

Kirala L S M   24 | 14 | 16 | $29
2100 Ward St. (Shattuck Ave.), Berkeley, 510-549-3486
■ "If you can survive the wait", "treasures await" at this Berkeley Japanese that's in the process of remodeling and adding a sake bar to complement its "excellent robata"-grilled dishes and sushi that's "quite simply the best" in the East Bay; now "how about accepting reservations?"

Lalime's S M   24 | 19 | 22 | $37
1329 Gilman St. (bet. Neilson St. & Peralta Ave.), Berkeley, 510-527-9838
◪ "Mood-elevating" "hanging quilts" add to the atmosphere of this "hospitable" Berkeley Med-Eclectic with "innovative" prix fixe dinners that come with "well- chosen wines"; P.S. "get on the mailing list" for the newsletter so that you can "plan ahead" for "some great meals."

La Mediterranée L S M   18 | 14 | 17 | $19
2936 College Ave. (Ashby Ave.), Berkeley, 510-540-7773
See review in San Francisco Directory.

La Note L S M   – | – | – | M
2377 Shattuck Ave. (bet. Channing Way & Durant Ave.), Berkeley, 510-843-1535
Berkeley residents gladly "queue up" for the "excellent breakfast goodies" offered at this "cute", "intimate" ("but not claustrophobic") French bistro, which sports a "gorgeous garden" that's ideal for a lunch of "Provençal comfort food" such as "the best salad niçoise in the Bay Area"; N.B. dinner on Friday and Saturday only.

Lark Creek L S M   21 | 20 | 20 | $35
1360 Locust St. (Mt. Diablo Blvd.), Walnut Creek, 925-256-1234
◪ "Try the meatloaf", "best Caesar salad" and "old-fashioned desserts" when dining at these Walnut Creek and South of SF outposts of Bradley Ogden's original Larkspur source for "American home cooking"; while most think they're a lark for "attractive food in a comfortable setting", foes find the menu "boring" and the experience "overrated."

Le Cheval L S M   22 | 15 | 16 | $21
1007 Clay St. (10th St.), Oakland, 510-763-8495
■ This "clean" Oakland Vietnamese has a range of "excellent" dishes that's "matched only by the variety of its clientele", which often shows up in "big groups"; a "loud dining room" can't detract from the fact that this is one of "the best in the East Bay" for its category.

Long Life Noodle Co. L S M   14 | 14 | 12 | $16
2261 Shattuck Ave. (Kittredge St.), Berkeley, 510-548-8083
See review in San Francisco Directory.

Long Life Vegi House L S M   14 | 5 | 12 | $13
2129 University Ave. (Shattuck Ave.), Berkeley, 510-845-6072
☑ "A student sort of place", this "quick", "cheap" Chinese-
Vegetarian in Berkeley serves "massive portions" of
"faux-meat" concoctions that make you "feel healthier",
but taste "largely unmemorable"; a "dumpy-looking"
setting argues for taking your order back to the dorm.

Mama's Royal Cafe L S M ≠   19 | 14 | 16 | $14
4012 Broadway (40th St.), Oakland, 510-547-7600
☑ "Sweet child, get your bones down to Mama's" command
surveyors smitten with this Oakland retro coffee shop that
whips up "some outstanding dishes", especially at breakfast
when the "best omelets on earth" come in endless varieties;
while eating here will "sure beat IHOP", even diehards
concede that the wait is "too long for Sunday brunch."

Mazzini L S M   22 | 21 | 20 | $32
*2826 Telegraph Ave. (bet. Oregon & Stuart Sts.), Berkeley,
510-848-5599*
■ "Even Berkeley dresses well" when dining at this Tuscan
trattoria, a "much-needed" "bright spot in a dark corner"
of town, with a "beautiful interior", "terrific" cuisine, a
"good wine list" and a "disciplined", "attentive" staff; factor
in "fair prices" and you have an "impressive newcomer."

Nan Yang Rockridge L S   22 | 15 | 19 | $21
6048 College Ave. (Claremont Ave.), Oakland, 510-655-3298
■ "Anything with mango" and a "delicious" curried-
spinach-and-tomato dish that "will curl your toes" are a few
of the many recommended choices at this vegetarian-
friendly Rockridge Burmese, which is "safer than a trip to
Myanmar"; moreover, the family owners are "helpful" and
the prices are good too, which further explains why this
place "works" "year in and year out."

Nava Restaurant L S M   – | – | – | M
5478 College Ave. (Lawton Ave.), Oakland, 510-655-4770
Groups of diners who can't agree on what type of cuisine
they want to eat should consider a visit to this "relaxed"
Rockridge-area Eclectic where the varied menu has "lots
of good choices" from around the world, including chicken
tagine, smoked salmon in a tequila-lime cure and *coq au vin*.

Oak Town Cafe L S M   – | – | – | M
499 Ninth St. (Washington St.), Oakland, 510-763-4999
Another nice addition to the East Bay dining scene, this
informal Downtown Oakland Cal-Eclectic (located in a 120-
year-old building) sports a glass-walled dining room that
makes an attractive setting for sampling the pizza, fish and
meat from a wood-fired oven, or one of the creative pastas.

Obelisque 🆂Ⓜ   ▽ 19 | 20 | 21 | $43
5421 College Ave. (Hudson St.), Oakland, 510-923-9691
◪ Aesthetes note that this Rockridge New French has a high ceiling, "beautiful" mahogany-wood paneling, a "quiet", "soothing" atmosphere and a "pleasant" staff; however, initial reports on the food indicate that the kitchen "doesn't quite have it" yet, especially relative to the "high prices", but perhaps the addition of a Mediterranean tapas bar will add to its appeal.

O Chamé ⓁⓂ   23 | 21 | 20 | $28
1830 Fourth St. (Hearst St.), Berkeley, 510-841-8783
◪ "This is Zen cuisine" remark converts to this "serene" Berkeley Japanese where a "healthy" "bowl of noodles will gratify your soul" and "to-die-for pancakes" epitomize the "simply prepared" but "exquisite" food; dissenters find the menu limited (no sushi) and think that the "beautiful presentations" don't offset the "small", "pricey" portions.

OLIVETO   24 | 21 | 21 | $42
CAFE & RESTAURANT Ⓛ🆂Ⓜ
5655 College Ave. (Shafter Ave.), Oakland, 510-547-5356
◪ "Shades of Tuscany" await visitors to Paul Bertolli's Oakland Northern Italian where diners "love the purity" of the flavors in the "simple", "unadorned" dishes; there's an open kitchen and decor that epitomizes "rustic elegance" too, but that doesn't stop a chorus of dissenters from declaring that the place is "overpriced" and "not as good as its rep"; N.B. to hedge your bets, consider the less-expensive cafe downstairs.

Pasta Pomodoro Ⓛ🆂Ⓜ   14 | 11 | 14 | $15
2379 Telegraph Ave. (bet. Channing & Durant Sts.), Berkeley, 510-666-1100
5500 College Ave. (Lawton St.), Oakland, 510-923-0900
See review in San Francisco Directory.

Phuping Thai Cuisine Ⓛ🆂Ⓜ   – | – | – | M
Pacific East Mall, 3288 Pierce St. (Central Ave.), Richmond, 510-558-3242
The new Pacific East Mall in Richmond is the setting for this joint venture that's co-owned by the people behind SF's top-rated Thep Phanom; that being the case, you're guaranteed some authentic dishes plus an added bonus – the complex's Asian supermarket and specialty shops are ideal for finding exotic ingredients and seasonings.

Picante Cocina Mexicana Ⓛ🆂Ⓜ   19 | 12 | 13 | $14
1328 Sixth St. (bet. Camelia & Gilman Sts.), Berkeley, 510-525-3121
◪ "Better than most Mexicans" in the Berkeley area, this "reasonably priced", "kid-friendly" taqueria offers "fast", "semi self-service" and a menu that showcases "great tostadas"and a "surprisingly large vegetarian selection."

Plearn Thai Cuisine 🅛🅢🅜   18 │ 12 │ 14 │ $19 │
2050 University Ave. (bet. Milvia St. & Shattuck Ave.),
Berkeley, 510-841-2148
◪ Surveyors are split on this "old standby" Berkeley Thai:
some say it's been "wonderful through the years" and still
puts out some "very authentic" dishes such as "to-die-for
tom ka gai"; others detect a "fall from grace", or perhaps
it's just that there's "so much competition" these days.

Postino 🅛🅢🅜   20 │ 23 │ 19 │ $40 │
3565 Mt. Diablo Blvd. (Oak Hill Rd.), Lafayette, 925-299-8700
◪ Michael Chiarello and the other folks behind Napa Valley's
Tra Vigne have opened this "very stylish" Lafayette Italian
in a "beautiful" building that formerly housed Tourelle; the
"everybody-looks-rich" crowd calls it a "very good suburban
restaurant" that shows "creativity with simple ingredients";
nonetheless, it's clear that the kitchen is not yet at the
level of its sibling.

Prima 🅛🅢🅜   23 │ 20 │ 22 │ $38 │
1522 N. Main St. (bet. Bonanza & Lincoln Sts.), Walnut Creek,
925-935-7780
◼ A "phenomenal" 1,600-label cellar, weekly changing
flights, "inventive" vino dinners and a staff that knows the
selection means "wine is the thing" are the draws at this
"lively" Walnut Creek Italian; while the cooking might be
an "afterthought" for oenophiles, the high food rating means
no one "needs an excuse to eat here."

Pyramid Alehouse 🅛🅢🅜   13 │ 15 │ 14 │ $19 │
901 Gilman St. (bet. 7th & 8th Sts.), Berkeley, 510-528-9880
◪ Situated in a "large warehouse", this Berkeley brewpub is
called "a pleasure" for its suds ("especially the apricot
ale"), but its bar grub is dubbed "lackluster"; so "drink
more, eat less" and bring earplugs ("say what?") and
you'll have a good time.

Restaurant Peony 🅛🅢🅜   ▽ 19 │ 14 │ 12 │ $22 │
Pacific Renaissance Plaza, 388 Ninth St. (bet. Franklin &
Webster Sts.), Oakland, 510-286-8866
◼ This "busy" Downtown Oakland Chinese has "good dim
sum" and Peking duck, but the few who know it say next
time they'll bring a friend who speaks the language ("only
way to go").

Rick & Ann's 🅛🅢🅜   – │ – │ – │ M │
2922 Domingo Ave. (bet. Ashby & Claremont Aves.),
Berkeley, 510-649-8538
Another contender for the "best breakfast in the Bay
Area", thanks to omelets and stacked pancakes that are
"worth the wait", this Berkeley favorite serves "homey"
American fare in a country-style dining room that's casual
enough for you to bring the whole family.

RIVOLI ⑤Ⓜ   25 | 21 | 23 | $38
1539 Solano Ave. (bet. Neilson St. & Peralta Ave.), Berkeley, 510-526-2542

■ "Intimate", "side-by-side" seating allows diners at this Berkeley Cal-Mediterranean to simultaneously watch the "raccoons and skunks gambol in the garden" as the "wonderful staff" serves Wendy Brucker's "incredible", "really creative" dishes ("amazing portobello fritters"), including plenty of vegetarian options; overall, this is an "East Bay treasure" that garners passionate praise.

Rue de Main ⓁⓂ   ▽ 20 | 20 | 20 | $37
22622 Main St. (bet. B & C Sts.), Hayward, 510-537-0812

◪ This "reliable" Classic French veteran has "delightful murals" and a "romantic atmosphere"; foodwise, the "old-fashioned" fare may be rather "predictable", but for Hayward it ranks as a "cultural oasis."

Salute Ristorante Ⓛ⑤Ⓜ   19 | 19 | 19 | $32
1900 Esplanade, Marina Bay (Melville Sq.), Richmond, 510-215-0803

◪ Reviewers of this Richmond Italian say try to get a "coveted table by the window" to take full advantage of the "wonderful views"; the victuals play to mixed reviews, so a safe bet might be to "stick with the pizzas"; N.B. there's a North of SF location, but it lacks the vista.

Santa Fe Bar & Grill Ⓛ⑤Ⓜ   20 | 19 | 19 | $33
1310 University Ave. (bet. Acton & Chestnut Sts.), Berkeley, 510-841-4740

◪ "Check out the herb garden" when dining at this "relaxing" Berkeley Californian, which some mistakenly think serves Southwestern fare because of its name and its location in a "pretty" former Santa Fe Railroad train station; while it's undergone lots of changes over the years ("yet another rebirth?"), solid ratings and comments lauding the "committed owners" suggest that it's largely on track.

Saul's Restaurant & Delicatessen Ⓛ⑤Ⓜ   18 | 11 | 16 | $15
1475 Shattuck Ave. (bet. Rose & Vine Sts.), Berkeley, 510-848-3354

◪ Boosters of this Berkeley deli "love the bowls of pickles on the tables", plus the "best Reubens" and "authentic bakery items", claiming they're "close (well, almost)" to the real NYC experience; mavens observe it's "not very Jewish", but concede that it's "the closest you can get to the Lower East Side" here.

Scott's Ⓛ⑤Ⓜ   17 | 17 | 17 | $32
2 Broadway (Embarcadero), Oakland, 510-444-3456
1333 N. California Blvd. (Mt. Diablo Blvd.), Walnut Creek, 925-934-1300
See review in San Francisco Directory.

Soizic 🄻 🅂   22 | 19 | 20 | $30
300 Broadway (3rd St.), Oakland, 510-251-8100
◪ An "interesting" "up-and-comer" in an "offbeat" area near Oakland's Jack London Square, this Cal-French bistro is known for its "gracious host", "well-prepared fish dishes and salads" and eclectic, "art-filled" setting; overall, it "deserves more frequent visits."

Spiedini 🄻 🅂 🄼   22 | 21 | 21 | $34
101 Ygnacio Valley Rd. (Oakland Blvd.), Walnut Creek, 925-939-2100
◪ "Get a booth in the back" to avoid the "too-damn-noisy" atmosphere at this Walnut Creek Italian trattoria, a "dependable" choice, especially for those who order the "good rotisserie meats"; dissenters say it may be "one of the area's best", but it's "not a destination."

Thornhill Cafe 🄻 🅂 🄼   ▽ 20 | 17 | 21 | $33
5761 Thornhill Dr. (Grisborne Ave.), Oakland, 510-339-0646
◪ "They try hard" at this Asian-influenced New French "sleeper", a "quaint neighborhood spot" in Oakland with a chef who was doing "fusion before it was in"; while most feel it "deserves more attention", a few think the formerly avant-garde menu "could use an overhaul", even if the "duck is still terrific."

Uzen 🄻 🄼   ▽ 22 | 17 | 18 | $26
5415 College Ave. (bet. Hudson St. & Kales Ave.), Oakland, 510-654-7753
◪ Sushi that's "elegant" "visual art" is the draw at this minimalist-looking Oakland Japanese, which gets surprisingly few votes considering that some think chef "Kazu is a fish master"; there are cooked items on the menu, but they receive scant attention.

Venezia 🄻 🅂 🄼   19 | 19 | 18 | $25
1799 University Ave. (Grant St.), Berkeley, 510-849-4681
◼ Clothing hanging from a wash line contributes to the "cute", Venice-street-scene decor at this "warm, airy" Berkeley trattoria, a "jolly" "standby" "for kids" as well as dates; regulars strongly suggest that you "don't skip the appetizers" and remember to make a reservation when dining on the weekend.

Vic Stewart's 🄻 🅂 🄼   21 | 21 | 20 | $43
850 S. Broadway (bet. Mt. Diablo Blvd. & Newell Ave.), Walnut Creek, 925-943-5666
◪ "If you're a beef lover, this is the place in the East Bay" declare devotees of this American steakhouse with "wonderful cuts" (including an ostrich alternative), snazzy sides and railroad-motif decor that would have especially appealed to the cattle barons of yesteryear; but at these prices, you might want to "save it for a special occasion."

Wente Vineyards 🅛🅢🅜   25 | 25 | 22 | $41
5050 Arroyo Rd. (Wetmore Rd.), Livermore, 925-456-2450
■ "Try the smoked pork chop" ("best in the world") on chef Kimball Jones' "fresh, seasonal and regional" Californian menu when dining at this "secluded and sedate" Livermore destination located in a "beautiful" vineyard ("sit outside"); an "excellent wine list" that's well-paired with the food further boosts the reputation of this "expensive but justified" "class act", a "perfect anniversary spot."

Xanadu 🅛🅢🅜   – | – | – | M
700 University Ave. (4th St.), Berkeley, 510-548-7880
If your yin's been feeling heavier than your yang, visit this new entry from George Chen (of Betelnut Pejiu Wu, Shanghai 1930 and Long Life Noodle Co. fame), where the restorative Asian cooking is linked to Chinese herbal medicine and designed to promote health and well-being; sure, it's another only-in-Berkeley spot, but who would expect the food to taste this good?

Yoshi's at
Jack London Square 🅛🅢🅜   16 | 20 | 16 | $30
510 Embarcadero W. (Washington St.), Oakland, 510-238-9200
◨ In theory, jazz and sushi make a "perfect date combo", but this Jack London Square venue, which relocated a few years ago, still plays to mixed reviews: advocates call the food "decent", the club's "digs" "cool" and the music "great" ("makes this place happen"); those not in harmony find the setting "too big" ("lost its charm") and the "so-so" food "overpriced."

Zachary's Chicago Pizza 🅛🅢🅜∌   24 | 10 | 13 | $16
5801 College Ave. (Oak Grove St.), Oakland, 510-655-6385
1853 Solano Ave. (bet. Colusa & Fresno Aves.), Berkeley, 510-525-5950
■ "Still the best Chicago-style pizza in the Bay area" sums up opinion on these "loud", "congested" twins adorned with "interesting" posters drawn by kids; while some honestly insist that they "would wait longer and pay more" for their favorite spinach-and-mushroom pie, most recommend that if you don't want to sit around for "an hour" "call ahead and take out."

Zza's Trattoria 🅛🅢🅜   17 | 13 | 16 | $20
552 Grand Ave. (bet. Euclid Ave. & MacArthur Blvd.), Oakland, 510-839-9124
◨ Parents love to bring "small children" to this "brightly lit", "unpretentious" Oakland trattoria because the little ones are given crayons to draw on the communal tables and the Italian cooking comes in "copious servings" that won't bust the budget.

North of San Francisco

F | D | S | C

Albion River Inn 🛇Ⓜ   24 | 23 | 23 | $42
Albion River Inn, 3790 Hwy. 1 N., Albion, 707-937-1919
■ "The ambiance mirrors the location" at this expensive and "phenomenally romantic" Mendocino "hideaway" serving American coastal cuisine and offering guest rooms for overnight stays; it boasts a "great ocean view", the "best dinner within 50 miles" and a "good wine list too."

Alta Mira Ⓛ🛇Ⓜ   14 | 21 | 16 | $37
Alta Mira Hotel, 125 Bulkley Ave. (bet. Bridgeway & Princess St.), Sausalito, 415-332-1350
☑ It's a good thing there's a "stunning view of the Bay" at this Sausalito American-Continental housed in a historic hotel, because foes find the food "institutional" and say it "needs an update"; the best bet is having a drink on the outdoor patio.

Atlas Peak Grill 🛇   ▽ 14 | 20 | 18 | $31
3342 Vichy Ave. (Monticello Rd.), Napa, 707-253-1455
☑ While few surveyors know this long-standing Napa New American–Mediterranean housed in a stone country cottage, they say it has a "beautiful garden setting" and call it a "well-kept secret"; but the less enthused sniff that the menu is "limited" and the food is "ordinary."

AUBERGE DU SOLEIL Ⓛ🛇Ⓜ   25 | 28 | 24 | $58
Auberge du Soleil Inn, 180 Rutherford Hill Rd. (Silverado Trail), Rutherford, 707-967-3111
■ "Your wish is their command" at this "glorious" Rutherford American that many consider a "highlight of the wine country" and "worth the trip from anywhere"; budget-conscious critics carp about "insane prices", but with a "world-class wine list" and a "well-organized menu" of "the most incredible food" served in an "unbeatable setting" with a "phenomenal view", most maintain "life doesn't get much better" – just "bring your sugar daddy!"

Avenue Grill 🛇Ⓜ   20 | 17 | 19 | $31
44 E. Blithedale Ave. (Sunnyside Ave.), Mill Valley, 415-388-6003
■ "Definitive meat loaf" and other "good", "creative" dishes that combine "Cal cuisine with your grandmother's favorites" can be yours at this long-standing American; it can be "damn noisy", but it offers the "real Mill Valley experience" and our envious critics from elsewhere think "locals are lucky to have it!"

Bistro Don Giovanni L S M   24 | 22 | 23 | $39
4110 St. Helena Hwy. (bet. Oak Knoll & Salvador Aves.), Napa, 707-224-3300

■ Our reviewers find "so many things we want" on the "well-executed, tasty" menu at this "handsome" Napa bistro (sib to SF's Scala's Bistro) with a "great patio"; the cognoscenti call it "my favorite Italian restaurant that's not in Milan", while romantics simply sigh that "after a cocktail overlooking the vineyards, nothing could go wrong."

BISTRO JEANTY L S M   25 | 21 | 22 | $39
6510 Washington St. (east of Hwy. 29), Yountville, 707-944-0103

■ "Forget Berkeley" – there's "absolutely authentic bistro food" at Philippe Jeanty's jaunty French spot in Yountville, which "hits on all cylinders" and "wow, wow, wow's" our wide-eyed critics with "outstanding food" at "fair prices" and "convivial" ambiance; if the "Paris ouest" menu makes it "hard to decide what to eat", then just "order everything."

Bistro Ralph L S M   23 | 18 | 21 | $36
109 Plaza St. (Healdsburg Ave.), Healdsburg, 707-433-1380

☑ "There's a reason why locals with good taste" head for chef Ralph Tingle's "minuscule" Healdsburg New American, and it's a "perfect getaway" for visitors too; the menu is "limited", but "what we got was great" and the "fine food" draws on the freshness of "Sonoma's bounty"; "extremely attentive service" adds to the "delightful" experience.

Bolero L S M   16 | 24 | 17 | $34
125 E. Sir Francis Drake Blvd. (ferry terminal at Larkspur), Larkspur, 415-925-9391

☑ "Oodles of atmo" and flamenco entertainment add to the "fun" at this "exotic" Larkspur Spanish; while critics claim the "theme overtakes the dining experience" and say they "can't remember the food", revelers retort "where else can you eat suckling pig in a brick kiln?"

Boonville Hotel L S M   23 | 21 | 22 | $32
Boonville Hotel, Hwy. 128 (Lambert Ln.), Boonville, 707-895-2210

■ Alright, this Boonville New American–Mexican *is* out in the boonies in the Anderson Valley, but it offers some "wonderful, interesting food" that's "done with love" and comes in "ample portions"; the occasionally "slow service" goes with the "relaxed" and "friendly" atmosphere.

Bouchon ◗ L S M   23 | 25 | 22 | $42
6534 Washington St. (east of Hwy. 29), Yountville, 707-944-8037

■ Highly touted chef Thomas Keller (of the No. 1 rated French Laundry) and his brother Joseph are behind this "beautiful" Yountville yearling with a "NY-Parisian" feel and "excellent" French bistro food; a few feel the menu "doesn't reach far enough" and dub the service "disjointed", but the majority maintains "what's there is stellar" and it's a "wonderful addition to the Napa Valley scene."

Brannan's Grill L S M | 18 | 22 | 19 | $36 |
1374 Lincoln Ave. (bet. Cedar & Washington Sts.), Calistoga,
707-942-2233
◪ A "very creative" new chef is putting out some "inventive food" at this Calistoga New American, and some say it's "much improved after its initial opening"; service can be "spotty", but eyeing the "trendy decor" helps pass the time.

Brava Terrace L S M | 19 | 21 | 19 | $38 |
3010 St. Helena Hwy. N. (bet. Hwy. 29 & Lodi Ln.), St. Helena,
707-963-9300
◪ This "typical Napa Valley" eclectic Cal-Italian has a "beautiful setting", and some think it's "rock steady" for "country dining as you imagine it should be"; others say that the "descriptions are often better than the tastes" and find themselves asking "is anyone training the staff?"; still, spending time on the "lovely" terrace is "a great way to end the day."

Brix L S M | 22 | 23 | 20 | $40 |
7377 St. Helena Hwy. (Washington St.), Napa, 707-944-2749
■ Not only is the Asian-Fusion cooking at this "outstandingly creative" Napa spot a "happy marriage of East and West", it's matched with a "wine list I'd like to take home with me", "stunning decor" and a "beautiful garden" in a "restful vineyard setting"; the "service needs work"("it's gotten popular faster than the staff can keep up"), but the food is so "delicious" fans "can't wait to go back."

Bubba's Diner L S M | 20 | 14 | 18 | $21 |
566 San Anselmo Ave. (bet. Bridge & Magnolia Sts.),
San Anselmo, 415-459-6862
■ "Come as you are" to this "plain" San Amselmo American "institution" for a "wonderfully creative twist on comfort food" ("good breakfasts" and "innovative blackboard specials"); since fans feel that this small, "friendly" spot is the "ultimate neighborhood diner", you may have to "wait outside."

Buckeye Roadhouse L S M | 21 | 22 | 20 | $34 |
15 Shoreline Hwy. (west of Hwy. 101), Mill Valley, 415-331-2600
■ There's "never a dull moment" at this "sprawling" 1937 roadhouse with "upscale rustic" decor and "hunting lodge ambiance", located just short of the Golden Gate Bridge; the fact that it features "hearty", "scrumptious" American food like barbecue and "wonderful desserts" means it's a "must stop" for most when coming back from Marin.

Cacti L S M | 16 | 17 | 17 | $28 |
1200 Grant Ave. (2nd St.), Novato, 415-898-2234
■ "Nice place, nice people, nice food" sums up this "delightful" Novato Southwestern that's set in a former church; the menu is "creative" and "the margaritas ain't bad either", pard'ner.

Cactus Cafe **L S M**   ▽ 18 | 9 | 14 | $20
393 Miller Ave. (bet. Evergreen Ave. & LaGoma St.), Mill Valley,
415-388-8226

■ This "hole-in-the-wall" Mill Valley taqueria has "minimal
facilities", but it puts out some "delightful, innovative
Mexican" cooking at "cheap" prices; it's "pretty basic",
but don't get prickly – "just go for the food and don't
worry about the rest."

Cafe Beaujolais **S M**   24 | 20 | 22 | $41
961 Ukiah St. (bet. Evergreen & School Sts.), Mendocino,
707-937-5614

■ While the legendary breakfasts here are no more,
this Mendocino French-International with the "homey
atmosphere" is still the "queen of the North" for dinner; a
few think it's "not quite as good as we remembered" and
remark that costs have "escalated to city prices", but
many still say "eating in the garden is an unforgettable
experience", and San Franciscans lament "why, oh why,
is it so far away?"

Cafe Citti **L S M**   18 | 11 | 15 | $22
9049 Sonoma Hwy. (Hwy. 12), Kenwood, 707-833-2690

■ Modest Kenwood Italian and "country deli" that turns
out the "best roasted chicken" from its "crackling rotisserie"
at reasonable prices; it's "an unexpected pleasant stop"
in wine country and "always a delight if you can get in."

Café La Haye **S**   24 | 18 | 23 | $29
140 E. Napa St. (bet. 1st & 2nd Sts. E.), Sonoma, 707-935-5994

■ "Friendly" American-International in Sonoma with a
"welcoming and professional" staff, "personable" owners
and a kitchen that "does great things with meat"; the room is
"a little cramped", but the rotating art exhibits make it a
"cute little place" and the reasonable prices make it a
"perfect wine country stop."

California Cafe **L S M**   18 | 18 | 18 | $31
The Village, 1736 Redwood Hwy. (Paradise Dr.), Corte Madera,
415-924-2233

■ "Consistently good" "salads, sandwiches and other light"
California fare, and service that's "better than expected",
are the hallmarks of this national chain whose East, South
and North of SF branches were all recently refurbished.

Caprice, The **S M**   21 | 25 | 21 | $44
2000 Paradise Dr. (Mar West St.), Tiburon, 415-435-3400

◪ Long-standing Tiburon spot boasting a "billion dollar
view" (do they mean the nearby real estate or the Bay?),
but whether the restaurant's self-styled Cal-Continental
cuisine is even "better" than the scenery or "doesn't
match" it is a matter of debate; in any case, the "stunning
location" alone makes it a "worthwhile destination."

Catahoula
Restaurant & Saloon L S M

23 │ 20 │ 19 │ $38

Mount View Hotel, 1457 Lincoln Ave. (bet. Fair Way & Washington St.), Calistoga, 707-942-2275

■ Jan Birnbaum's "always novel, always delicious" Southern regional cuisine is the main attraction at this "ragin' Cajun" Calistoga American; for a restaurant that's in wine country, its "forgettable" vino list takes a few jibes, but the "gutsy", "flavorful" food and "fun" atmosphere pack in a "noisy, rowdy crowd."

Celadon L M

24 │ 20 │ 24 │ $32

1040 Main St. (bet. 1st & Pearl Sts.), Napa, 707-254-9690

■ "Lucky Napa!" say supporters of this "little wine country gem" with a "small, imaginative menu" of "delicious" New American–International food from a "very talented chef" (owner Greg Cole), plus "attentive service"; it's an "ideal neighborhood cafe" – "wish they took reservations."

CHATEAU SOUVERAIN CAFE
AT THE WINERY L S

21 │ 26 │ 22 │ $43

400 Souverain Rd. (Hwy. 101, Independence Ln. exit), Geyserville, 707-433-3141

■ "France meets Sonoma" at this Geyserville country French in the Chateau Souverain Winery; the "fantastic" setting, the "glow" in the "stylish dining room" and the "excellent food" make for "grand dining"; N.B. lunch daily, dinner Friday–Sunday.

Chevys L S M

12 │ 12 │ 13 │ $18

Bon Air Shopping Ctr., 302 Bon Air Ctr. (Sir Francis Drake Blvd.), Greenbrae, 415-461-3203
24 Fourth St. (Wilson St.), Santa Rosa, 707-571-1082
See review in San Francisco Directory.

Christophe S

22 │ 18 │ 21 │ $31

1919 Bridgeway (Spring St.), Sausalito, 415-332-9244

■ "Small" Sausalito French bistro whose "bargain" prix fixe and early-bird menus are "hard to beat"; another plus is the "Parisian feel" to the place, which makes it "very romantic" and "comfortable."

Compadres L S M

16 │ 18 │ 18 │ $24

Vintage Estates, 6539 Washington St., Yountville, 707-944-2406
See review in South of San Francisco Directory.

Cucina Jackson Fillmore S

▽ 20 │ 18 │ 17 │ $32

337 San Anselmo Ave. (bet. Pine St. & Woodland Ave.), San Anselmo, 415-454-2942

■ "Lively" San Anselmo spinoff of the popular San Francisco trattoria that's a "new hot spot for Italian in Marin" and a "great addition to the dining scene"; they "need better acoustics" (you "have to scream to be heard"), but there's a "trained, friendly staff" and locals are lining up to say (or shout) "welcome."

Della Santina's L S M
22 | 20 | 20 | $31 |
133 E. Napa St. (1st St. E.), Sonoma, 707-935-0576

☑ "Best pasta, nicest people" is the take on this "classic" Sonoma Northern Italian whose rotisserie items get high marks too; "wonderful outdoor dining" is another plus.

DOMAINE CHANDON L S M
26 | 25 | 25 | $53 |
1 California Dr. (Hwy. 29), Yountville, 707-944-2892

■ "We oohed and aahed over every course" at this long-standing Yountville French-Californian with a "spectacular setting" in the vineyards ("be sure to sit outside if possible"); a "fine wine list" complements the "fantastic food", and an "attentive, knowledgeable staff pampers" diners; in sum, it's still a "quintessential wine country destination" – just remember to "rob a bank" before you come here.

DOWNTOWN
BAKERY & CREAMERY L S M ⊜
25 | 13 | 17 | $12 |
308A Center St. (Matheson St.), Healdsburg, 707-431-2719

■ "Nirvana in Healdsburg?"; yep, the "addictive sticky buns" and other "delicious baked goods" at this Sonoma bakery/ice-cream parlor provide "a great taste to kick off a day of wine tasting."

EL PASEO S
23 | 26 | 23 | $44 |
17 Throckmorton Ave. (bet. E. Blithedale & Miller Aves.), Mill Valley, 415-388-0741

■ Pricey and "gorgeous" Mill Valley French stalwart with a curiously Spanish name that's "the definition of romantic dining" in some of our reviewers' dictionaries; a "consistent menu", "exquisite presentation" and "timeless decor" add up to a "Mill Valley classic."

Felix & Louie's L S M
16 | 17 | 17 | $29 |
106 Matheson St. (Healdsburg Ave.), Healdsburg, 707-433-6966

☑ A "fun place to eat comfort food" is what some say about this Healdsburg yearling that's the "more casual" American Regional–Italian sib of Bistro Ralph; although service can be "friendly", it reportedly still "needs work."

Filou S
– | – | – | E |
198 Sir Francis Drake Blvd. (Tunstead Ave.), San Anselmo, 415-256-2436

Chef-owner Nikolaus Kaubisch (ex La Folie) turns out "surprisingly sophisticated French cuisine" at this "small", San Anselmo spot with a "friendly staff"; the few surveyors who know it say they've "never had a bad meal" here.

FOOTHILL CAFE S
25 | 14 | 22 | $31 |
J&P Shopping Ctr., 2766 Old Sonoma Rd. (Foothill Blvd.), Napa, 707-252-6178

■ Napa American offering "consistently delicious" "great eats"; just "ignore the decor" and "dumb location" "off the beaten path" in a strip mall and go for the "good barbecue" ("one word – ribs!").

Frantoio ⓁⓈⓂ   19 │ 20 │ 19 │ $35 │
152 Shoreline Hwy. (west of Hwy. 101), Mill Valley, 415-289-5777
☒ "Stylish" Mill Valley Northern Italian whose food ("very good" vs. "fair") gets mixed marks from our surveyors; however, there is consensus about the "terrific decor", which includes an "impressive" olive oil press, and the dessert of choice – "save room for the chocolate tower!"

FRENCH LAUNDRY ⓁⓈⓂ   29 │ 26 │ 27 │ $78 │
6640 Washington St. (Creek St.), Yountville, 707-944-2380
■ "Two whole days on redial" might score you a reservation at Thomas Keller's "dazzling" and deliriously expensive Yountville Contemporary American with French influences that's voted No. 1 for Food in this *Survey*; the "whimsical, playfully serious" cuisine is backed by the "finest service ever", and "monastic" decor adds to the "religious experience"; the spiritual predict it's "how we'll eat in heaven" and caution it's "just about as easy to get in to."

Fresco ⓁⓂ   – │ – │ – │ M │
13 Ross Common (Poplar Ave.), Ross, 415-464-0915
Marco Franceschini's small, new trattoria in Downtown Ross features Florentine-inspired fare (like classic pastas) that's served up from a tiny kitchen; a friendly atmo adds to its appeal.

General's Daughter ⓁⓈⓂ   20 │ 23 │ 22 │ $37 │
400 W. Spain St. (4th St. W.), Sonoma, 707-938-4004
☒ A "stunning remake of a historic house" serves as the Victorian-style setting for this New American, which has "hearty, unpretentious food"; several refuse to salute the "boring", "generic" cuisine, but it's still "one of the better places to go in Sonoma", and with its "charming decor" and "pretty" patio, it's great for "lunch with the girls."

Gira Polli ⓈⓂ   21 │ 13 │ 16 │ $22 │
590 E. Blithedale Ave. (Camino Alto), Mill Valley, 415-383-6040
See review in San Francisco Directory.

girl & the fig, the ⓈⓂ   23 │ 21 │ 21 │ $36 │
13690 Arnold Dr. (Warm Springs Rd.), Glen Ellen,
707-938-3634
☒ "Quaint", "unpretentious" and "promising" Glen Ellen French Bistro serving some "offbeat food" that's "good", "not great"; the "fun wine list" features Rhône varietals rather than the usual Sonoma suspects.

Glen Ellen Inn Restaurant ⓈⓂ   – │ – │ – │ M │
13670 Arnold Dr. (Warm Springs Rd.), Glen Ellen,
707-996-6409
"Quaint, romantic" and recently remodeled Glen Ellen Fusion-Californian with "innovative dishes" that's a "real find"; P.S. some surveyors say it's got the "best outdoor patio around", but despite the 'Inn' in its name, what it doesn't have is overnight accommodations – yet.

Gordon's L S   ▽ 21 | 17 | 18 | $24
6770 Washington St. (Madison St.), Yountville,
707-944-8246
■ "Hang with the locals" for breakfast at this modest,
"informal" Yountville New American with "quality family-
style" fare; it's "a bit discombobulated at times" because
the "space is crowded", but that doesn't keep fans from
"wishing it were open every night for dinner", which is
served on Friday only.

Guaymas L S M   18 | 22 | 17 | $29
5 Main St. (Tiburon Blvd.), Tiburon, 415-435-6300
☑ With the "best patio view in the Bay Area" at your
disposal, "it's easy to linger" at this "fun" Tiburon Mexican
that "looks and feels wonderful"; "hit-or-miss" food "needs
a new shot of life" according to some, but appetizers,
"great margaritas" and the "priceless" panorama make it
"worth crossing the Bridge for" (or taking the ferry).

Guernica S M   ▽ 18 | 15 | 20 | $31
2009 Bridgeway (Spring St.), Sausalito, 415-332-1512
■ "Nice, nice people", "wonderful service" and an owner
who "makes you feel as though you're his houseguest"
have some of our respondents painting a happy picture
of this French-Basque in Sausalito; the food is "never
disappointing", particularly the "wonderful paella."

Heirloom Restaurant L S M   – | – | – | M
Sonoma Hotel, 110 W. Spain St. (1st St. W.), Sonoma,
707-939-6955
This new New American inherited the revolving-door
restaurant space on the first floor of the Sonoma Hotel; with
its three "rustic" rooms and "well-done creative food",
it's "much needed in the area" and "should be a winner."

Horizons L S M   ▽ 14 | 20 | 15 | $30
558 Bridgeway (Princess St.), Sausalito, 415-331-3232
☑ The terrace of this moderate Sausalito American has a
"super view" that takes in an admirable expanse of the
Bay; however, if you're looking to broaden your culinary
Horizons here, forget it, because the "food needs work."

Il Fornaio L S M   19 | 21 | 18 | $30
Town Ctr., 222 Town Ctr., Corte Madera, 415-927-4400
See review in San Francisco Directory.

Insalata's Restaurant L S M   23 | 21 | 21 | $36
120 Sir Francis Drake Blvd. (Barber St.), San Anselmo,
415-457-7700
■ Locals say Heidi Kranling's "bright and airy" San Anselmo
Mediterranean is "a Marin restaurant we don't have to be
embarrassed about"; surveyors single out an "inventive
menu" that delivers such an "exquisite blend of flavors"
that "one meal made me a believer."

John Ash & Co. L S M   23 | 23 | 22 | $48
4330 Barnes Rd. (River Rd.), Santa Rosa, 707-527-7687
■ "Refined" and pricey wine country American in Santa Rosa that puts on a "good solid performance", with "interesting preparations", "excellent service" and a "strong wine list"; in addition, the "delightful setting amidst the vineyards" makes "patio dining especially enjoyable" here.

Kasbah Moroccan S   ▽ 24 | 25 | 21 | $36
200 Merrydale Rd. (Willow St.), San Rafael, 415-472-6666
■ Take "a fanciful trip to Morocco for under 50 bucks" at this San Rafael spot serving "sensual food" in a "most hospitable environment"; "fun and entertaining" belly dancing adds to the authenticity, and fans fez up "we always feel taken away."

Kenwood L S   24 | 21 | 22 | $40
9900 Hwy. 12, Kenwood, 707-833-6326
■ Contemporary French–New American in Kenwood whose "robust food", "nice wine list" and "friendly, professional staff" display "amazing consistency and staying power"; "try to sit on the patio" because "in warm weather" the garden makes for "lovely outdoor dining."

La Ginestra S   ▽ 17 | 11 | 17 | $22
127 Throckmorton Ave. (Miller Ave.), Mill Valley, 415-388-0224
■ Mill Valley Southern Italian where "the ravioli is just like mama's" and the "big booths are just made for kids"; it's "nothing fancy", but the "good, basic" home cooking and welcoming owners "make you feel at home" and keep locals "coming back."

Lark Creek Inn L S M   24 | 24 | 23 | $45
234 Magnolia Ave. (Madrone Ave.), Larkspur, 415-924-7766
■ "Tried and true" with "top-notch" food is what surveyors say about Brad Ogden's "charming" Larkspur American in a "delightful old house"; considered a "classic", "Bradley's benchmark" is a "sentimental favorite" and "what a country restaurant should be."

Las Camelias L S M   22 | 16 | 19 | $23
912 Lincoln Ave. (bet. 3rd & 4th Sts.), San Rafael, 415-453-5850
■ The "best mole this side of the border" and other "sophisticated Mexican" fare can be had at this modest, "offbeat" San Rafael stalwart; the "really authentic" dishes and moderate prices have our critics calling it "a keeper."

La Toque S   25 | 21 | 24 | $67
1140 Rutherford Rd. (east of Hwy. 29), Rutherford, 707-963-9770
■ LA transplant and top toque Ken Frank is "taking Napa by storm" with this ambitious Rutherford New French yearling, featuring a "fresh, refined approach" in the kitchen and a weekly-changing, prix fixe tasting menu of "lovely" dishes; while a few find the food "too rich" and the tab "expensive", most maintain that it's a "fab addition to the area."

Left Bank L S M   21 | 21 | 19 | $37
507 Magnolia Ave. (Ward St.), Larkspur, 415-927-3331
■ "A restaurant of character" from Rolland Passot of the
highly rated La Folie, this "outstandingly comfortable"
Larkspur French bistro (with a newer Peninsula sibling)
has an "open, bright feeling" and a "lovely" patio where
"happy patrons" enjoy "great home-style French" food
and an "awesome wine list"; in sum, "this place has soul"
and "you'd have to try very hard to have a bad time" here.

Live Fire   16 | 19 | 17 | $35
Grill & Smokehouse L S M
6518 Washington St. (Yount St.), Yountville, 707-944-1500
☑ Our critics don't get too fired up about this Yountville
barbecue place; fans feel it "does grilled meats nicely",
producing "basic but tasty stuff", but detractors demand
"turn up the heat" on the "rather bland, commercial menu"
and "uneven" service.

Madrona Manor S M   ▽ 22 | 23 | 21 | $51
*Madrona Manor Hotel, 1001 Westside Rd. (W. Dry Creek Rd.),
Healdsburg, 707-433-4231*
☑ "Charming wine-country ambiance" is the draw at
this "pleasant" Healdsburg Classic French housed in a
"Victorian setting" with "fabulous flower gardens";
comments on the food range from "refined" and "creative"
to "pretentious" and "inconsistent", but with atmosphere
to burn, most maintain it's "perfect for a romantic dinner."

Manka's Inverness Lodge S M   22 | 24 | 21 | $43
*Manka's Inverness Lodge, 30 Callendar Way (Argyle St.),
Inverness, 415-669-1034*
☑ Inverness American restaurant and lodge where the
"flavorful, gamy, rustic" cuisine is based on local Tomales
Bay produce; the "magical" atmosphere ("flickering
candles") makes for "extraordinary dining" by some
accounts, while wallet-watchers whine that the experience
is "overpriced"; in any case, it's "the only place there."

Marin Joe's ◐ L S M   19 | 12 | 18 | $28
*1585 Casa Buena Dr. (Tamalpais Dr.), Corte Madera,
415-924-2081*
■ Corte Madera Northern Italian "institution" where there
are "no surprises – just big portions of good food"; most
ignore the "tacky decor" and shrug "hey, it's a time warp"
but "it still works."

Meadowood Grill L S M   22 | 22 | 22 | $40
*Meadowood Resort, 900 Meadowood Ln. (bet. Howell
Mtn. Rd. & Silverado Trail), St. Helena, 707-963-3646*
■ "Well-prepared food", "elegant, understated" decor and
an "accommodating staff" make this pricey St. Helena Cal-
American "great for a business engagement"; the "great
view of the golf course" doesn't T-off anyone either.

Mikayla at the Casa Madrona S M ▽ 24 | 26 | 23 | $38 |
Casa Madrona, 801 Bridgeway (near El Monte Ln.), Sausalito,
415-331-5888
■ It's "so romantic you'll swoon" at this Californian
"sleeper-by-the-Bay" in Sausalito's Casa Madrona hotel; the
"breathtaking" view is "unbelievable" and the cuisine is
"delicious"; N.B. at press time, the restaurant is scheduled
to relocate to the hotel's new extension next door, so
surveyors "hope it doesn't lose its charm when it moves."

Mustards Grill L S M   24 | 19 | 21 | $37 |
7399 St. Helena Hwy. (Hwy. 29), Napa, 707-944-2424
■ "Some places know how to make friends", and this "busy,
bustling, bright and boffo" Napa New American stalwart
seems to be one of them; there's "always a reason to go
back", whether for the "well-prepared and well-presented
classic fare", the "knockout specials", the "enticing wine
flights" or the "energetic, happy staff"; it's most people's
idea of the "quintessential wine country bistro" and "should
be there for many years to come."

Napa Valley Grille L S M   21 | 19 | 20 | $34 |
Washington Sq., 6795 Washington St. (Madison St.), Yountville,
707-944-8686
■ Yountville Cal-Med whose "large portions" of "solid food"
served by an "attentive staff" make it a "perfect rest stop
after a day of wine tasting"; P.S. a recent remodeling might
even enhance the already "nice setting."

Napa Valley Wine Train L S M   17 | 25 | 19 | $51 |
1275 McKinstry St. (bet. 1st St. & Soscol Ave.), Napa,
707-253-2111
■ Sure, it's a "gimmicky venue", but "the dining cars are
beautiful" and the food is "good" on this Californian train
where the price of your meal includes a rail tour of Napa
Valley; the route is reportedly "less scenic than expected",
but there's "pretty good service for 40 mph"; most maintain
"give it chance" 'cause "it's fun for a day."

North Sea Village L S M   19 | 15 | 14 | $27 |
300 Turney St. (Bridgeway), Sausalito, 415-331-3300
■ Thank goodness there's a "Bay view bonus" at this
Sausalito Chinese with a "beautiful waterfront location",
because the decor's not much to look at; on the food front,
however, there's "delicious dim sum" and "reliable" seafood.

Olema Inn L S M   19 | 20 | 20 | $33 |
Olema Inn, 10000 Sir Francis Drake Blvd. (Hwy. 1), Olema,
415-663-9559
☑ It's a "long way to go for dinner", but this "romantic"
North Coast New American is housed in a B&B in an "old
farm house" in case you want to spend the night; while
loyalists like the "good" "home cooking", the less enthused
shrug "nice but nothing special except for the location."

Ondine 🆂🅼　　– | – | – | E
558 Bridgeway (Princess Ave.), Sausalito, 415-331-1133
"A classic restaurant reborn" (the original opened in 1956 and closed ten years ago), this beautiful and costly Sausalito newcomer has been resuscitated; chef Seiji Wakabayashi's menu has Asian accents combined with Cal ingredients and French technique; the question is, can the cuisine live up to the breathtaking views of the Bay and the SF skyline?

Pasta Pomodoro 🅻🆂🅼　　14 | 11 | 14 | $15
421 Third St. (Irving St.), San Rafael, 415-256-2401
See review in San Francisco Directory.

Piatti 🅻🆂🅼　　19 | 19 | 18 | $33
6480 Washington St. (Oak Circle), Yountville, 707-944-2070
El Dorado Hotel, 405 First St. W. (Spain St.), Sonoma, 707-996-2351
625 Redwood Hwy. (Seminary Dr.), Mill Valley, 415-380-2525
☑ Fans of these "friendly" and "fresh" Cal-Italians say that "for a chain the quality is incredible" and they make for a "great anytime eatery", but foes feel that there are "better choices all around."

Piazza D'Angelo 🅻🆂🅼　　18 | 19 | 18 | $31
22 Miller Ave. (Throckmorton Ave.), Mill Valley, 415-388-2000
☑ The site of the "scene in scenic Mill Valley" is this Southern Italian with "personality", an attractive crowd at the bar and "dependable", "competent food"; phobes feel that it's "loud, crowded and mediocre", but insiders say take your pick: "quieter outside, prettier inside" – either way's ok for a "typical yuppie Marin experience."

Pinot Blanc 🅻🆂🅼　　22 | 22 | 21 | $44
641 Main St. (Grayson St.), St. Helena, 707-963-6191
■ "Hollywood meets Napa Valley" at LA superchef Joachim Splichal's St. Helena New French that's "hitting its stride now" with executive chef Shawn Knight's "delicious food" and "artistic presentations"; there's also "cheery new decor" that "invites you back" (adieu to "dark and scary" digs), along with a "great patio."

PlumpJack Cafe 🅻🆂🅼　　24 | 22 | 23 | $44
PlumpJack Squaw Valley Inn, 1920 Squaw Valley Rd., Olympic Valley, 530-583-1576
See review in San Francisco Directory.

Ravenous 🅻🆂　　– | – | – | M
117 North St. (bet. Center & Healdsburg Sts.), Healdsburg, 707-431-1770
The name of this "tiny" Healdsburg eatery is actually a pun, since it's located in the same building as the Raven Theater, but it could also describe our reviewers' hunger for the "increasingly creative" cuisine coming from a Californian-Eclectic "seasonal menu that changes daily", as well as a "great local wine" list; N.B. closed Monday–Tuesday.

Restaurant at Meadowood S M   25 │ 25 │ 24 │ $54
Meadowood Resort, 900 Meadowood Ln. (bet. Howell Mtn. Rd. & Silverado Trail), St. Helena, 707-963-3646
■ Pros praise the "innovative and beautifully presented food" and the "excellent wine list" at this pricey St. Helena American in a lush golf resort; the dining room exudes "country elegance" and the patio offers the "finest outdoor seating in Napa Valley"; the only question is "where do they find the fantastic, friendly staff?"

Rice Table S   ▽ 19 │ 15 │ 19 │ $26
1617 Fourth St. (G St.), San Rafael, 415-456-1808
■ "Some of the nicest, most accommodating people around" run this San Rafael Indonesian where the traditional rijsttafel has "wonderful flavors"; the "tacky decor" is a drawback, but the place is still a "unique experience" that's "nice for everyone", at least once.

Ristorante Fabrizio L S M   20 │ 16 │ 20 │ $31
455 Magnolia Ave. (Cane St.), Larkspur, 415-924-3332
■ "Cute" Larkspur stalwart that's "one of a gaggle of good [Northern] Italian places" in Marin, but is a "sentimental favorite" because chef-owner "Fabrizio takes good care of his customers" and the "welcoming, helpful staff" follows suit; regulars at this "old faithful" swear by the evening specials ("Monday is lobster night!") and say it's "less discovered than it deserves" to be.

Robata Grill & Sushi L S M   20 │ 17 │ 17 │ $29
591 Redwood Hwy. (Hwy. 101, Seminary Dr. exit), Mill Valley, 415-381-8400
■ "Flamboyant sushi chefs add spice" to this Mill Valley Japanese while slicing some "fresh, good-quality" fish; the fact that there's also a "fantastic variety of dishes" on the grill menu makes it a "perennial favorite" for some.

Royal Thai L S M   22 │ 15 │ 18 │ $24
610 Third St. (Irwin St.), San Rafael, 415-485-1074
■ Surveyors say this "simple" San Rafael Thai (with a sib in the City) is a "solid performer" with "amazingly good" food and "unusual, innovative" offerings; the decor may be "ho-hum", but you'll get the Royal treatment with "gracious, charming service" and a "relaxing atmosphere"; all in all, "always a pleasant experience."

Rutherford Grill L S M   20 │ 19 │ 20 │ $30
1180 Rutherford Rd. (Hwy. 29), Rutherford, 707-963-1792
■ This American in Rutherford (a spinoff of the Houston's chain) is "just what the doctor ordered after a day of wine tasting" and some drivers on Highway 29 report you'll "have to stop because of your nose" when you smell the "excellent meats and chicken"; "getting a table is tough", but their ribs "will stick to yours", and "overall it's a good value."

Salute Ristorante L S M　　19　19　19　$32
706 Third St. (Tamalpais Ave.), San Rafael,
415-453-7596
See review in East of San Francisco Directory.

Sam's Anchor Cafe L S M　　13　19　14　$23
27 Main St. (Tiburon Blvd.), Tiburon, 415-435-4527
■ Tiburon American that's a "meat market on a deck" (aka
"beautiful people central") and rather "seedy looking",
but fans with tans argue "decor? how about all of SF
Bay!"; the food is "barely ok", if anyone really cares, but
those who anchor themselves here say it's the "perfect
sunny afternoon hangout" – just "beware the gulls"
("bring a hat").

Sand Dollar L S M　　▽　12　12　15　$22
3458 Shoreline Hwy., Stinson Beach, 415-868-0434
☒ Ok, the food is "not terribly good" and service can be
"slow" at this "throwback" American in Stinson Beach;
however, it's one of the few eateries in the area, and "locals
love it", mainly because of the "great bar."

Savanna Grill L S M　　–　–　–　E
Marketplace, 55 Tamalvista Blvd. (Tamalpais Dr.),
Corte Madera, 415-924-6774
This once-popular Corte Madera American has resurfaced,
reopening on the site of what was McCormick & Schmick's,
with a newly revamped decor that reflects a classy, retro
look; a menu of regional American eats reinterpreted for
the sophisticated tastes of today, live jazz and an exhibition
kitchen make it a come-back kid that's contemporary.

Scoma's L S M　　19　17　18　$33
588 Bridgeway (Princess St.), Sausalito,
415-332-9551
See review in San Francisco Directory.

Showley's Restaurant L S　　▽　21　18　20　$39
Miramonte Inn, 1327 Railroad Ave. (bet. Adams & Hunt Sts.),
St. Helena, 707-963-1200
☒ The few surveyors who know this "quiet" St. Helena
stalwart say that it "tries hard" with "good" Californian
cooking; while they "could do more with the spare decor",
there's a "nice outdoor patio" with "lovely trees."

Sonoma Mission Inn Grille S M　　21　21　21　$42
Sonoma Mission Inn, 18140 Hwy. 12 (Boyes Blvd.), Sonoma,
707-939-2415
■ Sybarites say "go for the whole shebang – hotel and
dinner" at this "great getaway" in a "perfect" Sonoma
setting, with "excellent" Californian cooking (including
some reduced-calorie and -cholesterol spa dishes) and a
"great wine list"; spendthrifts shrug: it's "very expensive
and totally worth it."

Station House Cafe L S M   19 | 15 | 16 | $25
11180 State Rte. 1 (Hwy. 1), Point Reyes Station, 415-663-1515
◪ An "oasis in West Marin" in the "hinterlands" of Point Reyes Station, this long-standing New American serves up "good" "basic comfort food" with an emphasis on seafood ("don't pass up oysters in any form"); it's "very nice if you're in the neighborhood", especially if you eat out on the "beautifully landscaped patio."

SUSHI RAN L S M   26 | 19 | 20 | $35
107 Caledonia St. (bet. Pine & Turney Sts.), Sausalito, 415-332-3620
■ "Who knew about this sushi haven in Sausalito?", where there's "fresh", "exquisite" raw fish that's "artfully presented", accompanied by "great sakes"; Ran fans advise it's "not cheap, but it's worth the money."

Syrah L   – | – | – | M
205 Fifth St. (Davis St.), Santa Rosa, 707-568-4002
"Very new, really good" is the early word on chef-owner Josh Silver's Santa Rosa Franco-Californian; with its monthly changing menu and small but upscale space, it's an "exciting bistro" in a town that deserves more sophisticated spots like this one.

TERRA S M   27 | 25 | 25 | $52
1345 Railroad Ave. (bet. Adams & Hunt Sts.), St. Helena, 707-963-8931
■ Husband-and-wife team Hiro Sone and Lissa Doumani's highly-rated St. Helena Franco-Californian with Asian accents "has it all" – "gorgeous, unusual, unforgettable" cuisine served by an "amazing staff" in a "romantic", "quietly elegant" stone-walled dining room; a few are Terra-fied by the prices, but everyone agrees it's "definitely a destination place that always delivers."

Tomales Bay Foods L S   ▽ 24 | 18 | 19 | $20
80 Fourth St. (B St.), Point Reyes Station, 415-663-8153
■ A "picnickers' dream come true", this Tomales Bay "fabulous food emporium" offers homemade ice creams and charcuterie, "super fresh", organically-grown produce, cheeses and other "quality" regional specialties overseen by chef Peggy Smith (ex Chez Panisse); surveyors just "wish they had a restaurant!"

Tomatina L S M   18 | 15 | 14 | $20
Inn at Southbridge, 1016 Main St. (bet. Charter Oak Ave. & Pope St.), St. Helena, 707-967-9999
◪ This St. Helena Southern Italian from the folks at Real Restaurants is an "affordable" alternative to more pricey places, offering "quick Italian fare" like "nice thin pizzas"; it's "fun for the whole family" (translation: "beware of babies and kids galore").

TRA VIGNE ⓁⓈⓂ   24 | 26 | 22 | $42 |
1050 Charter Oak Ave. (Hwy. 29), St. Helena, 707-963-4444
☑ "Hang out with the who's who of Napa Valley" at this "brassy, classy, sassy" St. Helena Italian; they come for chef Michael Chiarello's "marvelous food that's made with love", a "lovely", "spacious" setting with a "fabulous interior design" that evokes Tuscany and an outdoor terrace that's "truly sublime" in summer.

Wappo Bar Bistro ⓁⓈⓂ   23 | 20 | 20 | $34 |
1226 Washington St. (Lincoln Ave.), Calistoga, 707-942-4712
■ Check out the "wonderful combination of tastes" at this "casual" and "cute" Calistoga Global cuisine spot that offers "inventive", "eclectic" cooking, "eccentric decor" and "electric" ambiance; but it's biggest plus seems to be the "best summer patio around" where you can "dine beneath the vines."

WILLOWSIDE CAFE Ⓢ   25 | 17 | 22 | $42 |
3535 Guerneville Rd. (Willowside Rd.), Santa Rosa, 707-523-4814
☑ "A gem in an unusual spot" ("I thought we were pulling into my uncle Bill's house") is what surveyors say about this loaded-with-character Santa Rosa Californian; chef Richard Allen's "fabulous" food is backed up by an award-winning and "very intelligent wine list" – no wonder that it's a hangout for local vintners.

Wine Spectator Greystone ⓁⓈⓂ   20 | 23 | 19 | $39 |
2555 Main St. (Deer Park Rd.), St. Helena, 707-967-1010
■ The presence of new chef Todd Humphries (ex Campton Place) "should really up the quality" of the cooking at this St. Helena Mediterranean-American on the West Coast campus of the Culinary Institute of America; while service can be "nerve-wracking" at times ("they're students" after all), the dining room (in the former Christian Brothers winery) is "stunning", with an "open kitchen that's a kick"; N.B. there's an excellent wine list, natch.

World Wrapps ⓁⓈⓂ⊅   13 | 8 | 11 | $10 |
208 Corte Madera Town Ctr. (Madera Blvd.), Corte Madera, 415-927-3663
See review in San Francisco Directory.

Yet Wah ⓁⓈⓂ   14 | 10 | 13 | $20 |
2019 Larkspur Landing Circle (Sir Francis Drake Blvd.), Larkspur, 415-461-3631
See review in San Francisco Directory.

South of San Francisco

| F | D | S | C |

Agenda
Restaurant & Lounge 🅛🅢 | − | − | − | E |
399 S. First St. (San Salvador St.), San Jose, 408-287-3991
If you like live jazz, salsa and swing, add this tony, multilevel
San Jose Californian to your agenda; a happening bar
scene with inventive cocktails also amps up the action.

Amber India 🅛🅢🅜 | 23 | 19 | 19 | $26 |
*Olive Tree Shopping Ctr., 2290 El Camino Real (Rengstorff Ave.),
Mountain View, 650-968-7511*
■ You'd "never know by looking at it", but the "unlikely mall
location" of this Mountain Viewer "hides a gem" with
"refined" food that achieves "a new level of Indian cooking",
at least for the Bay Area; P.S. "don't forget the lunch buffet."

A.P. Stump's 🅛🅢🅜 | 25 | 25 | 23 | $46 |
163 W. Santa Clara St. (Almaden Ave.), San Jose, 408-292-9928
■ San Jose New American hot spot that isn't Stumping
surveyors 'cause it's "off to an excellent start", with
"innovative" food and "fab decor"; it's "fairly expensive",
but it's also "setting a new standard for the South Bay."

Aqui Cal-Mex Grill 🅛🅢🅜 ▽ | 21 | 18 | 16 | $16 |
*1145 Lincoln Ave. (bet. Minnesota & Willow Sts.), San Jose,
408-995-0381*
■ "Variety, flavor, and flair" is the secret to this San Jose
Cal-Mexican serving "tasty but not necessarily authentic"
fare; throw in "low prices" and a "great patio" and no
wonder it's "much loved" by locals.

Bacchanal 🅛🅜 | − | − | − | E |
265 Grand Ave. (Linden Ave.), South San Francisco, 650-742-6600
Things are looking up culinarily for The Industrial City: the
1915-era Metropolitan Hotel has been transformed into an
upscale American featuring a menu of such SF classics as
cioppino; owner-sommelier Ken Taylor's 45,000-bottle wine
cellar, plus a shortlist of amazingly affordable offerings, also
makes this one a definite destination for oenophiles.

Basque Cultural Center 🅛🅢 | 19 | 13 | 18 | $26 |
*599 Railroad Ave. (bet. Orange & Spruce Aves.),
South San Francisco, 650-583-8091*
☑ "Hearty food at cheap prices" is the pull at this South
SF "old standby" serving "genuine" Basque cooking; it
provides a "nice change from too much California cuisine."

Beauséjour 🅛🅢🅜   ▽ 17 | 19 | 18 | $36

170 State St. (bet. 3rd & 4th Sts.), Los Altos, 650-948-1382

◪ While this Los Altos French-Asian has a "romantic atmosphere" and a "pretty setting", unfortunately most maintain that the "mundane food and service" make for an "uneventful" evening; it's definitely "quiet" alright, but "is there anyone under 60 who eats here?"

Bella Vista 🅜   22 | 23 | 23 | $47

13451 Skyline Blvd. (5 mi. south of I-92), Woodside, 650-851-1229

◪ A sky-high, "mountain-retreat" location and matching prices characterize this Woodside Continental with a "sensational view" ("as long as it isn't foggy") and tuxedoed waiters; most maintain that the food is "consistently good" (like the "gotta have it" soufflés), and "wow, what a wine list!"; P.S. "out-of-towners love it."

Benihana 🅛🅢🅜   16 | 15 | 18 | $30

1496 Old Bayshore Hwy. (bet. Broadway & Millbrae Ave.), Burlingame, 650-342-5202
2074 Valco Fashion Park (Wolfe Rd.), Cupertino, 408-253-1221
See review in San Francisco Directory.

Bistro Vida 🅛🅢🅜   – | – | – | M

641 Santa Cruz Ave. (El Camino Real), Menlo Park, 650-462-1686
It's no relation to the LA spot of the same name, but this Menlo Park yearling offers "good" "traditional French bistro fare" in an "inviting atmosphere" that's overseen by a "great host."

Blue Chalk Cafe 🅛🅜   13 | 14 | 14 | $24

630 Ramona St. (bet. Forest & Hamilton Aves.), Palo Alto, 650-326-1020

◪ Cynics chalk this Palo Alto American-cum-poolroom up to being a "meat market and a reunion joint for Stanford" grads, but cue connoisseurs counter the "food may be poor, but it's great for pool parties."

Buck's 🅛🅢🅜   – | – | – | M

3062 Woodside Rd. (Cañada Rd.), Woodside, 650-851-8010
"Cowboys meet venture capitalists" at this "friendly" Woodside American and western-style diner known for its "power breakfasts"; the "wacky" and "conspicuously downscale" decor and the "outré collections" on the walls and ceiling don't keep the deals from getting done.

Buffalo Grill 🅛🅢🅜   18 | 20 | 18 | $33

Hillsdale Mall, 66 31st Ave. (El Camino Real), San Mateo, 650-358-8777

◪ "Food too big to eat" is the hallmark of this San Mateo American that our reviewers say is "sometimes good, sometimes not"; it's convenient "after shopping" at the mall, but "who needs animal heads on the wall?"

Cafe Marcella **L S**   23 | 19 | 22 | $34
368 Village Ln. (Santa Cruz Ave.), Los Gatos, 408-354-8006
☑ Opinion is divided on this Franco-Italian bistro: pros point out that it provides "tasty", "good food for the trendy Los Gatos crowd" and an "up" atmosphere; but cons contend that it's "noisy" (they "stack people at the bar when it's busy") and "overrated."

California Cafe **L S M**   18 | 18 | 18 | $31
Old Town Shopping Ctr., 50 University Ave. (Main St.), Los Gatos, 408-354-8118
Stanford Barn, 700 Welch Rd. (Quarry St.), Palo Alto, 650-325-2233
Valley Fair Shopping Ctr., 2855 Stevens Creek Blvd. (Hwy. 280), Santa Clara, 408-296-2233
See review in North of San Francisco Directory.

Camranh Bay **L S**   – | – | – | M
201 E. Third Ave. (Ellsworth Ave.), San Mateo, 650-342-7577
This stylish, upscale new Vietnamese has opened in the tony San Mateo digs that formerly housed Gibson; look for elegant Asian fare with a French flair from chef Son Truong (ex Le Cheval in Oakland).

Capellini **L S M**   20 | 21 | 19 | $33
310 Baldwin Ave. (South B St.), San Mateo, 650-348-2296
■ There's "solid" cooking (the namesake "classic capellini dish is superb") and the "veal melts in your mouth") at this "pretty" and "comfortable" Northern Italian in San Mateo; while it can be "noisy", most maintain it's a "consistently good choice for fun and food."

Carpaccio **L S M**   19 | 18 | 19 | $34
1120 Crane St. (Santa Cruz Ave.), Menlo Park, 650-322-1211
■ "What a scene" at this Menlo Park Northern Italian designed by Pat Kuleto that serves "reliable", "honest cooking"; there's also a "friendly bar" where you can "sit and sample wine."

Casanova **L S M**   22 | 24 | 21 | $41
Fifth St. (bet. Mission & San Carlos Sts.), Carmel, 831-625-0501
☑ Those enamored of this long-standing "Carmel charmer", with a "cozy", "casually elegant" interior and "lovely garden for outdoor dining", say it's "as good as ever", with "artistic, inventive" Franco-Italian fare and a "huge wine list"; the less loving feel the food is only "decent" and warn that the experience is "not for the faint of pocketbook."

Chef Chu's **L S M**   20 | 14 | 16 | $24
1067 N. San Antonio Rd. (El Camino Real), Los Altos, 650-948-2696
☑ For those who Chu's, there's "tremendous variety" on the menu at this Los Altos Chinese, an "old-time favorite" and an "institution" in San Jose whose owner is "paying attention and it shows"; however, cynics snipe that "it's lost its edge", dubbing the "disappointing" food and decor "tired."

Chevys 🇱🇸🇲   12 | 12 | 13 | $18
979A Edgewater Blvd. (Beach Park Blvd.), Foster City, 650-572-8441
5305 Almaden Expy. (Blossom Hill Rd.), San Jose, 408-266-1815
141 Hickey Blvd. (El Camino Real), South San Francisco, 650-755-1617
204 S. Mathilda Ave. (Washington Ave.), Sunnyvale, 408-737-7395
See review in San Francisco Directory.

Chez Renee 🇱   ▽ 23 | 20 | 20 | $43
9051 Soquel Dr. (Rio del Mar), Aptos, 831-688-5566
■ The few surveyors who know this "gem hidden away in Aptos" call it "a winner", with "thoroughly delicious" Eclectic-French cuisine ("ravishing rack of lamb") and "warm, gracious service"; in sum, they say "more restaurants should be like this."

Chez T.J.   24 | 21 | 22 | $67
938 Villa St. (bet. Castro St. & Shoreline Blvd.), Mountain View, 650-964-7466
▨ It's "very experimental, so you have to gamble" at this Mountain View French: some report "wonderful prix fixe menus" coupled with "imaginative wine parings", making it the "place to go for weddings and anniversaries"; but critics counter that with these "absurd prices" the stakes are too high, and point out that since the clientele is mostly "Silicon Valley techno"-types, you may not fit in unless "you have a pocket protector."

Cielo 🇱🇸🇲   – | – | – | E
Ventana Inn & Spa, Hwy. 1, Big Sur, 831-667-4242
"Beautiful views" overlooking the Pacific Ocean and the mountains are the attraction at this New American in the Ventana Inn & Spa in Big Sur; the "lodgelike setting" and "lovely service" also make it a great for a weekend getaway.

Club XIX 🇱🇸🇲   25 | 26 | 25 | $54
The Lodge at Pebble Beach, 2700 17 Mile Dr. (Cypress Dr.), Pebble Beach, 831-625-8519
■ "People don't know how great it is" insist insiders about this "posh", "pricey" Contemporary French in The Lodge at Pebble Beach, with its "elegant, sophisticated" surroundings and a birdie-eye view of the famous 18th-hole; while a few feel that it "needs a menu update", most maintain the "top-notch" cuisine and "pampering service" are almost on a par with the setting.

Compadres 🇱🇸🇲   16 | 18 | 18 | $24
3877 El Camino Real (Curtner Ave.), Palo Alto, 650-858-1141
▨ Surveyors say the food is only "so-so" at this modestly priced Palo Alto Mexican, but "outside dining is fun" and, inside, there's a "nice, cozy fireplace for cold winter nights"; a large tequila selection and "great margaritas" keep compadres coming; N.B. there's a sib in Yountville too.

Covey, The 🅢🅜　　　▽　24　24　23　$50
Quail Lodge Resort & Golf Club, 8205 Valley Greens Dr.
(Carmel Valley Rd.), Carmel, 831-624-1581

☑ Long-standing Carmel Californian-French in the Quail Lodge Resort & Golf Club with "excellent food", "great service" and a "romantic" terrace overlooking the lake that make it a "special-occasion" spot; N.B. breakfast and dinner only.

Crow's Nest 🅛🅢🅜　　　16　20　16　$27
2218 E. Cliff Dr. (5th Ave.), Santa Cruz, 831-476-4560

☑ While our critics can't quite crow about the food here, this "fun", "casual" stalwart for seafood has a "cute view of Santa Cruz harbor"; a recently remodeled dining room and a new deck add to the aesthetic appeal.

Dal Baffo 🅛🅜　　　21　20　22　$53
878 Santa Cruz Ave. (bet. Crane St. & University Dr.),
Menlo Park, 650-325-1588

☑ Traditionalists trying to "find that classic restaurant" head for this Menlo Park Franco-Italian where they encounter "old-school charm" and "good food and service" at "expense-account prices"; but others are baffled by "blah" cuisine and shrug "it's seen better days."

Duarte's Tavern 🅛🅢🅜　　　20　13　18　$24
202 Stage Rd. (Pescadero Rd.), Pescadero,
650-879-0464

☑ It's a "delicious dive" where "you can still hear the stagecoaches" is what surveyors say about this "funky and fun" roadhouse tavern in Pescadero; the unassuming American food is "nothing fancy", but has earned a passel of fanatical fans because it's their "favorite getaway for fresh fish and pies" ("my god, the olallieberry pie! – did I mention the pie?").

Duck Club ❶🅛🅢🅜　　　▽　20　17　21　$37
Stanford Park Hotel, 100 El Camino Real (University Ave.),
Menlo Park, 650-322-1234

■ "The duck is good but so is the fish" at this Menlo Park American-International in the Stanford Park Hotel; in addition, there are "wonderful [Sunday] brunches and holiday dinners", and since the place is "always open" (til midnight anyway), you can always duck in.

EMILE'S　　　26　21　23　$51
545 S. Second St. (bet. Reed & William Sts.), San Jose,
408-289-1960

■ "High-powered brokers and celebrities" dine at this pricey San Jose pioneer featuring "great" "classic French with modern edges"; "knowledgeable", "caring service", an "elegant" atmosphere and "fine wines" are other reasons why it's "always a treat."

ERNA'S
ELDERBERRY HOUSE 🅛🆂🅜   26 | 27 | 27 | $66

48688 Victoria Ln. (Hwy. 41), Oakhurst, 209-683-6800

■ Our furthest-flung restaurant is this "first-class" American-French in Oakhurst (right outside Yosemite National Park), a "special getaway that creates memories" with an "elegant but comfortable" atmosphere and a "dining experience that's four-star from beginning to end"; you can overnight at the adjoining Château du Sureau, but some frustrated foodies still whine: "why is it so good yet so far?"

Estampas Peruanas 🅛🆂   ▽ 19 | 9 | 17 | $22

715 El Camino Real (Brewster St.), Redwood City, 650-368-9340

☑ "Hole-in-the wall" Peruvian in Redwood City, where there are "huge portions" of "filling food" like "tasty fish stew"; affordable tabs and the fact that it's "trying hard" help make up for "no ambiance."

Eulipia 🅛🆂   21 | 18 | 20 | $38

374 S. First St. (bet. San Carlos & San Salvador Sts.),
San Jose, 408-280-6161

☑ Opinion is divided on this pricey San Jose New American–Continental: pros praise the "innovative food and decor", but foes sniff that "despite the nice ambiance", the fare is "more miss than hit"; however, the new chef might put an end to questions like "wonder why it's not more popular?"

Evvia 🅛🆂🅜   24 | 23 | 21 | $37

420 Emerson St. (bet. Lytton & University Aves.), Palo Alto,
650-326-0983

■ For "Greek food raised to an art form", try this "taverna-like" Palo Alto spot with "wonderful" "nouvelle Hellenistic" cuisine; throw in "transporting decor" and it becomes a "feast for the senses"; the only complaint is that it's one of the "toughest reservations" in the area to score.

Fandango 🅛🆂🅜   – | – | – | E

223 17th St. (Lighthouse Ave.), Pacific Grove, 831-372-3456

High-spirited Mediterranean that's housed in a "wonderful building" in Pacific Grove that gets write-in votes for its "excellent" rustic food, "hospitable owners" and "lovely atmosphere"; there's dining out on the patio, in the glassed-in terrace room and the wine cellar as well.

Faz 🅛🆂🅜   18 | 18 | 18 | $29

1108 N. Mathilda Ave. (Hwy. 237), Sunnyvale, 408-752-8000
See review in San Francisco Directory.

Flea St. Cafe 🅛🆂   22 | 19 | 21 | $35

3607 Alameda de las Pulgas (Avy St.), Menlo Park, 650-854-1226

■ "Marvelous" Menlo Park New American offering "cleverly prepared" food made with "fresh ingredients" and served by a "personable" staff; a recently redecorated dining room (relax, it's still like "eating at home"), and new chef Mark Stark may make Flea fans jump even higher.

Fook Yuen 🅛🅢🅜   23 | 13 | 15 | $25

195 El Camino Real (Millbrae Ave.), Millbrae,
650-692-8600

☑ "Popular" and "authentic" Millbrae Asian that's "always packed with Chinese families" ("a good omen"); once you taste the "most imaginative dim-sum preparations around" (even though "decor and service don't match them"), "you'll know why you waited in line."

FRESH CREAM 🅢🅜   25 | 24 | 24 | $52

Heritage Harbor, 99 Pacific St. (Scott St.), Monterey,
831-375-9798

☑ This expensive New French stalwart in Monterey is "a good place to spend your on-line day-trading profits" on a "leisurely, romantic dinner" that consists of "simply wonderful food", "*très* elegant service" and a "beautiful" setting (some tables have "great [Bay] views"); aficionados ask: "can it get any better?"

Fung Lum 🅛🅢🅜   ▽ 17 | 19 | 14 | $28

1815 S. Bascom Ave. (bet. Campbell & Hamilton Aves.),
Campbell, 408-377-6955

☑ Pros praise this Campbell Chinese for its "delicious food" (like the "unbeatable" signature lemon chicken) and "beautiful decor", which add up to a "delight for the senses"; but critics snipe about the "rude service" and over-the-top setting, saying it "looks, feels and tastes like a movie set" – i.e. "not the real thing."

Gaylord India 🅛🅢🅜   17 | 16 | 16 | $28

1706 El Camino Real (Encinal Ave.), Menlo Park,
650-326-8761

See review in San Francisco Directory.

Gordon Biersch Brewery 🅛🅢🅜   14 | 15 | 14 | $23

640 Emerson St. (bet. Forest & Hamilton Sts.), Palo Alto,
650-323-7723
33 E. San Fernando St. (bet. 1st & 2nd Sts.), San Jose,
408-294-6785

☑ "Noisy" Palo Alto and San Jose brewpubs that function as "yuppie after-work hangouts" (translation: "talk about a pickup joint!"), with "formulaic" American fare and "communication-impaired" service"; party animals simply shrug "bag the food, bring on the brewskies"; N. B. there's also a branch in SF.

Grandview 🅛🅢🅜   ▽ 23 | 11 | 20 | $25

1107 Howard Ave. (bet. Highland & Lorton Aves.), Burlingame,
650-348-3888

■ There's "good" Shanghai cuisine to be had at this Burlingame Chinese with "interesting " dishes; it's "one step above the rest", so you might want to "try everything" – just don't expect anything when it comes to the "plain" decor.

Grill, The 🇱🇸🇲   – | – | – | E |
Fairmont Hotel, 172 S. Market St. (San Fernando St.), San Jose,
408-998-1900
LA power-dining arrived in San Jose with the advent of this
offshoot of a renowned Beverly Hills American; located in
the Fairmont Hotel, it's a prime steak-and-chop house that's
pricey, posh and perfect for closing that deal.

Hong Kong Flower Lounge 🇱🇸🇲 21 | 15 | 15 | $27 |
51 Millbrae Ave. (El Camino Real), Millbrae, 650-692-6666
560 Waverly St. (Hamilton St.), Palo Alto, 650-326-3830
■ The "duck rocks", as does the "tasty" seafood and "very
authentic dim sum" at this "vast, glitzy" Millbrae Chinese
with a clientele of "rich Hong Kong expats"; it's "noisy"
and service isn't the swiftest, but most maintain that it's
"worth the wait"; N.B. there's also a sib in Palo Alto.

Iberia 🇱🇸🇲   19 | 19 | 17 | $40 |
Ladera Country Shopper, 3130 Alpine Rd. (La Cuesta),
Portola Valley, 650-854-1746
◪ A "nondescript mall" setting for this pricey Portola
Valley pioneer hides "one of the few Spanish places in
this area", but surveyors are split on whether the food is
"interesting" or "inconsistent"; the "glacial service" is
less noticeable if "you are able to eat outside" in the garden.

Il Fornaio 🇱🇸🇲   19 | 21 | 18 | $30 |
327 Lorton Ave. (bet. Burlingame Ave. & California St.),
Burlingame, 650-375-8000
Garden Court Hotel, 520 Cowper St. (bet. Hamilton St. &
University Ave.), Palo Alto, 650-853-3888
Hyatt Sainte Claire, 302 S. Market St. (San Carlos St.), San Jose,
408-271-3366
See review in San Francisco Directory.

Isobune Sushi 🇱🇸🇲   16 | 14 | 14 | $22 |
1451 Burlingame Ave. (El Camino Real), Burlingame,
650-344-8433
See review in San Francisco Directory.

JoAnn's Cafe 🇱🇸🇲🇵   22 | 12 | 19 | $16 |
1131 El Camino Real (bet. Hickey & Westborough Blvds.),
South San Francisco, 650-872-2810
■ "JoAnn couldn't be nicer, nor the food better" at her
"no-frills" South SF coffee shop where the "best breakfasts"
come in "huge, farm-style portions" and "everything is fresh
and yummy"; N.B. breakfast and lunch only.

Jocco's Restaurant 🇱🇸🇲   ∇ 21 | 15 | 20 | $39 |
236 Central Plaza (bet. 2nd & 3rd Sts.), Los Altos, 650-948-6809
■ A "small" "neighborhood restaurant with a big-city quality
chef" is what surveyors say about Jaime Carpenter's New
American yearling in Los Altos; "innovative food" means that
the "simple but comfortable room" can become "cramped"
and "noisy" because it's "always jammed with crowds."

Juban **L S M**   18 | 17 | 15 | $28
1204 Broadway (Laguna Ave.), Burlingame, 650-347-2300
712 Santa Cruz Ave. (bet. El Camino Real & Santa Cruz Ave.),
Menlo Park, 650-473-6458
☑ "If you don't mind doing the cooking yourself", these
Burlingame and Menlo Park Japanese (with a sib in
SF's Japantown) are an apt option, sending out "quality"
ingredients to your tabletop grill for you to turn into
"flavorful" dishes; of course, grumps gripe "who likes to
cook when they go out to eat?"

Kathmandu West **L S M**   ▽ 18 | 14 | 21 | $20
20916A Homestead Rd. (Hollenbeck Rd.), Cupertino, 408-996-0940
■ Some who have trekked to this Cupertino spot serving
Nepalese cuisine say it's "better than Indian food", with
"more interesting spices"; "cheerful service" and low prices
add to its appeal.

Kincaid's Bistro **L S M**   23 | 22 | 21 | $39
Crossroads Shopping Ctr., 217 Crossroads Blvd. (Hwy. 1),
Carmel, 831-624-9626
■ "Elegant" Carmel French bistro offering "artfully
presented food that melts in your mouth" and "smooth
service"; "don't let the shopping center location fool you –
this is a keeper" that's both "charming and consistent."

Kuleto's Trattoria **L S M**   19 | 20 | 19 | $33
1095 Rollins Rd. (Broadway), Burlingame, 415-342-4922
■ Burlingame Italian with "consistently good food, a
comfortable atmosphere and friendly service"; this
offshoot may "not have the magic" of its sib in SF, but if
you're looking for the "best place near the airport",
surveyors say this is it.

La Cumbre Taqueria **L S M**   21 | 9 | 13 | $9
28 North B St. (bet. 1st & Tilton Aves.), San Mateo, 650-344-8989
See review in San Francisco Directory.

L'AMIE DONIA   25 | 18 | 20 | $41
530 Bryant St. (bet. Hamilton & University Aves.), Palo Alto,
650-323-7614
■ "Up tempo" Palo Alto French bistro with "dynamite food";
true, the "tables are too close together", the setting is a
"little hard-edged" and wallet-watchers feel jabbed by
the "skyrocketing prices", but most maintain that you can
always count on a "high-quality meal" here.

La Pastaia **L S M**   20 | 21 | 20 | $35
Hotel De Anza, 233 W. Santa Clara St. (Almaden Blvd.),
San Jose, 408-286-8686
☑ Surveyors can't reach a consensus as to whether the
food at this hotel Italian in the "heart of San Jose" is "good"
and "flavorful" or only "fair"; what is certain is that it's
"comfortable" and convenient if you're heading to a sporting
event 'cause it's "close to the Arena."

Lark Creek 🅛🅢🅜   21 | 20 | 20 | $35
Benjamin Franklin Hotel, 50 E. Third Ave. (El Camino Real), San Mateo, 650-344-9444
See review in East of San Francisco Directory.

La Taqueria 🅛🅜⇄   23 | 10 | 13 | $11
15 S. First St. (Santa Clara Ave.), San Jose, 408-287-1542
See review in San Francisco Directory.

Left at Albuquerque 🅛🅢🅜   13 | 15 | 14 | $21
445 Emerson St. (bet Lytton & University Aves.), Palo Alto, 650-326-1011
1100 Burlingame Ave. (California Ave.), Burlingame, 650-401-5700
Pruneyard Shopping Ctr., 1875 S. Bascom Ave.
(bet. Campbell & Hamilton Aves.), Campbell, 408-558-1680
☑ "Loud, lively" Tex-Mexers that are "a frat boy's dream", what with their "singles scene" and "great selection of tequilas"; but others can't get enthused about the "so-so" chain food, so they hang a sharp right and steer clear.

Left Bank 🅛🅢🅜   21 | 21 | 19 | $37
635 Santa Cruz Ave. (Doyle St.), Menlo Park, 650-473-6543
See review in North of San Francisco Directory.

LE MOUTON NOIR 🅢🅜   25 | 23 | 24 | $49
14560 Big Basin Way (bet. 4th & 5th Sts.), Saratoga, 408-867-7017
■ Saratoga stalwart with "excellent" French food, "great service", "outstanding wine" and recently renovated, romantic "country decor"; it's "pricey" but "good for impressing dates or clients."

Le Papillon 🅛🅢🅜   ▽ 26 | 23 | 25 | $51
410 Saratoga Ave. (Kiely Blvd.), San Jose, 408-296-3730
☑ The few who know this long-standing San Jose New French say it features "excellent food", which is "presented in an artistic manner"; in addition, the "classy" atmosphere bodes well for a "romantic evening."

Lion & Compass 🅛🅜   ▽ 19 | 18 | 19 | $37
1023 N. Fair Oaks Ave. (Weddell Dr.), Sunnyvale, 408-745-1260
☑ While local corporate types set their compass for this "old-school Silicon Valley institution", surveyors can't get their bearings as to whether the New American food here is "good" or "just ok"; still, the "comfortable atmosphere" is "great for business."

Los Gatos Brewing Co. 🅛🅢🅜   18 | 18 | 18 | $26
130G N. Santa Cruz Ave. (Grays Ln.), Los Gatos, 408-395-9929
☑ Watch out for "groping men at the bar" at this "loud", "lively" Los Gatos brewpub "where Silicon Valley yuppies go"; foam fans feel that the food can be "surprisingly good" or "unnecessarily mediocre", depending on how many beers you've had.

131

MacArthur Park L S M   17 | 18 | 18 | $30
27 University Ave. (El Camino Real), Palo Alto, 650-321-9990
See review in San Francisco Directory.

Marinus L S M   – | – | – | VE
Bernardus Lodge, 415 Carmel Valley Rd. (Laureles Grade Rd.),
Carmel Valley, 831-659-3131
Veteran Bay-Area chef Cal Stamenov moved from the highly
rated Pacific's Edge in the Highlands Inn to this Cal-French
in Carmel Valley's luxurious new Bernardus Lodge (owned
by the interests behind Bernardus Winery); with its old-world
wine country charm and garden and mountain views, watch
this one sail straight to the forefront as a dining destination.

Max's Opera Café L S M   17 | 14 | 16 | $22
1250 Old Bayshore (Airport Blvd.), Burlingame, 650-342-6297
711 Stanford Shopping Ctr. (El Camino Real), Palo Alto,
650-323-6297
See review in San Francisco Directory.

Mio Vicino L S M   ▽ 20 | 14 | 17 | $23
384 E. Campbell Ave. (Central Ave.), Campbell, 408-378-0335
1140-8 Lincoln Ave. (bet. Meredith Ave. & Willow St.),
San Jose, 408-286-6027
1290 Benton St. (Monroe St.), Santa Clara, 408-241-9414
◪ "Value-packed Italian fare" and nice local wine lists
are yours at these Campbell, San Jose and Santa Clara
trattorias; they make "good drop-in places" or "great fall-
back" spots for "reliable" cooking right in your own nabe.

Montrio L S M   23 | 22 | 21 | $39
414 Calle Principal (Franklin St.), Monterey, 831-648-8880
■ "If I could live there, I would!" exclaim fans of this
"boisterous" Monterey American bistro set "in a converted
firehouse" that features "outstanding food" and a "great
wine list"; it's "always a delight", so "tell your friends."

Moss Beach Distillery L S M   13 | 20 | 15 | $30
Beach Way & Ocean Blvd. (off Hwy. 1), Moss Beach,
650-728-5595
◪ Ok, the food is only "so-so", but "even if they only served
Tang and Spam, you'd still have to come for the view of
the Pacific" at this landmark 1927 American on the coast;
it may be a "dowdy, dated dud" that's grown a bit mossy
over the years, but the resident ghost is an invisible
attraction and the vista "makes you forget everything else."

Nepenthe L S M   15 | 25 | 16 | $27
Hwy. 1, Big Sur, 831-667-2345
■ "The '60s are alive and well" at this Big Sur American in
an "awesome location", perched on a "breathtaking cliffside
site" high above the Pacific, giving it quite possibly the
"planet's best view"; the food is only "an afterthought",
so stick to a drink, a burger or just "sit outside with a cup
of coffee" and tune in to the universe.

L S M   – | – | – | M
...mona St. (bet. Hamilton & University Aves.), Palo Alto,
...8-2722
...e flavor of New Orleans" comes to Downtown Palo
...a this "wonderfully hip restaurant" where "Cajun
...Californian" and the result is "creative food"; it's
not related to the establishment of the same name in the
Big Easy, but you'll "feel like you're on Bourbon Street"
because it's "fun" and a "great scene."

Osteria L M   21 | 16 | 17 | $31
Cardinal Hotel, 247 Hamilton Ave. (Ramona St.), Palo Alto,
650-328-5700
☑ "Friendly" Palo Alto Northern Italian with "consistent",
"good" food, "especially the pastas"; the space is small
and "claustrophobic", but the "portions are large" and
the price is right.

PACIFIC'S EDGE L S M   26 | 28 | 24 | $57
Highlands Inn, Hwy. 1 (Highland Dr.), Carmel, 831-622-5445
■ "Nature provides the ambiance" at this top-dollar
Californian in the Highlands Inn, which is voted No. 1 for
Decor and situated on a "spectacular stretch" of the
Carmel coast; however, the vista "doesn't overshadow
the truly fine food", which is likely to remain highly rated
despite the departure of chef Cal Stamenov (now at
Marinus); since it "excels in every way", the only question
is whether the "world-class views" are "best at lunch at a
window table" or "right before sunset."

Palace, The   ▽ 21 | 25 | 18 | $41
146 S. Murphy Ave. (bet. Evelyn & Washington Aves.),
Sunnyvale, 408-739-5179
■ This '30s Sunnyvale movie theater, which has been
transformed into a supper club with multiple bars, jazz and
dancing, exudes a "great atmosphere" that's "like going to a
show"; there are "always new, unusual dishes" on the
New American menu, as well as a large tapas selection; it
all adds up to a "good scene place", so "party on!"

Paolo's L S M   ▽ 23 | 22 | 19 | $43
River Park Tower, 333 W. San Carlos St. (Woz Way), San Jose,
408-294-2558
■ "Upscale" Italian with "exceptional food and service"
that's an "outstanding favorite"; it's on the "pricey" side,
but some swear it's been the "best in San Jose for decades."

Pasta Moon L S M   21 | 17 | 19 | $31
315 Main St. (Mill St.), Half Moon Bay, 650-726-5125
☑ There's a "small-town feel" to this "clean, neat" Italian
in Half Moon Bay that specializes in home-made pastas
and wood-oven roasted pizzas that are generally "always
good"; while service can be "lackluster" and "slow", most
maintain that the place is an "old favorite."

Piatti L S M
     19 | 19 | 18 | $33 |
2 Stanford Shopping Ctr. (El Camino Real), Palo Alto, 650-324-9733
NW corner of 6th St. & Junipero, Carmel, 831-625-1766
See review in North of San Francisco Directory.

Plumed Horse M
     24 | 22 | 24 | $50 |
14555 Big Basin Way (4th St.), Saratoga, 408-867-4711
■ High-ticket Saratoga stalwart whose New French food is "sometimes excellent, always good"; other pluses are a pretty, romantic room, "exceptional service" and an award-winning wine list.

Pluto's L S M
     18 | 11 | 12 | $13 |
482 University Ave. (Cowper St.), Palo Alto, 650-853-1556
See review in San Francisco Directory.

Rio Grill L S M
     22 | 20 | 21 | $35 |
Crossroads Shopping Ctr., 101 Crossroads Blvd. (Rio Rd.), Carmel, 831-625-5436
■ "Consistently consistent" Carmel Cal-Southwestern in a shopping mall that "still delivers", with a "great menu", an "appealing" (albeit "noisy") ambiance and a "friendly", "helpful staff" that makes it a good choice "when the kids are in tow"; since it's "blue ribbon in every way", surveyors surmise that "it will never go out of style."

Roy's at Pebble Beach L S M
     25 | 26 | 23 | $45 |
The Inn at Spanish Bay, 2700 17 Mile Dr. (Congress Rd.), Pebble Beach, 831-647-7423
■ "Can you beat the setting?" – probably not because Hawaiian super-chef Roy Yamaguchi's Euro-Asian "special-occasion" spot in The Inn at Spanish Bay "lives up to its reputation" with a "dreamlike" location overlooking Pebble Beach and a "beautiful, stylish room"; the fusion fare is "innovative" and "amazing", and the staff "treats you like royalty", but "bring a calculator" because the tab "adds up."

San Benito House L S M
     ▽ 19 | 18 | 18 | $37 |
San Benito House, 356 Main St. (Mill St.), Half Moon Bay, 650-726-3425
■ "You'd better like doilies" if you're going to this Half Moon Bay Cal-Med in an historic 1905 hotel; while the Victorian-style dining room is "lovely, funky" and old-fashioned, in contrast, the "delicious" menu is strictly modern.

Santa Barbara Grill L S M
     ▽ 17 | 17 | 17 | $34 |
10745 N. De Anza Blvd. (bet. Hwy. 280 & Valley Green Dr.), Cupertino, 408-253-2233
◪ Surveyors are split over this Cupertino BYO New American yearling: while cynics say it "feels like a chain", grateful locals retort that it's a "nice neighborhood place" in an area where "there aren't many options."

Scott's L S M
| 17 | 17 | 17 | $32 |

2300 E. Bayshore Rd. (Embarcadero), Palo Alto,
650-856-1046
185 Park Ave. (bet. Almaden Blvd. & Market St.), San Jose,
408-971-1700
See review in San Francisco Directory.

SENT SOVI S
| 28 | 22 | 25 | $56 |

14583 Big Basin Way (5th St.), Saratoga, 408-867-3110
■ The "treasure of Saratoga" is David Kinch's "perfect small restaurant", an "exquisite find" with "imaginative" and "outstanding" New French food, which is backed up by highly rated service; it's "pricey", but the experience is "always extremely enjoyable."

71 Saint Peter L M
▽ | 23 | 18 | 22 | $37 |

71 N. San Pedro St. (bet. Santa Clara & St. John Sts.), San Jose,
408-971-8523
■ In spite of its "postage stamp–sized kitchen", fans say you can "always count on an excellent meal" at this "friendly" Mediterranean grill with brick walls and wooden beams; not only does it make "Downtown San Jose bearable", but it's "great for a romantic dinner."

Sierra Mar L S M
▽ | 28 | 30 | 25 | $61 |

Post Ranch Inn, Hwy. 1 (26 mi. south of Carmel), Big Sur,
831-667-2800
■ "If money is no object", go for "one of life's rare treats" to this "spectacular" "cliff-hanger" – "the restaurant at the end of the universe" suspended 1200 feet above the Pacific in Big Sur; since the Cal-French "food and the view are heaven on earth!", it's no wonder surveyors sigh it's the "most romantic spot on the coast."

Spago Palo Alto L S M
| 24 | 23 | 22 | $51 |

265 Lytton Ave. (Bryant St.), Palo Alto,
650-833-1000
■ "Wolfgang works his magic" at this "chi-chi" ("just smell all that new money") Palo Alto hot spot and "sequel" to the original in LA, with the trademark "hip decor" and "fabulous people-watching" ("get off the cell phone already"); while some sniff it's "noisy", "overrated" and "trading on its reputation", the majority maintains that the Californian food is "excellent" – as usual, "Puck knows what he's doing."

Stokes Adobe L S M
▽ | 20 | 22 | 21 | $42 |

500 Hartnell St. (bet. Madison & Polk Sts.), Monterey,
831-373-1110
■ This "wonderful revamp" of an 1830s-era Monterey adobe dwelling houses a "charming", "customer-friendly" Franco-Italian with a "creative menu" from chef Brandon Miller; devotees detect "a future star" with "great potential" here.

Straits Cafe 🄻🅂Ⓜ   22 | 18 | 18 | $29
3295 El Camino Real (Lambert Ave.), Palo Alto, 650-494-7168
See review in San Francisco Directory.

Swagat Indian Cuisine 🄻🅂Ⓜ   20 | 12 | 14 | $21
2700 W. El Camino Real (bet. Los Altos Ave. & San Antonio Rd.), Mountain View, 650-948-7727
■ The "wide choices" and "cheap" prices make this Mountain View Indian a "good value"; it's "not fancy", but don't let the "tacky setting" deter you from discovering what some say is "more food than I've ever seen anywhere."

Tapestry 🄻Ⓜ   ▽ 27 | 24 | 23 | $40
11 College Ave. (E. Main St.), Los Gatos, 408-395-2808
■ "Cute little" yearling in Los Gatos that features an "excellent, innovative", monthly changing menu of 'Global' cuisine (California cooking with International influences); it can be a bit noisy, but the heated patio makes for an appealing alfresco alternative.

Tarpy's Roadhouse 🄻🅂Ⓜ   22 | 22 | 21 | $37
2999 Monterey-Salinas Hwy. (Canyon Del Rey), Monterey, 831-647-1444
■ While it's in "the middle of nowhere", this "fun" American roadhouse near the Monterey Airport features "good, creative fare without pretense"; "if you dine outdoors" on the "wonderful" patio, you can get a buzz without booze from watching the "planes overhead."

2030 🄻Ⓜ   ▽ 20 | 18 | 20 | $33
2030 Broadway (Main St.), Redwood City, 650-363-2030
■ Midrange Redwood City American-International bistro and local "favorite" that's "many steps above its neighbors"; an outdoor patio is another plus.

231 ELLSWORTH 🄻   25 | 22 | 24 | $47
231 S. Ellsworth Ave. (bet. 2nd & 3rd Aves.), San Mateo, 650-347-7231
■ High-end French "gem" in San Mateo with "elegant, refined food" that's "never a disappointment", making it the "nearby choice for special occasions"; while the "dull interior" doesn't excite those with design on their minds, the prix fixe lunch offers a "great deal on gourmet dining."

Viognier 🄻🅂Ⓜ   25 | 22 | 21 | $43
Draeger's Mkt., 222 E. Fourth Ave. (bet. B St. & Ellsworth Ave.), San Mateo, 650-685-3727
■ "A food lover's restaurant", this San Mateo Med (located upstairs from Draeger's "super supermarket") is "one of the few worth a trip down 101"; while star chef Gary Danko is now at his own spot in SF, his legacy lives on in the "imaginative, delicious" cuisine; with its "wonderfully spacious" dining room, "friendly service" and "good wine list", it's "a repeater."

136

Wild Hare 🄻🅂🄼   - | - | - | E
1029 El Camino Real (bet. Menlo & Santa Cruz Aves.),
Menlo Park, 650-327-4273
There's a large menu featuring Californian cuisine with an
emphasis on game dishes at this new Menlo Park spot,
making it a "nice addition to the Peninsula" – maybe reason
enough for city dwellers to head south on a Wild Hare chase.

World Wrapps 🄻🅂🄼⊘   13 | 8 | 11 | $10
1318 Burlingame Ave. (bet. California Ave. & El Camino Real),
Burlingame, 650-342-9777
201 University Ave. (Emerson St.), Palo Alto, 650-327-9777
Mercado Ctr., 3125 Mission College Blvd.
(Great America Pkwy.), Santa Clara, 408-486-9727
See review in San Francisco Directory.

Zibibbo 🄻🅂🄼   20 | 21 | 18 | $36
430 Kipling St. (bet. Lytton & University Aves.), Palo Alto,
650-328-6722
◪ Here comes "LuLu's country cousin" – this "fun" Palo
Alto Mediterranean can be "a little overwhelming", what
with "all those choices" on the menu and the "noisy",
happening "scene"; while the food is "good" ("marvelous"
signature mussels), most maintain that there's more "flash
and sizzle" in the dining room than the kitchen.

Indexes to Restaurants

Special Features and Appeals

CUISINES

Afghan
Helmand

American (New)
A.P. Stump's/S
Aqua
Atlas Peak Grill/N
Avenue Grill/N
Avenue 9
Big Four
Bistro Ralph/N
Bix
Boonville Hotel/N
Boulevard
Brannan's Grill/N
Bubba's Diner/N
Buffalo Grill/S
Cafe Flore
Cafe Kati
Café La Haye/N
Carnelian Room
Celadon/N
Cielo/S
Cypress Club
Duck Club/S
Eddie Rickenbacker's
Elan Vital
Ella's
Elroys
Erna's Elderberry/S
Eulipia/S
First Crush
Flea St. Cafe/S
French Laundry/N
Gary Danko
General's Daughter/N
Ginger Island/E
Globe
Gordon's/N
Gordon's Hse.
Harry Denton's Starlight
Heirloom/N
Horizons/N
House
Indigo
Infusion
Jocco's/S
Kenwood/N
Liberty Cafe
Lion & Compass/S
Live Fire/N
Meadowood Grill/N
Mecca

Meetinghouse
Miss Millie's
Montage
Mustards Grill/N
Occidental Grill
Olema Inn/N
One Market
Palace/S
Park Grill
Pauli's Cafe
Planet Hollywood
Pyramid Alehse./E
Red Herring
Ricochet
Rotunda
Rumpus
Santa Barbara Grill/S
Sent Sovi/S
Slow Club
Station Hse. Cafe/N
Terra/N
Tomales Bay/N
Town's End
2223 Rest.
Universal Cafe
Wine Spectator/N
Woodward's Garden

American (Regional)
Albion River Inn/N
Auberge du Soleil/N
Bacchanal/S
Biscuits & Blues
Black Cat
Buckeye Roadhse./N
Catahoula/N
Connecticut Yankee
dame
Duarte's Tavern/S
Eastside West
Felix & Louie's/N
Foothill Cafe/N
Gordon's Hse.
John Ash/N
Lark Creek/E
Lark Creek/S
Lark Creek Inn/N
Manka's Inverness/N
Montrio/S
Rest. at Meadowood/N
Savanna Grill/N

American (Traditional)

Alta Mira/N
Autumn Moon/E
Balboa Cafe
Beach Chalet
Bette's Oceanview/E
Bill's Place
Bitterroot
Blue Chalk Cafe/S
Brazen Head
Bubba's Diner/N
Buchanan Grill
Buckeye Roadhse./N
Buck's/S
Cafe For All Seasons
Cheers
Chow
Clement St. B&G
Cliff Hse.
Connecticut Yankee
Curbside Too
Delancey St.
Doidge's Cafe
Dottie's True Blue
FatApple's/E
Fly Trap
Fog City Diner
Gordon Biersch
Gordon Biersch/S
Grill/S
Hamburger Mary's
Hard Rock Cafe
Hayes St. Grill
Houston's
Izzy's
JoAnn's Cafe/S
John's Grill
Kate's Kitchen
Lark Creek/E
Lark Creek/S
Lark Creek Inn/N
Liverpool Lil's
London Wine Bar
Los Gatos/S
MacArthur Park
MacArthur Park/S
Magnolia Pub
Mama's on Washington
Mama's Royal Cafe/E
Mel's Drive-In
MoMo's
Mo's Burgers
Moss Beach Distillery/S
Nepenthe/S
Northstar & Little Dipper

Original Joe's
Park Chow
Perry's
Perry's Downtown
Pier 23 Cafe
Pluto's
Pluto's/S
Rick & Ann's/E
Rutherford Grill/N
Sam's Anchor Cafe/N
Sam's Grill
Sand Dollar/N
Sears Fine Food
Tarpy's Roadhse./S
Tommy's Joynt
2030/S
Vic Stewart's/E
Washington Sq. B&G

Asian

Angkor Wat
AsiaSF
Beausejour/S
Betelnut Pejiu Wu
Brix/N
E&O Trading
Eos
Firecracker
Fook Yuen/S
House
Kathmandu West/S
Ondine/N
Oodles
Oritalia
Park Chow
Roy's/Pebble Beach/S
Silks
Tin-Pan
Watergate
Xanadu/E
Yoyo Bistro

Bakeries

Citizen Cake
Downtown Bakery/N
Northstar & Little Dipper
Town's End

Bar-B-Q

Cordon Bleu
Foothill Cafe/N
Korea Hse.
Live Fire/N
MacArthur Park
MacArthur Park/S
Moonshine

Brazilian
Mozzarella Di Bufala
Terra Brazilis

Burmese
Irrawaddy
Mandalay
Nan Yang Rockridge/E

Cajun/Creole
Catahoula/N
Elite Cafe
Jessie's
Nola/S
PJ's Oyster Bed

Californian
Agenda/S
Aqui/S
Avenue Grill/N
Backflip
Bay Wolf/E
Belon
Bistro Viola/E
Blackhawk Grille/E
Blue Point
Brava Terrace/N
Bridges/E
Cafe Majestic
Cafe Mozart
California Cafe/E
California Cafe/N
California Cafe/S
California Pizza Kit.
California Pizza Kit./E
Caprice/N
Charles Nob Hill
Chez Panisse/E
Chez Panisse Cafe/E
Covey/S
Domaine Chandon/N
Erna's Elderberry/S
Farallon
Food Inc.
Frascati
Garden Court
Garibaldis/College/E
Glen Ellen Inn/N
Grand Cafe
Hawthorne Lane
Insalata's/N
Jordan's/E
Julie's Supper Club
Kelly's Mission Rock
Marinus/S
Ma Tante Sumi

mc^2
Meadowood Grill/N
Mikayla/Casa Madrona/N
Millennium
Montage
Moose's
Napa Valley Grille/N
Napa Valley Wine Train/N
Nola/S
Oak Town Cafe/E
Pacific
Pacific's Edge/S
Piatti/N
Piatti/S
Postrio
Presidio Cafe
Ravenous/N
Redwood Rm.
Rio Grill/S
Rivoli/E
Rubicon
San Benito Hse./S
Santa Fe B&G/E
Showley's/N
Sierra Mar/S
Silks
Soizic/E
Sonoma Mission Inn Grille/N
Spago Palo Alto/S
Syrah/N
Tapestry/S
Terra/N
Top of the Mark
Tortola
Viognier/S
Waterfront
Wente Vineyards/E
Wild Hare/S
Willowside Cafe/N
Xyz
Yoyo Bistro

Cambodian
Angkor Wat
Battambang/E

Caribbean
Caribbean Zone
Cha Cha Cha
Cha Cha Cha/Orig. McCarthy's
Charanga
Primo Patio

Chinese
Alice's
Brandy Ho's

Chef Chu's/S
Dragon Well
Eliza's
Empress of China
Eric's
Firecracker
Fook Yuen/S
Fountain Court
Fung Lum/S
Grandview/S
Great Eastern
Harbor Village
Hong Kong Flower
Hong Kong Flower/S
House of Nanking
Hunan
Jade Villa/E
Lichee Garden
Long Life Noodle
Long Life Noodle/E
Long Life Vegi/E
Mandarin
Mayflower
North Sea Village/N
Rest. Peony/E
Shanghai 1930
Taiwan
Tommy Toy's
Tonga
Ton Kiang
Yank Sing
Yet Wah
Yet Wah/N
Yuet Lee

Coffee Shops/Diners

Bette's Oceanview/E
Bubba's Diner/N
Buck's/S
Caffe Centro
Dottie's True Blue
Fog City Diner
JoAnn's Cafe/S
Mama's Royal Cafe/E
Mario's Bohemian
Max's Diner
Mel's Drive-In
Sears Fine Food

Continental

Alta Mira/N
Bella Vista/S
Caprice/N
Eulipia/S
Fournou's Ovens
Gordon's Hse.

Hotel Mac/E
Jacks
Ovation
Rocco's

Delis/Sandwich Shops

Cafe Citti/N
Max's Diner
Max's on Square
Max's Opera Café
Max's Opera Café/S
Saul's/E
Vivande Porta Via

Dim Sum

Fook Yuen/S
Harbor Village
Hong Kong Flower
Hong Kong Flower/S
Jade Villa/E
Lichee Garden
Mayflower
North Sea Village/N
Rest. Peony/E
Ton Kiang
Yank Sing

Eclectic/International

AsiaSF
Bam
Black Cat
Blue Plate
Bubble Lounge
Cafe Akimbo
Cafe Beaujolais/N
Café La Haye/N
Carta
Celadon/N
Chez Renee/S
Chow
Duck Club/S
Entros
Firefly
Fuzio
Glen Ellen Inn/N
Gramercy Grill
Hayes & Vine
Lalime's/E
Nava/E
Northstar & Little Dipper
Oak Town Cafe/E
Ondine/N
Oodles
Primo Patio
Ravenous/N
Rick's

Rooster
Savor
Tapestry/S
2030/S
Wappo Bar/N
World Wrapps
World Wrapps/N
World Wrapps/S

English
Liverpool Lil's

Ethiopian
Blue Nile/E
Massawa
Rasselas

French
Bandol
Basque Cultural Ctr./S
Cafe de la Presse
Cafe Jacqueline
Cafe Mozart
Campton Place
Citron/E
Dal Baffo/S
El Paseo/N
Emile's/S
Filou/N
French Laundry/N
La Bergerie
Le Cyrano
Le Mouton Noir/S
L'Olivier
Madrona Manor/N
Marinus/S
Rest. Marais
Rue de Main/E
Ti Couz
231 Ellsworth/S

French Bistro
Absinthe
Alamo Square
Anjou
Baker St. Bistro
Bistro Clovis
Bistro Jeanty/N
Bistro Vida/S
Bistro Viola/E
Bizou
Bocca Rotis
Bouchon/N
Cafe Bastille
Cafe Claude
Cafe de Paris

Cafe Marcella/S
Cafe Rouge/E
Caffe Proust
Casanova/S
Cassis
Chapeau!
Christophe/N
Clementine
Florio
Foreign Cinema
Fringale
girl & the fig/N
Guernica/N
Hyde St. Bistro
Kincaid's Bistro/S
L'Amie Donia/S
La Note/E
La Scene
Le Central Bistro
Le Charm
Left Bank/N
Left Bank/S
LuLu
Plouf
Scala's Bistro
Soizic/E
South Park Cafe
Stokes Adobe/S
Syrah/N
Zazie

French (New)
Aux Delices
Beausejour/S
Brasserie Savoy
Cafe Beaujolais/N
Cafe Fanny/E
Charles Nob Hill
Chateau Souverain/N
Chez Renee/S
Chez T.J./S
Club XIX/S
Covey/S
Domaine Chandon/N
Elan Vital
Erna's Elderberry/S
Fifth Floor
Fleur de Lys
Flying Saucer
French Laundry/N
Fresh Cream/S
Grand Cafe
Jardinière
Kenwood/N
La Folie

La Toque/N
Le Papillon/S
Maria Therese
Masa's
mc^2
Obelisque/E
Ondine/N
Ovation
Pastis
Piaf's
Pinot Blanc/N
Plouf
Plumed Horse/S
Rest. Marais
Ritz-Carlton Din. Rm.
Rubicon
Sent Sovi/S
Sierra Mar/S
Terra/N
Thornhill Cafe/E
231 Ellsworth/S
Watergate

German

Schroeder's
Suppenküche
Tommy's Joynt

Greek

Evvia/S
Kokkari

Hamburgers

Autumn Moon/E
Balboa Cafe
Barney's
Bill's Place
FatApple's/E
Hamburger Mary's
Hard Rock Cafe
Houston's
Liverpool Lil's
Mel's Drive-In
Mo's Burgers
Nepenthe/S
Planet Hollywood
Presidio Cafe

Hawaiian

Tita's

Health Food

Millennium
Raw

Hungarian

Hungarian Sausage

Indian

Ajanta/E
Amber India/S
Breads of India/E
Gaylord India
Gaylord India/S
Indian Oven
Maharani
North India
Swagat/S

Indonesian

Jakarta
Rice Table/N

Irish

O'Reilly's

Italian

(N=Northern; S=Southern;
N&S=Includes both)
Acquerello (N)
Albona Rist. (N)
Allegro (N&S)
Antica Trattoria (N&S)
Aperto (N&S)
Armani Cafe (N&S)
Baraonda (N&S)
Basta Pasta (N)
Bella Trattoria (N&S)
Bistro Don Giovanni/N (N&S)
Bocca Rotis (N&S)
Bocce Cafe (N&S)
Bontà Rist. (N&S)
Brava Terrace/N (N&S)
Brazio/E (N)
Buca Giovanni (N&S)
Cafe Citti/N (N)
Cafe 817/E (N)
Cafe Marcella/S (N&S)
Cafe Riggio (N&S)
Cafe Tiramisu (N)
Caffe Delle Stelle (N)
Caffe Greco (N&S)
Caffe Macaroni (S)
Caffe Proust (N&S)
Caffe Sport (S)
Calzone's (N)
Capellini/S (N)
Capp's Corner (N&S)
Carpaccio/S (N)
Casanova/S (N&S)
Castagnola's (N&S)

Columbus Rist. (N)
Cucina Jackson Fillmore/N (S)
Dal Baffo/S (N&S)
dalla Torre (N)
Delfina (N&S)
Della Santina's/N (N)
E'Angelo (N)
Enrico's (N&S)
Ernesto's (N&S)
Felix & Louie's/N (N&S)
Fior d'Italia (N)
Firewood Cafe (N&S)
Frantoio/N (N)
Frascati (S)
Fresco/N (N&S)
Gira Polli (N&S)
Gira Polli/E (N&S)
Gira Polli/N (N&S)
I Fratelli (N&S)
Il Fornaio (N)
Il Fornaio/E (N)
Il Fornaio/N (N)
Il Fornaio/S (N)
Iron Horse (N)
Jackson Fillmore (S)
Julius' Castle (N)
Kuleto's (N)
Kuleto's Trattoria/S (N&S)
La Felce (N)
Laghi (N)
La Ginestra/N (S)
La Pastaia/S (N&S)
La Traviata (N&S)
Little City (N&S)
Little Italy (S)
Little Joe's (N&S)
L'Osteria Del Forno (N)
Macaroni Sciue Sciue (S)
Mangiafuoco (N)
Marin Joe's/N (N)
Mario's Bohemian (N&S)
Maye's Oyster Hse. (N&S)
Mazzini/E (N)
Mescolanza (N)
Michelangelo Cafe (N&S)
Mio Vicino/S (N&S)
Mozzarella Di Bufala (N&S)
New Joe's (N&S)
New Pisa (N)
Nob Hill Cafe (N&S)
North Beach (N)
Oliveto/E (N)
Original Joe's (N&S)
Osteria (N)
Osteria/S (N)

Palio d'Asti (N&S)
Pane e Vino (N)
Paolo's/S (N&S)
Park Chow (N&S)
Parma (N)
Pasta Moon/S (N)
Pasta Pomodoro (N&S)
Pasta Pomodoro/E (N&S)
Pasta Pomodoro/N (N&S)
Pazzia (N&S)
Piatti/N (N&S)
Piatti/S (N&S)
Piazza D'Angelo/N (S)
Postino/E (N&S)
Prego (N&S)
Prima/E (N)
Puccini & Pinetti (N&S)
Radicchio (N)
Rist. Bacco (N&S)
Rist. Ecco (N&S)
Rist. Fabrizio/N (N)
Rist. Ideale (N&S)
Rist. Milano (N)
Rose Pistola (N)
Rose's Cafe (N)
Rosti (N)
Salute/E (N&S)
Salute/N (N&S)
Scala's Bistro (N&S)
Spiedini/E (N&S)
Splendido (N&S)
Stars (N&S)
Stelline (N)
Stinking Rose (N)
Stokes Adobe/S (N)
Tavolino (N)
Tomatina/N (S)
Tommaso's (N&S)
Trattoria Contadina (N&S)
Tra Vigne/N (N&S)
Venezia/E (N&S)
Venticello (N)
Via Vai (N&S)
Vicolo (N&S)
Vineria (N)
Vivande Porta Via (N&S)
Vivande Rist. (N&S)
Zinzino (N&S)
Zza's Trattoria/E (N&S)

Japanese
Ace Wasabi's
Anzu
Benihana
Benihana/E

Benihana/S
Blowfish Sushi
Ebisu
Godzilla Sushi
Grandeho's
Hamano Sushi
Hotei
Iroha
Isobune Sushi
Isobune Sushi/S
Juban
Juban/S
Kabuto Sushi
Kirala/E
Kyo-Ya
Maki
Mifune
Nippon Sushi
O Chamé/E
Osaka Grill
Osome
Robata/N
Sanppo
Sanraku
Sushi Groove
Sushi Ran/N
Tanuki
Tokyo Go Go
Uzen/E
Yoshida-Ya
Yoshi's/E

Jewish
Autumn Moon/E
Max's on Square
Max's Opera Café
Max's Opera Café/S
Saul's/E

Korean
Korea Hse.
Seoul Garden

Mediterranean
Atlas Peak Grill/N
Backflip
Bay Wolf/E
Bistro Aix
Bistro Zaré
Bizou
Blackhawk Grille/E
Blue Point
Brazio/E
Bruno's
Bucci's/E
Chez Panisse/E

Chez Panisse Cafe/E
Citron/E
Delfina
Enrico's
Fandango/S
Faz
Faz/E
Faz/S
Firewood Cafe
Food Inc.
42°
Fournou's Ovens
Garibaldis/College/E
Garibaldis/Presidio
Insalata's/N
Kasbah/N
Lalime's/E
La Mediterranée
La Mediterranée/E
La Scene
LuLu
Moose's
Napa Valley Grille/N
Oberon
Oritalia
Palomino
PlumpJack Cafe
PlumpJack Cafe/N
Redwood Rm.
Ritz-Carlton Terrace
Rivoli/E
San Benito Hse./S
71 St. Peter/S
Socca
Viognier/S
Wine Spectator/N
Zaré
Zax
Zibibbo/S
Zodiac Club
Zuni Cafe

Mexican/Tex-Mex
Aqui/S
Boonville Hotel/N
Cactus Cafe/N
Cafe Marimba
Casa Aguila
Chevys
Chevys/E
Chevys/N
Chevys/S
Compadres/N
Compadres/S
El Balazo

Guaymas/N
La Cumbre
La Cumbre/S
La Rondalla
Las Camelias/N
La Taqueria
La Taqueria/S
Left at Albuquerque
Left at Albuquerque/S
Leticia's
Maya
Mom is Cooking
Pancho Villa
Picante Cocina/E
Roosevelt Tamale
Sweet Heat
Tortola
Wa-Ha-Ka

Middle Eastern

Faz
Faz/E
Faz/S
La Mediterranée
La Mediterranée/E
Ya-Ya Cuisine

Moroccan

Kasbah/N

Noodle Shops

Hotei
Iroha
Long Life Noodle
Long Life Noodle/E
Mifune

Pacific Rim

Bridges/E
Pacific
Roy's/Pebble Beach/S

Peruvian

Estampas Peruanas/S
Fresca

Pizza

Bucci's/E
California Pizza Kit.
California Pizza Kit./E
Ernesto's
Firewood Cafe
Il Fornaio
Il Fornaio/E
Il Fornaio/N
Il Fornaio/S

L'Osteria Del Forno
Mozzarella Di Bufala
Oak Town Cafe/E
Pasta Moon/S
Pauline's
Pazzia
Rosti
Salute/E
Salute/N
Tomatina/N
Tommaso's
Via Vai
Vicolo
Zachary's/E
Zinzino

Russian

Katia's

Seafood

Alamo Square
Alioto's
Aqua
A. Sabella's
Bacchanal/S
Belon
Blue Point
Castagnola's
Crow's Nest/S
Eastside West
Farallon
Great Eastern
Hayes St. Grill
Hong Kong Flower
House
John's Grill
Maye's Oyster Hse.
McCormick & Kuleto's
Michelangelo Cafe
Original Old Clam
Pacific Cafe
PJ's Oyster Bed
Plouf
Red Herring
Rocco's
Rose Pistola
Sam's Grill
Scoma's
Scoma's/N
Scott's
Scott's/E
Scott's/S
Station Hse. Cafe/N
Swan Oyster Depot
Tadich Grill
Thanh Long

Waterfront
Yabbies
Yuet Lee

Singaporean
Straits Cafe
Straits Cafe/S

South American
Estampas Peruanas/S
Fresca

Southern/Soul
Biscuits & Blues
Catahoula/N
Moonshine

Southwestern
Cacti/N
Left at Albuquerque
Left at Albuquerque/S
Rio Grill/S

Spanish
Alegrias
Basque Cultural Ctr./S
Bolero/N
César/E
Esperpento
Guernica/N
Iberia/S
Picaro
Pintxos
Thirsty Bear
Timo's
Vinga
Zarzuela

Steakhouses
Alfred's Steak Hse.
Anzu
Benihana
Benihana/E
Benihana/S
Bighorn Grill/E
Grill/S
Harris'
House of Prime Rib
Izzy's
John's Grill
Live Fire/N
Morton's of Chicago
Vic Stewart's/E

Swiss
Matterhorn Swiss

Taiwanese
Taiwan

Tapas
César/E
Cha Cha Cha
Cha Cha Cha/Orig. McCarthy's
Charanga
Palace/S
Thirsty Bear
Timo's

Thai
Cha Am Thai
Cha Am Thai/E
Dusit Thai
Khan Toke
Manora's
Marnee Thai
Narai
Neecha Thai
Phuping/E
Plearn Thai/E
Royal Thai
Royal Thai/N
Sukhothai
Thep Phanom
Yukol Place

Tibetan
Lhasa Moon

Vegetarian
(Most Chinese, Indian and
Thai restaurants)
Bontà Rist.
Fleur de Lys
Greens
Long Life Vegi/E
Millennium
Raw
Valentine's Cafe

Vietnamese
Aux Delices
Camranh Bay/S
Cordon Bleu
Crustacean
Golden Turtle
Jasmine Hse.
La Vie
Le Cheval/E
Le Colonial
Le Soleil
Slanted Door
Thanh Long
Tu Lan

LOCATIONS

SAN FRANCISCO

Bernal Heights
Hungarian Sausage
Liberty Cafe

Castro/Noe
Alice's
Barney's
Cafe Flore
Chow
dame
Eric's
Firefly
Firewood Cafe
Fuzio
Hamano Sushi
La Mediterranée
Leticia's
Little Italy
Ma Tante Sumi
Mecca
Miss Millie's
Nippon Sushi
Pasta Pomodoro
Rist. Bacco
Savor
Tin-Pan
Tita's
2223 Rest.
Valentine's Cafe
Yet Wah
Zodiac Club

Chinatown
Empress of China
Great Eastern
House of Nanking
Lichee Garden
Yuet Lee

Civic Center
Absinthe
Bistro Clovis
Caffe Delle Stelle
Carta
Chevys
Citizen Cake
Eliza's
Hayes & Vine
Hayes St. Grill
Indigo
Jardinière
Max's Opera Café

Millennium
Ovation
Piaf's
Stars
Stelline
Suppenküche
Terra Brazilis
Vicolo
Vivande Rist.
Zuni Cafe

Downtown
Alfred's Steak Hse.
Anjou
Anzu
Aqua
Armani Cafe
Belon
Biscuits & Blues
Brasserie Savoy
Cafe Akimbo
Cafe Bastille
Cafe Claude
Cafe de la Presse
Cafe Mozart
Cafe Tiramisu
California Pizza Kit.
Campton Place
Carnelian Room
Cha Am Thai
Chevys
Dottie's True Blue
E&O Trading
Farallon
Faz
Fifth Floor
First Crush
Fleur de Lys
Fog City Diner
Fuzio
Garden Court
Gaylord India
Globe
Grand Cafe
Harbor Village
Harry Denton's Starlight
Houston's
Hunan
Il Fornaio
Iron Horse
Jacks

150

John's Grill
Kokkari
Kuleto's
Kyo-Ya
La Scene
Le Central Bistro
Le Colonial
L'Olivier
London Wine Bar
MacArthur Park
Masa's
Max's on Square
mc^2
Morton's of Chicago
New Joe's
Occidental Grill
Oodles
Original Joe's
Oritalia
Pacific
Palio d'Asti
Park Grill
Pastis
Perry's Downtown
Pier 23 Cafe
Planet Hollywood
Plouf
Postrio
Puccini & Pinetti
Redwood Rm.
Rotunda
Rubicon
Rumpus
Sam's Grill
Sanraku
Scala's Bistro
Schroeder's
Scott's
Sears Fine Food
Silks
Splendido
Tadich Grill
Tommy Toy's
Tortola
Tu Lan
Yank Sing
Ya-Ya Cuisine
Zaré

Haight-Ashbury

Alamo Square
Caffe Proust
Cha Cha Cha
El Balazo
Eos

Grandeho's
Indian Oven
Kate's Kitchen
Magnolia Pub
Massawa
Sweet Heat
Thep Phanom
Zazie

Japantown

Benihana
Iroha
Isobune Sushi
Juban
Korea Hse.
Maki
Mifune
Pasta Pomodoro
Sanppo
Seoul Garden
Yoyo Bistro

Marina

Ace Wasabi's
Barney's
Bistro Aix
Buchanan Grill
Cafe Marimba
Columbus Rist.
Curbside Too
Dragon Well
E'Angelo
Fuzio
Greens
Izzy's
Maria Therese
Oberon
Parma
Pasta Pomodoro
Pluto's
Rosti
Sweet Heat
World Wrapps
Yukol Place
Zinzino

Mission

Bitterroot
Blowfish Sushi
Blue Plate
Bruno's
Cha Cha Cha/Orig. McCarthy's
Charanga
Delfina
Dusit Thai
Esperpento

Firecracker
Flying Saucer
Foreign Cinema
Gordon's Hse.
La Cumbre
La Rondalla
La Taqueria
La Traviata
Mangiafuoco
Mom is Cooking
Original Old Clam
Pancho Villa
Pauline's
Picaro
Pintxos
Roosevelt Tamale
Rooster
Slanted Door
Ti Couz
Timo's
Tokyo Go Go
Universal Cafe
Vineria
Watergate
Woodward's Garden
Yuet Lee

Nob Hill

Big Four
Charles Nob Hill
Fournou's Ovens
Gramercy Grill
Nob Hill Cafe
Rist. Milano
Ritz-Carlton Din. Rm.
Ritz-Carlton Terrace
Tonga
Top of the Mark
Venticello

North Beach

Allegro
Bandol
Basta Pasta
Bix
Black Cat
Bocce Cafe
Brandy Ho's
Bubble Lounge
Buca Giovanni
Cafe Jacqueline
Caffe Greco
Caffe Macaroni
Caffe Sport
Calzone's
Capp's Corner

Cypress Club
dalla Torre
Enrico's
Fior d'Italia
Gira Polli
Helmand
House
Julius' Castle
La Felce
Little City
Little Joe's
L'Osteria Del Forno
Macaroni Sciue Sciue
Mama's on Washington
Mario's Bohemian
Michelangelo Cafe
Moonshine
Moose's
Mo's Burgers
New Pisa
North Beach
O'Reilly's
Pasta Pomodoro
Rist. Ideale
Rose Pistola
Stinking Rose
Taiwan
Tavolino
Tommaso's
Trattoria Contadina
Washington Sq. B&G
Zax

Pacific Heights

Bam
Cafe Kati
Curbside Too
Elite Cafe
Ella's
Florio
Food Inc.
Garibaldis/Presidio
Godzilla Sushi
Jackson Fillmore
Laghi
La Mediterranée
Meetinghouse
Mozzarella Di Bufala
Osteria
Pauli's Cafe
Rasselas
Tortola
Vivande Porta Via

Potrero Hill

Aperto
Connecticut Yankee

Eliza's
Northstar & Little Dipper
Slow Club

Richmond
Angkor Wat
Beach Chalet
Bella Trattoria
Bill's Place
Blue Point
Cafe Riggio
Chapeau!
Cheers
Clementine
Clement St. B&G
Cliff Hse.
Ernesto's
Fountain Court
Hong Kong Flower
Jakarta
Jasmine Hse.
Kabuto Sushi
Katia's
Khan Toke
La Bergerie
La Vie
Le Cyrano
Le Soleil
Mandalay
Mayflower
Mel's Drive-In
Mescolanza
Narai
Pacific Cafe
Presidio Cafe
Royal Thai
Socca
Straits Cafe
Taiwan
Tanuki
Ton Kiang
Yet Wah

SoMa
AsiaSF
Bizou
Boulevard
Caffe Centro
Caribbean Zone
Cha Am Thai
Delancey St.
Eddie Rickenbacker's
ELROYS
Entros
Firewood Cafe
Fly Trap

42°
Fringale
Gordon Biersch
Hamburger Mary's
Hawthorne Lane
Hunan
Infusion
Jessie's
Julie's Supper Club
Kelly's Mission Rock
Le Charm
Long Life Noodle
LuLu
Manora's
Max's Diner
Maya
MoMo's
Montage
Mo's Burgers
One Market
Palomino
Pazzia
Primo Patio
Red Herring
Rest. Marais
Rist. Ecco
Sanraku
Shanghai 1930
South Park Cafe
Thirsty Bear
Town's End
Vinga
Wa-Ha-Ka
XYZ

Sunset
Avenue 9
Bocca Rotis
Cafe For All Seasons
Casa Aguila
Cha Am Thai
Chevys
Ebisu
Fresca
Hotei
House
Marnee Thai
Mozzarella Di Bufala
Park Chow
Pasta Pomodoro
PJ's Oyster Bed
Pluto's
Raw
Rick's
Ricochet

Sukhothai
Thanh Long
Tortola

Union Street

Alegrias
Baker St. Bistro
Balboa Cafe
Betelnut Pejiu Wu
Bontà Rist.
Brazen Head
Cafe de Paris
Cassis
Doidge's Cafe
Eastside West
Irrawaddy
Left at Albuquerque
Lhasa Moon
Liverpool Lil's
Mel's Drive-In
North India
Osome
Pane e Vino
Perry's
PlumpJack Cafe
Prego
Radicchio
Rose's Cafe
Via Vai
Wa-Ha-Ka
Yoshida-Ya

Van Ness/Polk

Acquerello
Antica Trattoria
Aux Delices
Backflip
Baraonda
Bistro Zaré
Cafe Majestic
Cordon Bleu

Crustacean
Elan Vital
Frascati
Golden Turtle
Hard Rock Cafe
Harris'
House of Prime Rib
Hyde St. Bistro
I Fratelli
La Folie
Maharani
Mario's Bohemian
Matterhorn Swiss
Maye's Oyster Hse.
Mel's Drive-In
Neecha Thai
Osaka Grill
Rocco's
Sushi Groove
Swan Oyster Depot
Sweet Heat
Tommy's Joynt
World Wrapps
Yabbies
Zarzuela

Wharf

Albona Rist.
Alioto's
A. Sabella's
Castagnola's
Gary Danko
Gaylord India
Grandeho's
Mandarin
McCormick & Kuleto's
Scoma's
Waterfront
Yet Wah

EAST OF SAN FRANCISCO

Berkeley

Ajanta
Bette's Oceanview
Bistro Viola
Blue Nile
Breads of India
Cafe Fanny
Cafe Rouge
César
Cha Am Thai
Chez Panisse

Chez Panisse Cafe
FatApple's
Ginger Island
Jordan's
Kirala
Lalime's
La Mediterranée
La Note
Long Life Noodle
Long Life Vegi
Mazzini
O Chamé

Pasta Pomodoro
Picante Cocina
Plearn Thai
Pyramid Alehse.
Rick & Ann's
Rivoli
Santa Fe B&G
Saul's
Venezia
Xanadu
Zachary's

Concord
Benihana

Danville
Blackhawk Grille
Brazio
Bridges
Faz

El Cerrito
FatApple's

Emeryville
Bucci's

Hayward
Rue de Main

Lafayette
Postino

Livermore
Wente Vineyards

Oakland
Autumn Moon
Battambang
Bay Wolf
Cafe 817
Citron
Garibaldis/College

Jade Villa
Le Cheval
Mama's Royal Cafe
Nan Yang Rockridge
Nava
Oak Town Cafe
Obelisque
Oliveto
Pasta Pomodoro
Rest. Peony
Scott's
Soizic
Thornhill Cafe
Uzen
Yoshi's
Zachary's
Zza's Trattoria

Pleasant Hill
Chevys

Pleasanton
Faz

Richmond
Hotel Mac
Phuping
Salute

San Ramon
Bighorn Grill

Walnut Creek
California Cafe
California Pizza Kit.
Gira Polli
Il Fornaio
Lark Creek
Prima
Scott's
Spiedini
Vic Stewart's

NORTH OF SAN FRANCISCO

Marin
Alta Mira
Avenue Grill
Bolero
Bubba's Diner
Buckeye Roadhse.
Cacti
Cactus Cafe
California Cafe
Caprice
Chevys

Christophe
Cucina Jackson Fillmore
El Paseo
Filou
Frantoio
Fresco
Gira Polli
Guaymas
Guernica
Horizons
Il Fornaio

Insalata's
Kasbah
La Ginestra
Lark Creek Inn
Las Camelias
Left Bank
Manka's Inverness
Marin Joe's
Mikayla/Casa Madrona
North Sea Village
Olema Inn
Ondine
Pasta Pomodoro
Piatti
Piazza D'Angelo
Rice Table
Rist. Fabrizio
Robata
Royal Thai
Salute
Sam's Anchor Cafe
Sand Dollar
Savanna Grill
Scoma's
Station Hse. Cafe
Sushi Ran
Tomales Bay
World Wrapps
Yet Wah

Mendocino

Albion River Inn
Boonville Hotel
Cafe Beaujolais

Napa

Atlas Peak Grill
Auberge du Soleil
Bistro Don Giovanni
Bistro Jeanty
Bouchon
Brannan's Grill
Brava Terrace
Brix
Catahoula
Celadon

Compadres
Domaine Chandon
Foothill Cafe
French Laundry
Gordon's
La Toque
Live Fire
Meadowood Grill
Mustards Grill
Napa Valley Grille
Napa Valley Wine Train
Piatti
Pinot Blanc
Rest. at Meadowood
Rutherford Grill
Showley's
Terra
Tomatina
Tra Vigne
Wappo Bar
Wine Spectator

Olympic Valley-Tahoe

PlumpJack Cafe

Sonoma

Bistro Ralph
Cafe Citti
Café La Haye
Chateau Souverain
Chevys
Della Santina's
Downtown Bakery
Felix & Louie's
General's Daughter
girl & the fig
Glen Ellen Inn
Heirloom
John Ash
Kenwood
Madrona Manor
Piatti
Ravenous
Sonoma Mission Inn Grille
Syrah
Willowside Cafe

SOUTH OF SAN FRANCISCO

Monterey/Carmel

Casanova
Cielo
Club XIX
Covey
Fandango
Fresh Cream

Kincaid's Bistro
Marinus
Montrio
Nepenthe
Pacific's Edge
Piatti
Rio Grill

Roy's/Pebble Beach
Sierra Mar
Stokes Adobe
Tarpy's Roadhse.

Peninsula
Bacchanal
Basque Cultural Ctr.
Bella Vista
Benihana
Bistro Vida
Blue Chalk Cafe
Buck's
Buffalo Grill
California Cafe
Camranh Bay
Capellini
Carpaccio
Chevys
Compadres
Dal Baffo
Duck Club
Estampas Peruanas
Evvia
Flea St. Cafe
Fook Yuen
Gaylord India
Gordon Biersch
Grandview
Hong Kong Flower
Iberia
Il Fornaio
Isobune Sushi
JoAnn's Cafe
Juban
Kuleto's Trattoria
La Cumbre
L'Amie Donia
Lark Creek
Left at Albuquerque
Left Bank
MacArthur Park
Max's Opera Café
Nola
Osteria
Piatti
Pluto's
Scott's
Spago Palo Alto
Straits Cafe
2030
231 Ellsworth
Viognier
Wild Hare
World Wrapps
Zibibbo

San Jose
Agenda
Amber India
A.P. Stump's
Aqui
Beausejour
Benihana
Cafe Marcella
California Cafe
Chef Chu's
Chevys
Chez T.J.
Emile's
Eulipia
Faz
Fung Lum
Gordon Biersch
Grill
Il Fornaio
Jocco's
Kathmandu West
La Pastaia
La Taqueria
Left at Albuquerque
Le Mouton Noir
Le Papillon
Lion & Compass
Los Gatos
Mio Vicino
Palace
Paolo's
Plumed Horse
Santa Barbara Grill
Scott's
Sent Sovi
71 St. Peter
Swagat
Tapestry
World Wrapps

Santa Cruz
Chez Renee
Crow's Nest

South Coast
Duarte's Tavern
Moss Beach Distillery
Pasta Moon
San Benito Hse.

Yosemite-Oakhurst
Erna's Elderberry

SPECIAL FEATURES AND APPEALS

Breakfast

(All hotels and the following standouts)

Baker St. Bistro
Bette's Oceanview/E
Bocca Rotis
Bubba's Diner/N
Cafe Fanny/E
Cafe Flore
Casa Aguila
Cheers
Citizen Cake
Curbside Cafe
Curbside Too
Doidge's Cafe
Dottie's True Blue
Downtown Bakery/N
Duarte's Tavern/S
Ella's
FatApple's/E
Il Fornaio/N
JoAnn's Cafe/S
Mama's on Washington
Mama's Royal Cafe/E
Miss Millie's
Mo's Burgers
New Joe's
Oliveto/E
Original Joe's
Pauli's Cafe
Pluto's
Pluto's/S
Rick & Ann's/E
Savor
Sears Fine Food
South Park Cafe
Station Hse. Cafe/N
Swan Oyster Depot
Tomales Bay/N
Town's End
Universal Cafe
Valentine's Cafe
Zazie
Zuni Cafe

Brunch

(Best of many)

Alamo Square
Aperto
Avenue 9
Baker St. Bistro
Balboa Cafe
Beach Chalet

Black Cat
Bubba's Diner/N
Buckeye Roadhse./N
Cafe Claude
Cafe Marimba
California Cafe/E
California Cafe/N
California Cafe/S
Campton Place
Caprice/N
Carnelian Room
Casanova/S
Cheers
dame
Dottie's True Blue
Ella's
Erna's Elderberry/S
Flea St. Cafe/S
Garibaldis/Presidio
General's Daughter/N
Il Fornaio
Il Fornaio/N
Il Fornaio/S
Insalata's/N
Kate's Kitchen
Lark Creek/S
Lark Creek Inn/N
Los Gatos/S
Mama's on Washington
Mama's Royal Cafe/E
Miss Millie's
MoMo's
Moose's
Moss Beach Distillery/S
Napa Valley Grille/N
Napa Valley Wine Train/N
Pacific
Pacific's Edge/S
Park Chow
Pasta Moon/S
Pauli's Cafe
Piaf's
Piazza D'Angelo/N
Pier 23 Cafe
Postrio
Rick & Ann's/E
Rio Grill/S
Saul's/E
Suppenküche
Tarpy's Roadhse./S
Thornhill Cafe/E
Tortola
Town's End

2223 Rest.
Universal Cafe
Valentine's Cafe
Viognier/S
Vivande Rist.
Washington Sq. B&G
Zazie
Zibibbo/S

Buffet Served
(Check prices, days
and times)
Amber India/S
Anzu
Cacti/N
Cliff Hse.
Duck Club/S
Empress of China
Garden Court
Gaylord India
Gaylord India/S
Gramercy Grill
Hunan
Indian Oven
Irrawaddy
Jakarta
Jasmine Hse.
Jessie's
Jordan's/E
Kathmandu West/S
Maharani
Mom is Cooking
Pacific's Edge/S
Pasta Moon/S
Piatti/N
Rest. at Meadowood/N
Rio Grill/S
Ritz-Carlton Terrace
Rooster
Salute/E
Santa Fe B&G/E
Swagat/S
Thornhill Cafe/E
Top of the Mark
Wappo Bar/N
Yuet Lee

Business Dining
Alegrias
Big Four
Boulevard
Campton Place
Carnelian Room
Cypress Club
Emile's/S

42°
Hawthorne Lane
Hayes St. Grill
House of Prime Rib
Il Fornaio/S
Iron Horse
Jakarta
John Ash/N
Kuleto's
Lion & Compass/S
London Wine Bar
LuLu
MacArthur Park
Mandarin
Masa's
MoMo's
Moose's
North Beach
One Market
Pacific
Pane e Vino
Park Grill
Postrio
Prima/E
Ritz-Carlton Din. Rm.
Rubicon
Sam's Grill
Scala's Bistro
Silks
Splendido
Stars
Tadich Grill
Tommy Toy's
231 Ellsworth/S
Vivande Rist.
Washington Sq. B&G
Waterfront
Xanadu/E
Yukol Place
Zuni Cafe

Caters
(Best of many)
Acquerello
Amber India/S
Aperto
Aqua
Aqui/S
Armani Cafe
Autumn Moon/E
Avenue 9
Bacchanal/S
Baker St. Bistro
Beausejour/S
Betelnut Pejiu Wu

Bix
Bizou
Blackhawk Grille/E
Blowfish Sushi
Bocca Rotis
Brandy Ho's
Brannan's Grill/N
Brava Terrace/N
Buffalo Grill/S
Cacti/N
Cafe Tiramisu
Caffe Delle Stelle
Caffe Macaroni
Camranh Bay/S
Casanova/S
Cha Am Thai
Chef Chu's/S
Cielo/S
Citizen Cake
Compadres/N
Compadres/S
Curbside Cafe
dame
Delancey St.
Dragon Well
Emile's/S
Erna's Elderberry/S
Farallon
Faz
Faz/E
Faz/S
Filou/N
First Crush
Flea St. Cafe/S
Fog City Diner
Food Inc.
Fountain Court
Frascati
Fresca
Fuzio
Gaylord India/S
Gira Polli
Gira Polli/N
Globe
Gordon's/N
Gordon's Hse.
Greens
Hamburger Mary's
Horizons/N
Hyde St. Bistro
Il Fornaio/S
Indian Oven
Insalata's/N
Jakarta
Jessie's

JoAnn's Cafe/S
Jocco's/S
John Ash/N
Katia's
Kokkari
Lalime's/E
La Mediterranée
La Mediterranée/E
La Note/E
Las Camelias/N
Left Bank/N
Left Bank/S
Le Papillon/S
Long Life Noodle
Long Life Vegi/E
LuLu
MacArthur Park
MacArthur Park/S
Mama's Royal Cafe/E
Mangiafuoco
Marinus/S
Meadowood Grill/N
Mecca
Millennium
Mio Vicino/S
Mom is Cooking
Montrio/S
Mo's Burgers
Mustards Grill/N
Napa Valley Grille/N
Nava/E
North India
Oak Town Cafe/E
Obelisque/E
Oodles
O'Reilly's
Original Joe's
Osaka Grill
Pacific's Edge/S
Palace/S
Palio d'Asti
Pane e Vino
Paolo's/S
Piazza D'Angelo/N
Pinot Blanc/N
Pluto's
Postrio
Raw
Redwood Rm.
Rest. at Meadowood/N
Rick & Ann's/E
Ricochet
Rio Grill/S
Rose's Cafe
Rumpus

San Benito Hse./S
Sanraku
Santa Barbara Grill/S
Scott's
Scott's/E
Shanghai 1930
Splendido
Straits Cafe
Straits Cafe/S
Sushi Ran/N
Tarpy's Roadhse./S
Terra Brazilis
Timo's
Ton Kiang
Tra Vigne/N
2030/S
Via Vai
Vic Stewart's/E
Vinga
Vivande Porta Via
Wente Vineyards/E
Yank Sing
Ya-Ya Cuisine
Zinzino
Zza's Trattoria/E

Dancing/Entertainment

(Check days, times and
performers for entertainment;
D=dancing; best of many)
Agenda/S (DJ/varies)
Albion River Inn/N (piano)
Alegrias (flamenco/guitar)
Angkor Wat (Cambodian)
AsiaSF (D/gender illusionists)
Bandol (piano)
Beausejour/S (piano)
Big Four (piano)
Biscuits & Blues (D/blues)
Bix (jazz)
Black Cat (jazz)
Blackhawk Grille/E (piano)
Blowfish Sushi (Japanese)
Bocce Cafe (jazz)
Brasserie Savoy (piano)
Bruno's (jazz)
Cafe Claude (blues/jazz)
Cafe de Paris (D/world)
Cafe Majestic (classical/varies)
Carta (jazz/piano)
Cha Cha Cha/McCarthy (bands/DJ)
Cielo/S (jazz trio)
Compadres/N (mariachi)
Covey/S (guitar)
Cypress Club (jazz)

E&O Trading (jazz)
Eastside West (jazz)
Enrico's (jazz)
Faz/E (jazz)
42° (jazz trio)
Fournou's Ovens (piano)
Frantoio/N (piano)
Garden Court (D/harp/piano)
Gordon Biersch/S (jazz/swing)
Gordon's Hse. (jazz)
Guaymas/N (mariachi)
Harris' (jazz/piano)
Hawthorne Lane (piano)
Houston's (piano)
Jardinière (jazz duo)
John's Grill (jazz)
Jordan's/E (D/piano/swing)
Kasbah/N (belly dancer)
Katia's (accordion/guitar)
Kelly's Mission Rock (bands)
Kuleto's (piano)
La Scene (jazz/piano)
Le Colonial (jazz)
Left Bank/N (jazz)
Marinus/S (jazz)
Max's Opera Café (singing)
Max's Opera Café/S (singing)
Mecca (jazz/R&B)
Moose's (jazz)
Nepenthe/S (D)
Oberon (gypsy music)
One Market (jazz/piano)
O'Reilly's (acoustic)
Ovation (guitar/piano)
Pacific (piano)
Pacific's Edge/S (D/piano)
Palace/S (D/jazz)
Paolo's/S (piano/vocals)
Park Grill (piano)
Pauline's (cabaret/jazz)
Piaf's (cabaret/piano)
Plumed Horse/S (D/band/piano)
Prima/E (jazz/piano)
Redwood Rm. (piano)
Ritz-Carlton Din. Rm. (harp)
Ritz-Carlton Terrace (jazz)
Rose Pistola (jazz)
Roy's/Pebble Beach/S (jazz)
Rue de Main/E (classical guitar)
Santa Fe B&G/E (piano)
Savanna Grill/N (D/bands/jazz)
Schroeder's (polka)
Scott's (jazz/piano)
Scott's/E (jazz/piano)
Shanghai 1930 (D/jazz)

Showley's/N (jazz)
Stars (jazz/piano)
Straits Cafe/S (jazz)
Top of the Mark (D/jazz/swing)
Vic Stewart's/E (varies)
Vinga (Spanish guitar)
Wappo Bar/N (Brazilian/jazz)
Washington Sq. B&G (jazz)
Yoshi's/E (jazz)

Delivers*/Takeout

(Nearly all Asians, coffee shops, delis, diners and pasta/pizzerias deliver or do takeout; here are some interesting possibilities; D=delivery, T=takeout; *call to check range and charges, if any)

Absinthe (T)
Agenda/S (T)
Ajanta/E (D,T)
Alamo Square (T)
Alegrias (T)
Allegro (T)
Amber India/S (T)
Aperto (T)
A.P. Stump's/S (T)
Aqui/S (T)
Armani Cafe (D,T)
A. Sabella's (T)
Autumn Moon/E (T)
Avenue Grill/N (T)
Avenue 9 (T)
Baker St. Bistro (T)
Balboa Cafe (T)
Bam (T)
Bandol (T)
Baraonda (T)
Bella Vista/S (T)
Big Four (T)
Bighorn Grill/E (T)
Biscuits & Blues (D,T)
Bistro Aix (T)
Bistro Vida/S (T)
Bistro Viola/E (T)
Bistro Zaré (T)
Bitterroot (T)
Bizou (T)
Black Cat (T)
Blackhawk Grille/E (D,T)
Blue Chalk Cafe/S (T)
Blue Point (T)
Bocca Rotis (T)
Bontà Rist. (T)

Boonville Hotel/N (T)
Brannan's Grill/N (T)
Brava Terrace/N (T)
Brazen Head (T)
Brazio/E (T)
Breads of India/E (T)
Buca Giovanni (T)
Buchanan Grill (T)
Buckeye Roadhse./N (T)
Buck's/S (T)
Buffalo Grill/S (T)
Cafe Akimbo (T)
Cafe Bastille (T)
Cafe Beaujolais/N (T)
Cafe Claude (T)
Cafe de Paris (D,T)
Cafe 817/E (T)
Cafe Fanny/E (T)
Cafe Flore (T)
Cafe Marcella/S (T)
Cafe Marimba (T)
Cafe Riggio (D,T)
Cafe Rouge/E (T)
Caffe Delle Stelle (T)
Caffe Macaroni (T)
California Cafe/N (T)
Capellini/S (T)
Caprice/N (T)
Carpaccio/S (T)
Carta (T)
Casanova/S (T)
Castagnola's (T)
Catahoula/N (T)
Cha Cha Cha (T)
Charanga (T)
Cheers (T)
Chevys/E (T)
Chevys/N (T)
Chevys/S (T)
Chow (T)
Citizen Cake (D,T)
Clement St. B&G (T)
Columbus Rist. (T)
Compadres/N (D,T)
Compadres/S (D,T)
Connecticut Yankee (T)
Curbside Cafe (T)
Della Santina's/N (T)
Doidge's Cafe (T)
Duarte's Tavern/S (T)
E'Angelo (T)
Eastside West (T)
Eddie Rickenbacker's (T)
Ella's (T)

ELROYS(T)
Enrico's (T)
Esperpento (T)
Estampas Peruanas/S (T)
Fandango/S (T)
Faz (D,T)
Faz/E (T)
First Crush (T)
Flea St. Cafe/S (T)
Florio (T)
Fly Trap (D,T)
Food Inc. (D,T)
Foothill Cafe/N (T)
Fresca (T)
Fringale (T)
Fuzio (T)
Garibaldis/Presidio (T)
Gaylord India (D,T)
Gaylord India/S (D,T)
Ginger Island/E (T)
Gira Polli (D,T)
Gira Polli/N (D,T)
girl & the fig/N (T)
Globe (T)
Gordon Biersch (T)
Gordon Biersch/S (T)
Gordon's/N (D,T)
Gordon's Hse. (T)
Greens (T)
Grill/S (T)
Guaymas/N (T)
Guernica/N (T)
Hamburger Mary's (T)
Hard Rock Cafe (T)
Horizons/N (T)
Hotel Mac/E (T)
House of Prime Rib (T)
Houston's (D)
Hungarian Sausage (T)
Hyde St. Bistro (T)
Iberia/S (T)
I Fratelli (T)
Indian Oven (T)
Indigo (T)
Infusion (T)
Insalata's/N (T)
Iroha (T)
Irrawaddy (D,T)
Izzy's (D,T)
Jakarta (T)
Jessie's (T)
Jocco's/S (T)
Kate's Kitchen (T)
Katia's (D,T)
Kuleto's Trattoria/S (T)

La Bergerie (T)
Laghi (T)
La Ginestra/N (T)
La Mediterranée (D,T)
La Mediterranée/E (D,T)
La Note/E (T)
La Pastaia/S (T)
Las Camelias/N (D,T)
La Traviata (T)
Le Central Bistro (T)
Le Cyrano (T)
Left at Albuquerque/S (T)
Left Bank/N (T)
Leticia's (T)
Liberty Cafe (T)
Little City (T)
Little Italy (T)
Little Joe's (T)
Live Fire/N (T)
Liverpool Lil's (T)
L'Olivier (T)
LuLu (T)
Macaroni Sciue Sciue (T)
MacArthur Park (T)
Magnolia Pub (T)
Mama's on Washington (T)
Mangiafuoco (T)
Maria Therese (T)
Marin Joe's/N (T)
Massawa (T)
Maya (T)
Maye's Oyster Hse. (T)
Mazzini/E (T)
Meadowood Grill/N (D,T)
Mescolanza (T)
Michelangelo Cafe (T)
Mikayla/Casa Madrona/N (T)
Mio Vicino/S (T)
Miss Millie's (T)
Mom is Cooking (D,T)
MoMo's (T)
Montrio/S (D,T)
Moonshine (T)
Moose's (T)
Mustards Grill/N (T)
Nava/E (T)
New Pisa (T)
Nob Hill Cafe (T)
Nola/S (T)
North India (D,T)
Northstar & Little Dipper (T)
O'Reilly's (D,T)
Original Joe's (D,T)
Original Old Clam (T)
Osteria/S (T)

163

Pacific (T)
Palio d'Asti (T)
Palomino (T)
Pane e Vino (T)
Paolo's/S (T)
Park Grill (T)
Parma (T)
Pasta Pomodoro (D,T)
Pasta Pomodoro/E (T)
Pasta Pomodoro/N (D,T)
Pastis (T)
Pauli's Cafe (T)
Perry's (T)
Piatti/N (T)
Piazza D'Angelo/N (T)
Picante Cocina/E (T)
Picaro (D,T)
Pier 23 Cafe (T)
Pinot Blanc/N (D,T)
Pintxos (T)
Plouf (T)
Pluto's (T)
Pluto's/S (T)
Postino/E (T)
Prego (T)
Primo Patio (D,T)
Puccini & Pinetti (T)
Pyramid Alehse./E (T)
Radicchio (T)
Rasselas (T)
Red Herring (T)
Rick's (T)
Ricochet (T)
Rio Grill/S (D,T)
Rist. Bacco (T)
Rist. Ecco (T)
Rist. Fabrizio/N (T)
Rist. Ideale (T)
Rist. Milano (T)
Rivoli/E (T)
Rocco's (D,T)
Rose Pistola (T)
Rose's Cafe (T)
Rumpus (T)
Rutherford Grill/N (T)
Sam's Anchor Cafe/N (T)
Sam's Grill (T)
Sand Dollar/N (T)
Savanna Grill/N (T)
Savor (T)
Scala's Bistro (T)
Scott's (T)
Scott's/E (T)
Scott's/S (D,T)
Sent Sovi/S (T)

71 St. Peter/S (T)
Showley's/N (T)
Sierra Mar/S (T)
Slow Club (T)
Socca (T)
Spiedini/E (T)
Splendido (T)
Stelline (T)
Stinking Rose (T)
Stokes Adobe/S (T)
Straits Cafe (T)
Suppenküche (T)
Swagat/S (D,T)
Swan Oyster Depot (D)
Syrah/N (T)
Tadich Grill (T)
Tarpy's Roadhse./S (D,T)
Tavolino (T)
Thornhill Cafe/E (T)
Timo's (T)
Tita's (T)
Tomales Bay/N (T)
Town's End (T)
Trattoria Contadina (T)
Tra Vigne/N (D,T)
2030/S (D,T)
2223 Rest. (T)
Valentine's Cafe (T)
Venezia/E (T)
Vineria (T)
Vinga (T)
Viognier/S (T)
Wappo Bar/N (T)
Wente Vineyards/E (T)
Zarzuela (T)
Zza's Trattoria/E (T)

Dining Alone
(Other than hotels, coffee
shops, sushi bars and places
with counter service)
Alegrias
Beach Chalet
Biscuits & Blues
Clement St. B&G
Cordon Bleu
Fior d'Italia
House of Nanking
Infusion
Jakarta
Long Life Noodle
Matterhorn Swiss
Mo's Burgers
Original Joe's
Pasta Pomodoro

Pasta Pomodoro/E
Prima/E
South Park Cafe
Waterfront
Yukol Place

Fireplaces

Albion River Inn/N
A. Sabella's
Atlas Peak Grill/N
Auberge du Soleil/N
Bella Vista/S
Betelnut Pejiu Wu
Big Four
Bistro Jeanty/N
Blue Chalk Cafe/S
Boonville Hotel/N
Brannan's Grill/N
Brava Terrace/N
Brazio/E
Brix/N
Buckeye Roadhse./N
Cafe Citti/N
Cafe Mozart
Caprice/N
Casanova/S
Chateau Souverain/N
Chez Renee/S
Chez T.J./S
Cielo/S
Clement St. B&G
Club XIX/S
Compadres/N
Compadres/S
Covey/S
Crow's Nest/S
Dal Baffo/S
Della Santina's/N
Domaine Chandon/N
El Paseo/N
Erna's Elderberry/S
Faz/E
Fifth Floor
Foreign Cinema
French Laundry/N
Fresh Cream/S
Gaylord India/S
Guaymas/N
Harris'
House of Prime Rib
Houston's
Iberia/S
Il Fornaio/E
Il Fornaio/N
Izzy's

John Ash/N
Kenwood/N
Kincaid's Bistro/S
Kokkari
Kuleto's
Lark Creek Inn/N
Left Bank/N
Live Fire/N
Los Gatos/S
LuLu
MacArthur Park
MacArthur Park/S
Manka's Inverness/N
Mikayla/Casa Madrona/N
Nepenthe/S
Oliveto/E
Ovation
Pacific
Pacific's Edge/S
Park Chow
Piatti/N
Piatti/S
Piazza D'Angelo/N
Pinot Blanc/N
Plouf
Plumed Horse/S
Postino/E
Presidio Cafe
Prima/E
Red Herring
Rest. at Meadowood/N
Ricochet
Rutherford Grill/N
Salute/E
Sand Dollar/N
Scott's/S
Showley's/N
Sierra Mar/S
Spago Palo Alto/S
Stokes Adobe/S
Tarpy's Roadhse./S
Vic Stewart's/E
Viognier/S
Wine Spectator/N

Health/Spa Menus

(Most places cook to order to
meet any dietary request;
call in advance to check;
almost all Chinese, Indian and
other ethnics have health-
conscious meals, as
do the following)
Aqui/S
Columbus Rist.

Delancey St.
Meadowood Grill/N
Millennium
Raw
Ritz-Carlton Terrace
Sonoma Mission Inn Grille/N
Station Hse. Cafe/N

Historic Interest

(Year opened; *building)
1849 Tadich Grill
1861 Original Old Clam
1862 General's Daughter/N*
1863 Cliff Hse.
1864 Jacks
1867 Maye's Oyster Hse.
1867 Sam's Grill
1868 Boonville Hotel/N
1870 Showley's/N*
1876 Woodward's Garden*
1882 Wine Spectator/N*
1884 Terra/N*
1886 Fior d'Italia
1893 Schroeder's
1900 Bandol
1902 Cafe Majestic
1904 Tarpy's Roadhse./S*
1905 San Benito Hse./S*
1908 John's Grill
1909 Garden Court*
1909 Rotunda*
1912 Swan Oyster Depot
1914 Balboa Cafe
1915 Jordan's/E*
1916 Castagnola's
1917 New Pisa
1920 A. Sabella's
1920 Sam's Anchor Cafe/N
1922 Julius' Castle*
1922 Roosevelt Tamale
1925 Beach Chalet*
1927 Bella Vista/N
1927 Harry Denton's Starlight
1927 Moss Beach Distillery/S
1928 Alfred's Steak Hse.
1928 Alioto's*
1933 Sears Fine Food
1934 Duarte's Tavern/S
1937 Buckeye Roadhse./N
1937 Original Joe's
1938 Bruno's

Hotel Dining

Abigail Hotel
  Millennium
Albion River Inn
  Albion River Inn/N
Alta Mira Hotel
  Alta Mira/N

Auberge du Soleil Inn
  Auberge du Soleil/N
Benjamin Franklin Hotel
  Lark Creek/S
Bernardus Lodge
  Marinus/S
Boonville Hotel
  Boonville Hotel/N
Campton Place Hotel
  Campton Place
Cardinal Hotel
  Osteria/S
Casa Madrona
  Mikayla/Casa Madrona/N
Claremont Resort
  Jordan's/E
Cliff Hotel
  Redwood Rm.
Fairmont Hotel
  Tonga
Fairmont Hotel (San Jose)
  Grill/S
Galleria Park Hotel
  Perry's Downtown
Garden Court Hotel
  Il Fornaio/S
Highlands Inn
  Pacific's Edge/S
Hotel De Anza
  La Pastaia/S
Hotel Griffon
  Red Herring
Hotel Mac
  Hotel Mac/E
Hotel Majestic
  Cafe Majestic
Hotel Metropolis
  Belon
Hotel Monaco
  Grand Cafe
Hotel Nikko
  Anzu
Hotel Vintage Court
  Masa's
Huntington Hotel
  Big Four
Hyatt Sainte Claire
  Il Fornaio/S
Inn at Southbridge
  Tomatina/N
Inn at Spanish Bay
  Roy's/Pebble Beach/S
Inn at the Opera
  Ovation

Juliana Hotel
  Oritalia
Lodge at Pebble Beach
  Club XIX/S
Madrona Manor Hotel
  Madrona Manor/N
Mandarin Oriental Hotel
  Silks
Manka's Inverness Lodge
  Manka's Inverness/N
Mark Hopkins InterContinental
  Top of the Mark
Meadowood Resort
  Meadowood Grill/N
  Rest. at Meadowood/N
Miramonte Inn
  Showley's/N
Miyako Hotel
  Yoyo Bistro
Monticello Inn
  Puccini & Pinetti
Mount View Hotel
  Catahoula/N
Olema Inn
  Olema Inn/N
Palace Hotel
  Garden Court
  Kyo-Ya
Palomar Hotel
  Fifth Floor
Pan Pacific Hotel
  Pacific
Park Hyatt Hotel
  Park Grill
Phoenix Hotel
  Backflip
PlumpJack Squaw Valley Inn
  PlumpJack Cafe/N
Post Ranch Inn
  Sierra Mar/S
Prescott Hotel
  Postrio
Quail Lodge Resort & Golf Club
  Covey/S
Renaissance Stanford Ct.
  Fournou's Ovens
Ritz-Carlton Hotel
  Ritz-Carlton Din. Rm.
  Ritz-Carlton Terrace
San Benito House
  San Benito Hse./S
Savoy Hotel
  Brasserie Savoy

Sir Francis Drake Hotel
  Harry Denton's Starlight
  Scala's Bistro
Sonoma Hotel
  Heirloom/N
Sonoma Mission Inn & Spa
  Sonoma Mission Inn Grille/N
Stanford Park Hotel
  Duck Club/S
Ventana Inn & Spa
  Cielo/S
Villa Florence Hotel
  Kuleto's
Warwick Regis
  La Scene
W Hotel
  Xyz

"In" Places

Aqua
AsiaSF
Balboa Cafe
Beach Chalet
Betelnut Pejiu Wu
Bette's Oceanview/E
Biscuits & Blues
Bix
Bizou
Black Cat
Boulevard
Brava Terrace/N
Brazen Head
Bridges/E
Bruno's
Buckeye Roadhse./N
Cafe Marimba
Calzone's
Catahoula/N
César/E
Chez Panisse/E
Chez Panisse Cafe/E
Cypress Club
Delfina
Elite Cafe
Emile's/S
Enrico's
Eos
Eric's
Farallon
Firefly
Fleur de Lys
Florio
Flying Saucer
Fog City Diner
Fringale

Gary Danko
Globe
Greens
Harry Denton's Starlight
Hawthorne Lane
Hayes & Vine
House
Jardinière
Julie's Supper Club
Kokkari
Lark Creek Inn/N
Left Bank/N
Little City
LuLu
Max's Opera Café/S
Maya
Mecca
Michelangelo Cafe
MoMo's
Montrio/S
Moose's
Mustards Grill/N
Oliveto/E
One Market
Pastis
Perry's
Plouf
PlumpJack Cafe
PlumpJack Cafe/N
Postrio
Prima/E
Rose Pistola
Rubicon
Slanted Door
South Park Cafe
Stars
Suppenküche
Tommaso's
Tra Vigne/N
Vivande Rist.
Washington Sq. B&G
Waterfront
Watergate
Zinzino
Zuni Cafe

Helmand
Masa's
Ovation
Pacific's Edge/S
Redwood Rm.
Rest. at Meadowood/N
Ritz-Carlton Din. Rm.
Ritz-Carlton Terrace
Tommy Toy's
Waterfront

Late Late – After 12:30
(All hours are AM)
Absinthe (1)
Black Cat (2)
Bouchon/N (2)
Brazen Head (1)
Calzone's (1)
Globe (1)
La Rondalla (3)
Liverpool Lil's (12:45)
Marin Joe's/N (12:45)
Mel's Drive-In (locations vary)
Mozzarella Di Bufala (4)
Original Joe's (1:30)
Tommy's Joynt (1:40)
Tonga (1:30)

Meet for a Drink
(Most top hotels and the
following standouts)
Absinthe
Bix
Bubble Lounge
Buchanan Grill
Cacti/N
Calzone's
Caribbean Zone
Cliff Hse.
Cypress Club
Eddie Rickenbacker's
Elroys
Gordon Biersch
Gordon Biersch/S
Guaymas/N
Hamburger Mary's
Hard Rock Cafe
Infusion
Izzy's
Julie's Supper Club
Left at Albuquerque
Left Bank/N
London Wine Bar
Max's Opera Café/S
Mecca

Jacket Required
Acquerello
Camranh Bay/S
Carnelian Room
Covey/S
Dal Baffo/S
Flying Saucer
French Laundry/N
Harry Denton's Starlight

Moose's
Mustards Grill/N
North Beach
One Market
O'Reilly's
Original Old Clam
Palomino
Plouf
Prego
Prima/E
Rick's
Rocco's
Rose Pistola
Santa Fe B&G/E
Slow Club
Stars
Tra Vigne/N
Vivande Rist.
Washington Sq. B&G
Zuni Cafe

Sushi Ran/N
Terra Brazilis
Watergate
Wild Hare/S
Xanadu/E
Xyz
Zodiac Club

Noteworthy Closings (22)
Adolfo's
Alta Plaza
Babette's/N
Cadillac Bar & Restaurant
Chez Michel
Eleven Restaurant & Bar
Freestyle/N
French Room, The
Gibson/S
Gracie's
Kiss
Loongbar
Olive's Gourmet Pizza
Pickled Ginger
Roti
Sol y Luna
Sputino
301 Restaurant & Sake Bar
Tutto Mare/N
U.S. Restaurant
Val 21
Vertigo

Noteworthy Newcomers (39)
Anzu
A.P. Stump's/S
Bandol
Bistro Zaré
Bitterroot
Café La Haye/N
Cielo/S
Connecticut Yankee
Cucina Jackson Fillmore/N
Delfina
Eastside West
Fifth Floor
Florio
Food Inc.
Foreign Cinema
Fresca
Gary Danko
Gordon's Hse.
Gramercy Grill
Heirloom/N
Hotei
Kelly's Mission Rock
Kokkari
La Toque/N
Maya
Northstar & Little Dipper
Ondine/N
Red Herring
Redwood Rm.
Rest. Marais
Stokes Adobe/S
Sushi Groove

Offbeat
AsiaSF
Backflip
Bandol
Betelnut Pejiu Wu
Biscuits & Blues
Cafe Fanny/E
Caffe Sport
Caribbean Zone
Carta
Cha Cha Cha
Cypress Club
Dottie's True Blue
Esperpento
Flying Saucer
Gaylord India
Hamburger Mary's
Helmand
Katia's
Khan Toke
La Rondalla
Lhasa Moon
Long Life Noodle
Mario's Bohemian

169

Millennium
Mom is Cooking
Napa Valley Wine Train/N
O'Reilly's
Pauline's
Picaro
Pier 23 Cafe
Plouf
Rasselas
Roosevelt Tamale
Rooster
Stinking Rose
Straits Cafe
Suppenküche
Ti Couz
Tommy's Joynt
Tonga
World Wrapps
World Wrapps/N
World Wrapps/S
Ya-Ya Cuisine
Yet Wah
Yoshi's/E

Outdoor Dining

(G=garden; P=patio;
S=sidewalk; T=terrace;
W=waterside; best of many)
Agenda/S (P)
Albion River Inn/N (W)
Alioto's (W)
Alta Mira/N (T)
A.P. Stump's/S (P,S)
Aqui/S (P)
Atlas Peak Grill/N (G,P)
Auberge du Soleil/N (T)
Autumn Moon/E (G,P)
Avenue 9 (P)
Backflip (P,W)
Baker St. Bistro (S)
Bandol (S)
Baraonda (S)
Barney's (P)
Bay Wolf/E (P,T)
Beach Chalet (W)
Beausejour/S (T)
Betelnut Pejiu Wu (S)
Bighorn Grill/E (P)
Bill's Place (G,P)
Bistro Aix (P)
Bistro Don Giovanni/N (P)
Bistro Jeanty/N (P)
Bistro Viola/E (P)
Bistro Zaré (P)
Bitterroot (S)

Blackhawk Grille/E (P,T,W)
Blue Plate (G,P)
Bocce Cafe (P)
Bolero/N (P)
Bouchon/N (P)
Brannan's Grill/N (S)
Brava Terrace/N (T)
Brazio/E (T,W)
Bridges/E (P)
Brix/N (P)
Bubble Lounge (P,S)
Bucci's/E (P)
Buckeye Roadhse./N (P)
Buffalo Grill/S (P)
Cacti/N (P)
Cafe Bastille (S,T)
Cafe Citti/N (P)
Cafe Claude (S,T)
Cafe de la Presse (S,T)
Cafe de Paris (P,S,T)
Cafe 817/E (S)
Cafe Flore (P)
Cafe Tiramisu (S)
Caffe Centro (G,S)
Caffe Delle Stelle (S)
Caffe Greco (S)
California Cafe/N (P)
California Pizza Kit./E (P)
Calzone's (S)
Caprice/N (W)
Casanova/S (G,P,T)
Celadon/N (T,W)
César/E (P)
Cha Am Thai/E (P)
Chateau Souverain/N (P)
Cheers (P)
Chez Renee/S (P)
Chez T.J./S (T)
Cielo/S (T,W)
Citron/E (P)
Clementine (T)
Cliff Hse. (W)
Club XIX/S (P)
Compadres/N (G,P)
Compadres/S (P)
Connecticut Yankee (P)
Covey/S (T,W)
Crow's Nest/S (T)
Crustacean (P)
Curbside (S)
Delancey St. (S)
Della Santina's/N (P)
Domaine Chandon/N (P)
Duck Club/S (P)
El Paseo/N (P)

ELROYS (P)
Enrico's (P,S)
Erna's Elderberry/S (G,T)
Fandango/S (P)
Faz (T)
Faz/E (P)
Felix & Louie's/N (P)
Fior d'Italia (P)
Flea St. Cafe/S (T)
Food Inc. (S)
42° (P)
Frantoio/N (P)
French Laundry/N (P)
Fresh Cream/S (W)
General's Daughter/N (G,P)
Ginger Island/E (P)
Gira Polli/N (P)
Glen Ellen Inn/N (P)
Globe (S)
Gordon Biersch (P,W)
Gordon Biersch/S (P)
Gordon's/N (S)
Gordon's Hse. (P)
Greens (W)
Guaymas/N (P,W)
Heirloom/N (G,P)
Horizons/N (T)
Houston's (P,W)
Hungarian Sausage (S)
Iberia/S (G)
Il Fornaio (P)
Il Fornaio/E (P)
Il Fornaio/N (P)
Il Fornaio/S (P)
Insalata's/N (P)
Iron Horse (P,S)
Jessie's (G)
John Ash/N (T)
Julius' Castle (T)
Kelly's Mission Rock (P)
Kenwood/N (G)
La Cumbre/S (G,P,S)
La Mediterranée/E (P,S)
L'Amie Donia/S (P)
La Note/E (P)
Lark Creek/E (P)
Lark Creek Inn/N (G,P,W)
La Toque/N (P)
Le Charm (P)
Le Colonial (P,T)
Left at Albuquerque (P,S)
Left Bank/N (P)
Left Bank/S (S)
Le Mouton Noir/S (P)
Lion & Compass/S (P)

Little City (P,S)
Live Fire/N (T)
Liverpool Lil's (P)
Macaroni Sciue Sciue (S)
MacArthur Park (P)
Madrona Manor/N (P)
Mandarin (W)
Marin Joe's/N (P)
Marinus/S (T)
Mario's Bohemian (S)
McCormick & Kuleto's (W)
Meadowood Grill/N (T)
Mel's Drive-In (P)
Mikayla/Casa Madrona/N (W)
Mio Vicino/S (S)
Miss Millie's (P)
Mom is Cooking (P)
MoMo's (P)
Montage (T)
Montrio/S (S)
Moose's (P)
Moss Beach Distillery/S (T,W)
Napa Valley Grille/N (P)
Nava/E (P)
Nepenthe/S
North Sea Village/N (W)
Oak Town Cafe/E (S)
O Chamé/E (P)
Olema Inn/N (G)
Oodles (P)
O'Reilly's (P)
Palace/S (S)
Palomino (P,W)
Paolo's/S (P,T,W)
Park Chow (P,T)
Park Grill (T)
Pasta Pomodoro/E (P)
Pastis (P)
Pazzia (P,S)
Piatti/N (G,P)
Piazza D'Angelo/N (P)
Picante Cocina/E (P)
Pier 23 Cafe (P,W)
Pinot Blanc/N (P)
Plouf (S,T)
Pluto's/S (S)
Postino/E (T)
Prego (P,S)
Presidio Cafe (P,T)
Prima/E (P,S)
Primo Patio (P)
Pyramid Alehse./E (P)
Rest. at Meadowood/N (P,T)
Rick & Ann's/E (P)

Rio Grill/S (P)
Rist. Fabrizio/N (P)
Ritz-Carlton Terrace (T)
Rooster (T)
Rose Pistola (S)
Rose's Cafe (S,T)
Roy's/Pebble Beach/S (P,W)
Rumpus (P)
Rutherford Grill/N (P)
Salute/E (W)
Sam's Anchor Cafe/N (P,W)
Sam's Grill (P)
Sand Dollar/N (P)
Santa Barbara Grill/S (P)
Santa Fe B&G/E (G,P)
Savanna Grill/N (P)
Savor (P)
Scoma's/N (P,W)
Scott's (P)
Scott's/E (P,W)
Sent Sovi/S (P)
Showley's/N (P)
Sierra Mar/S (T,W)
Sonoma Mission Inn Grille/N (T)
South Park Cafe (S)
Spago Palo Alto/S (G,P,T)
Spiedini/E (P)
Splendido (P)
Station Hse. Cafe/N (G)
Straits Cafe/S (P)
Sweet Heat (S,T)
Syrah/N (P)
Tarpy's Roadhse./S (P)
Tavolino (S)
Tomatina/N (P)
Tra Vigne/N (G,P,T)
2030/S (P)
Valentine's Cafe (S)
Via Vai (P)
Vinga (T)
Vivande Rist. (P)
Wappo Bar/N (G,P,T)
Wente Vineyards/E (P)
Wine Spectator/N (T)
Xanadu/E (P)
Yank Sing (P)
Yoshi's/E (W)
Zazie (G,P,T)
Zibibbo/S (G,P)
Zinzino (G,P,S,T)
Zza's Trattoria/E (P)

Outstanding Views

Albion River Inn/N
Alioto's
Alta Mira/N
A. Sabella's
Auberge du Soleil/N
Beach Chalet
Bella Vista/S
Blackhawk Grille/E
Caprice/N
Carnelian Room
Castagnola's
Cielo/S
Cliff Hse.
Club XIX/S
Covey/S
Crow's Nest/S
dalla Torre
Domaine Chandon/N
Empress of China
Fresh Cream/S
Gaylord India
Gordon Biersch/S
Greens
Guaymas/N
Harbor Village
Harry Denton's Starlight
Horizons/N
Jordan's/E
Julius' Castle
Mandarin
McCormick & Kuleto's
Mikayla/Casa Madrona/N
Moss Beach Distillery/S
Nepenthe/S
North Sea Village/N
Pacific's Edge/S
Palomino
Paolo's/S
Pier 23 Cafe
Red Herring
Rest. at Meadowood/N
Salute/E
Salute/N
Sam's Anchor Cafe/N
Scoma's
Sierra Mar/S
Tarpy's Roadhse./S
Top of the Mark
Waterfront

Parking/Valet

(L=parking lot;
V=valet parking;
*=validated parking)
Absinthe (V)
Acquerello (L)
Albion River Inn/N (L)

172

Albona Rist. (V)
Alfred's Steak Hse. (V)
Alioto's (L)
Alta Mira/N (L)
Amber India/S (L)
Antica Trattoria (V)
Anzu (L)
A.P. Stump's/S*
Aqua (V)
Aqui/S (L)
A. Sabella's*
AsiaSF (V)
Atlas Peak Grill/N (L)
Auberge du Soleil/N (V)
Aux Delices*
Backflip (V)
Balboa Cafe (V)
Bam (L)
Bandol (V)
Baraonda (V)
Basque Cultural Ctr./S (L)
Basta Pasta (V)
Battambang/E (V)
Beach Chalet (L)
Beausejour/S (L)
Bella Vista/S (L)
Belon (L)
Benihana (L)
Benihana/E (L)
Betelnut Pejiu Wu*
Big Four (V)
Bighorn Grill/E (L)
Biscuits & Blues (L)
Bistro Jeanty/N (L)
Bistro Viola/E (L)
Bistro Zaré*
Bix (V)
Black Cat (V)
Blackhawk Grille/E (L)
Blue Point*
Bocce Cafe (V)
Bolero/N (L)
Bouchon/N (L)
Boulevard (V)
Brannan's Grill/N (L)
Brasserie Savoy (V)
Brava Terrace/N (L)
Brazio/E (L)
Bridges/E (V)
Brix/N (L)
Bruno's (L)
Bubble Lounge (V)
Bucci's/E (L)
Buckeye Roadhse./N (V)
Buck's/S (L)

Buffalo Grill/S (L)
Cacti/N (L)
Cafe Citti/N (L)
Cafe de la Presse*
Cafe de Paris (L)
Cafe 817/E (L)
Cafe Fanny/E (L)
Cafe Flore (L)
Cafe Kati*
Cafe Majestic (V)
Cafe Marcella/S (L)
Cafe Rouge/E (L)
California Cafe/N (L)
California Pizza Kit./E (L)
Campton Place (V)
Capellini/S (V)
Capp's Corner*
Caprice/N*
Caribbean Zone (L)
Carnelian Room (L)
Carpaccio/S (L)
Carta (L)
Cassis (V)
Castagnola's*
Catahoula/N (L)
Celadon/N (L)
Cha Am Thai*
Charles Nob Hill (V)
Chateau Souverain/N (L)
Chez Renee/S (L)
Christophe/N (L)
Cielo/S (L)
Club XIX/S (L)
Columbus Rist. (L)
Compadres/N (L)
Covey/S (L)
Crow's Nest/S*
Cucina Jackson Fillmore/N (L)
Cypress Club (V)
Dal Baffo/S (L)
dalla Torre (V)
Domaine Chandon/N (L)
Duarte's Tavern/S (L)
Duck Club/S (L)
E&O Trading (L)
Eastside West (V)
Elan Vital (L)
ELROYS(V)
Emile's/S (V)
Enrico's (V)
Entros*
Erna's Elderberry/S (L)
Esperpento (L)
Evvia/S (V)
Fandango/S (L)

Farallon (V)
FatApple's/E (L)
Faz/E (L)
Faz/S (L)
Felix & Louie's/N (L)
Fifth Floor (V)
Fior d'Italia (V)
Flea St. Cafe/S (L)
Fleur de Lys (V)
Fly Trap (V)
Fook Yuen/S (V)
Foothill Cafe/N (L)
42° (L)
Fournou's Ovens*
Frantoio/N (L)
Frascati (V)
French Laundry/N (L)
Fresh Cream/S (L)
Fung Lum/S (L)
Garden Court*
Garibaldis/College/E (V)
Garibaldis/Presidio (V)
Gaylord India*
Gaylord India/S (L)
General's Daughter/N (L)
Ginger Island/E (L)
Gira Polli/N (L)
girl & the fig/N (L)
Glen Ellen Inn/N (L)
Gordon Biersch*
Gordon's/N (L)
Gordon's Hse. (V)
Gramercy Grill*
Grand Cafe*
Grandeho's*
Great Eastern*
Greens (L)
Grill/S (V)
Guaymas/N*
Guernica/N (L)
Harbor Village*
Hard Rock Cafe (V)
Harris' (V)
Harry Denton's Starlight*
Hawthorne Lane (V)
Helmand (L)
Hong Kong Flower/S*
Horizons/N (V)
House of Nanking (L)
House of Prime Rib*
Hyde St. Bistro*
Iberia/S (L)
I Fratelli*
Il Fornaio (V)
Il Fornaio/E*

Il Fornaio/S (V)
Indigo (V)
Insalata's/N (L)
Iroha (L)
Isobune Sushi*
Isobune Sushi/S*
Izzy's*
Jacks (V)
Jardinière (V)
Jasmine Hse. (L)
Jocco's/S (L)
John Ash/N (L)
Jordan's/E*
Juban (L)
Juban/S (L)
Julie's Supper Club (L)
Julius' Castle (V)
Kasbah/N (L)
Kate's Kitchen (L)
Katia's*
Kenwood/N (L)
Kincaid's Bistro/S (L)
Kirala/E (L)
Kokkari (V)
Kuleto's (V)
Kuleto's Trattoria/S*
Kyo-Ya (V)
La Cumbre/S (L)
La Felce*
La Folie (V)
Laghi (V)
La Mediterranée/E (L)
La Pastaia/S (L)
Lark Creek/E*
Lark Creek/S (L)
Lark Creek Inn/N (L)
La Scene (V)
Le Cheval/E (L)
Le Colonial (V)
Le Cyrano (L)
Left Bank/N (V)
Le Papillon/S (L)
Leticia's (L)
Lion & Compass/S (V)
Little City*
Little Joe's (V)
Live Fire/N (L)
L'Olivier (V)
Los Gatos/S (L)
LuLu (L)
MacArthur Park (V)
Maharani*
Maki (L)
Mandarin*
Maria Therese*

Marin Joe's/N (L)
Marinus/S (V)
Masa's (V)
Matterhorn Swiss (V)
Max's Opera Café/S (L)
McCormick & Kuleto's*
mc² (V)
Meadowood Grill/N (L)
Mecca (V)
Meetinghouse (V)
Mel's Drive-In (L)
Mifune*
Mikayla/Casa Madrona/N (V)
Mio Vicino/S (L)
MoMo's (V)
Montrio/S (L)
Moonshine (L)
Moose's*
Morton's of Chicago (V)
Moss Beach Distillery/S (L)
Mustards Grill/N (L)
Napa Valley Grille/N (L)
Napa Valley Wine Train/N (L)
Narai*
Nob Hill Cafe (V)
North Beach (V)
North India (L)
North Sea Village/N (L)
Oberon (V)
Olema Inn/N (L)
Oliveto/E*
Ondine/N (V)
One Market (V)
Oodles (V)
Original Joe's*
Oritalia (V)
Osaka Grill*
Ovation*
Pacific*
Pacific's Edge/S (V)
Palace/S (L)
Palio d'Asti (L)
Palomino*
Paolo's/S*
Pazzia (L)
Phuping/E (L)
Piatti/N (L)*
Piatti/S (L)
Piazza D'Angelo/N (L)
Picante Cocina/E (L)
Pinot Blanc/N (L)
Pintxos (V)
Plumed Horse/S (V)
PlumpJack Cafe (V)
PlumpJack Cafe/N (V)

Postino/E (L)
Postrio (V)
Presidio Cafe (L)
Prima/E*
Red Herring (V)
Redwood Rm. (L)
Rest. at Meadowood/N (L)
Rest. Marais (V)
Rick's*
Rio Grill/S (L)
Rist. Fabrizio/N (L)
Rist. Milano*
Ritz-Carlton Din. Rm.*
Ritz-Carlton Terrace*
Robata/N (L)
Rocco's*
Rooster (L)
Rose Pistola (V)
Roy's/Pebble Beach/S (L)
Rubicon (V)
Rue de Main/E (L)
Rutherford Grill/N (L)
Salute/E (L)
Salute/N (V)
Santa Barbara Grill/S (L)
Santa Fe B&G/E*
Savanna Grill/N (L)
Scala's Bistro (V)
Scoma's (V)
Scott's*
Scott's/E*
Scott's/S (L)*
Sent Sovi/S (L)
Seoul Garden*
71 St. Peter/S*
Shanghai 1930 (V)
Showley's/N (L)
Sierra Mar/S (L)
Silks (V)
Slanted Door (V)
Socca*
Sonoma Mission Inn Grille/N (L)
Spago Palo Alto/S (V)
Spiedini/E (L)
Splendido*
Stars (V)
Station Hse. Cafe/N (L)
Stokes Adobe/S (L)
Straits Cafe/S (L)
Sushi Groove (V)
Sushi Ran/N (L)
Swagat/S*
Syrah/N (L)
Tarpy's Roadhse./S (L)
Thirsty Bear (L)

Tomatina/N (L)
Tommy Toy's (V)
Top of the Mark*
Tortola (L)
Trattoria Contadina*
Tra Vigne/N (L)
2030/S (L)
2223 Rest. (L)
Venezia/E (L)
Venticello (V)
Vic Stewart's/E (L)
Vinga*
Viognier/S (L)
Vivande Rist.*
Wappo Bar/N (L)
Washington Sq. B&G (V)
Waterfront (V)
Wente Vineyards/E (L)
Wild Hare/S (V)
Willowside Cafe/N (L)
Wine Spectator/N (L)
World Wrapps/S (L)
Xanadu/E (L)
XYZ (V)
Yabbies*
Yank Sing*
Yet Wah (L)
Yoshida-Ya (V)
Yoshi's/E*
Yoyo Bistro*
Zibibbo/S (V)
Zinzino*
Zuni Cafe (V)

Parties & Private Rooms

(Any nightclub or restaurant
charges less at off-times;
* indicates private rooms
available; best of many)
Acquerello*
Agenda/S
Alamo Square*
Albion River Inn/N*
Alegrias*
Alfred's Steak Hse.*
Amber India/S*
Angkor Wat
Anjou*
Anzu
A.P. Stump's/S*
Aqua*
AsiaSF*
Auberge du Soleil/N*
Avenue 9*
Bacchanal/S*

Bandol*
Baraonda*
Basque Cultural Ctr./S*
Bay Wolf/E
Beach Chalet*
Bella Vista/S*
Belon*
Betelnut Pejiu Wu*
Bette's Oceanview/E*
Big Four*
Biscuits & Blues*
Bistro Aix*
Bistro Viola/E*
Bistro Zaré*
BIX*
Black Cat*
Blackhawk Grille/E*
Blue Nile/E*
Blue Plate*
Bocca Rotis*
Bocce Cafe*
Bolero/N*
Boulevard
Brasserie Savoy
Brava Terrace/N*
Brazio/E*
Bridges/E*
Brix/N*
Bruno's
Buckeye Roadhse./N*
Buck's/S*
Cafe Akimbo*
Cafe Bastille*
Cafe Beaujolais/N*
Cafe de Paris*
Cafe Kati*
Cafe Majestic*
Cafe Mozart
Cafe Riggio*
Cafe Tiramisu*
California Cafe/N
Calzone's
Campton Place
Camranh Bay/S*
Capellini/S*
Caprice/N*
Carnelian Room*
Carpaccio/S*
Carta*
Casanova/S*
Cassis
Catahoula/N*
Cha Am Thai*
Cha Am Thai/E*

Charles Nob Hill*
Chef Chu's/S*
Chevys*
Chevys/E*
Chevys/N*
Chevys/S*
Chez Renee/S
Chez T.J./S*
Christophe/N*
Cielo/S*
Citizen Cake*
Citron/E*
Cliff Hse.*
Club XIX/S*
Columbus Rist.*
Connecticut Yankee*
Covey/S*
Crow's Nest/S*
Crustacean
Cypress Club*
Dal Baffo/S
Delancey St.*
Della Santina's/N*
Dragon Well*
Duarte's Tavern/S*
Duck Club/S*
E&O Trading*
Eastside West*
Elan Vital*
El Paseo/N*
Emile's/S
Empress of China
Enrico's*
Erna's Elderberry/S*
Esperpento*
Fandango/S*
Farallon*
Faz*
Faz/E*
Faz/S*
Fifth Floor*
Fior d'Italia*
First Crush*
Flea St. Cafe/S*
Fleur de Lys
Florio
Fly Trap*
Fook Yuen/S*
42°*
Fountain Court*
Fournou's Ovens*
Frascati*
French Laundry/N*
Fresh Cream/S*
Fung Lum/S

Garibaldis/Presidio*
Gaylord India*
Gaylord India/S*
General's Daughter/N*
Gira Polli/N*
Glen Ellen Inn/N*
Globe*
Gordon's/N*
Gordon's Hse.*
Gramercy Grill
Grand Cafe*
Grandeho's*
Grandview/S*
Great Eastern*
Greens*
Grill/S*
Guaymas/N*
Harbor Village*
Harris'*
Harry Denton's Starlight*
Hawthorne Lane*
Heirloom/N
Hong Kong Flower/S
Horizons/N*
Hotel Mac/E*
House of Prime Rib*
Hunan*
Hungarian Sausage*
Iberia/S
I Fratelli*
Il Fornaio
Il Fornaio/E
Il Fornaio/S*
Indian Oven
Indigo*
Insalata's/N*
Iron Horse*
Izzy's*
Jade Villa/E*
Jakarta
Jardinière*
Jasmine Hse.*
Jocco's/S*
John Ash/N*
Jordan's/E*
Kasbah/N*
Kate's Kitchen*
Kenwood/N
Khan Toke
Kokkari*
Korea Hse.
Kuleto's
Kuleto's Trattoria/S*
La Bergerie*
La Felce*

La Folie*
La Pastaia/S*
Lark Creek/E*
Lark Creek/S
Lark Creek Inn/N*
La Rondalla*
Las Camelias/N*
La Scene*
La Traviata*
La Vie*
Le Central Bistro*
Le Cheval/E*
Le Colonial*
Left Bank/N*
Left Bank/S*
Le Mouton Noir/S*
Le Papillon/S*
Leticia's*
Lion & Compass/S*
Little Italy*
Little Joe's*
Live Fire/N*
L'Olivier*
Long Life Noodle*
LuLu*
Macaroni Sciue Sciue*
MacArthur Park*
Mandalay*
Mandarin*
Manka's Inverness/N*
Marin Joe's/N*
Marinus/S*
Masa's*
Maya*
Mayflower*
McCormick & Kuleto's*
mc²*
Meadowood Grill/N
Mecca*
Mel's Drive-In*
Mikayla/Casa Madrona/N*
Millennium
MoMo's*
Montage*
Montrio/S*
Moonshine*
Morton's of Chicago*
Moss Beach Distillery/S*
Nan Yang Rockridge/E*
Napa Valley Grille/N*
Nava/E
New Pisa
Nob Hill Cafe*
Nola/S
North Beach

North India*
North Sea Village/N*
Obelisque/E*
Oberon*
Olema Inn/N*
Oliveto/E
One Market*
Oodles*
O'Reilly's*
Oritalia*
Osaka Grill*
Osome
Pacific's Edge/S*
Palace/S*
Palio d'Asti
Paolo's/S*
Park Chow*
Park Grill*
Pasta Moon/S
Pauline's*
Pauli's Cafe*
Pazzia*
Perry's*
Piazza D'Angelo/N*
Picante Cocina/E*
Pier 23 Cafe*
Pinot Blanc/N*
PJ's Oyster Bed*
Plearn Thai/E
Plouf*
Plumed Horse/S*
PlumpJack Cafe*
PlumpJack Cafe/N*
Postino/E*
Postrio*
Presidio Cafe*
Prima/E*
Pyramid Alehse./E*
Radicchio*
Red Herring*
Redwood Rm.
Rest. at Meadowood/N*
Rice Table/N*
Rick's*
Ricochet*
Rio Grill/S*
Rist. Ecco*
Rist. Milano*
Ritz-Carlton Din. Rm.
Rocco's*
Rooster*
Rotunda*
Royal Thai/N*
Rubicon*
Rue de Main/E*

Rumpus*
Salute/E
Salute/N*
Sam's Anchor Cafe/N*
Sam's Grill*
San Benito Hse./S*
Sanraku*
Santa Fe B&G/E
Savanna Grill/N*
Scala's Bistro
Scoma's/N*
Scott's*
Scott's/E*
Scott's/S*
Sent Sovi/S*
Seoul Garden*
71 St. Peter/S*
Shanghai 1930*
Showley's/N*
Silks*
Socca*
Soizic/E
Sonoma Mission Inn Grille/N*
Spago Palo Alto/S*
Spiedini/E*
Splendido*
Stars
Stokes Adobe/S*
Suppenküche*
Swagat/S*
Tarpy's Roadhse./S*
Terra/N*
Thanh Long*
Thornhill Cafe/E*
Ti Couz*
Tomales Bay/N*
Tommy Toy's*
Ton Kiang*
Trattoria Contadina*
Tra Vigne/N*
2030/S*
2223 Rest.*
Uzen/E*
Venezia/E
Venticello*
Via Vai*
Vic Stewart's/E*
Vinga*
Viognier/S*
Vivande Rist.*
Wappo Bar/N*
Waterfront
Wente Vineyards/E*
Wine Spectator/N*
Xanadu/E*

Yank Sing*
Yoshida-Ya*
Yoshi's/E*
Yoyo Bistro
Zaré*
Zarzuela*
Zibibbo/S*
Zinzino*
Zza's Trattoria/E*

People-Watching

Ace Wasabi's
Avenue Grill/N
Beach Chalet
Betelnut Pejiu Wu
Bette's Oceanview/E
Black Cat
Bruno's
Buckeye Roadhse./N
Cafe Flore
Cafe Marimba
Caffe Centro
Calzone's
Cha Cha Cha
Chez Panisse/E
Chez Panisse Cafe/E
Cypress Club
Enrico's
Farallon
Fly Trap
Globe
Gordon Biersch/S
Hamburger Mary's
Jakarta
Jardinière
Le Central Bistro
Left at Albuquerque
Leticia's
Little City
Long Life Noodle
Max's Opera Café/S
Mecca
Moose's
One Market
Park Grill
Perry's Downtown
Postrio
Prima/E
Rose Pistola
Rubicon
Tavolino
Xanadu/E
Zuni Cafe

Power Scenes

Aqua
Bistro Jeanty/N
Bix

Blackhawk Grille/E
Bouchon/N
Boulevard
Chez Panisse/E
Cypress Club
42°
Hawthorne Lane
Jacks
La Folie
Le Central Bistro
Le Colonial
LuLu
Masa's
MoMo's
Moose's
North Beach
Occidental Grill
One Market
Park Grill
Postrio
Prima/E
Ritz-Carlton Din. Rm.
Rubicon
Stars
Vivande Rist.
Washington Sq. B&G
Waterfront
Zuni Cafe

Pre-Theater Dining
(Call to check prices,
days and times)
Absinthe
Alamo Square
Anzu
Avenue 9
Biscuits & Blues
Buchanan Grill
Firewood Cafe
First Crush
Gira Polli
Gira Polli/N
Indigo
Juban
Juban/S
Kate's Kitchen
Katia's
La Scene
Little Italy
North India
Obelisque/E
Oritalia
Puccini & Pinetti
Rick's
Saul's/E

Scott's/S
Terra Brazilis

Prix Fixe Menus
(Call to check prices,
days and times)
Ajanta/E
Alamo Square
Anjou
Anzu
Aqua
Auberge du Soleil/N
Baker St. Bistro
Battambang/E
Bistro Aix
Bistro Viola/E
Bix
Bocca Rotis
Cafe Claude
Cafe Tiramisu
Campton Place
Capp's Corner
Carnelian Room
Carta
Castagnola's
Cha Am Thai/E
Chapeau!
Citron/E
Emile's/S
Entros
Erna's Elderberry/S
Esperpento
First Crush
Fournou's Ovens
French Laundry/N
Garden Court
Gaylord India/S
Gira Polli
Golden Turtle
Greens
Hunan
Hyde St. Bistro
Indigo
Jordan's/E
Juban
Juban/S
Kasbah/N
Kate's Kitchen
Kincaid's Bistro/S
Kyo-Ya
La Scene
Le Charm
L'Olivier
Los Gatos/S
Maharani

Manka's Inverness/N
Maria Therese
Mario's Bohemian
Masa's
Mom is Cooking
Moss Beach Distillery/S
Napa Valley Wine Train/N
New Pisa
North India
North Sea Village/N
Oberon
One Market
Oodles
Pacific
Pacific's Edge/S
Palace/S
Paolo's/S
Pastis
Piaf's
Rest. at Meadowood/N
Rice Table/N
Ritz-Carlton Din. Rm.
Rubicon
Rue de Main/E
Sanraku
Scoma's/N
Sent Sovi/S
Sierra Mar/S
Socca
Sonoma Mission Inn Grille/N
Splendido
Stelline
Stokes Adobe/S
Tommy Toy's
231 Ellsworth/S
Viognier/S
Wente Vineyards/E
Zaré

Pubs/Bars/ Microbreweries

Beach Chalet
Buchanan Grill
Crow's Nest/S
Gordon Biersch
Gordon Biersch/S
Liverpool Lil's
Los Gatos/S
Magnolia Pub
O'Reilly's
Perry's
Tommy's Joynt
Washington Sq. B&G

Quiet Conversation

Alegrias
Alioto's
Bella Vista/S
Cafe Mozart
Campton Place
Charles Nob Hill
Chez Panisse/E
El Paseo/N
Fior d'Italia
Fournou's Ovens
Garden Court
Jakarta
John Ash/N
La Felce
Lalime's/E
Liberty Cafe
L'Olivier
Long Life Noodle
Madrona Manor/N
Masa's
Meetinghouse
Napa Valley Wine Train/N
Oberon
PlumpJack Cafe
PlumpJack Cafe/N
Ritz-Carlton Din. Rm.
San Benito Hse./S
Sent Sovi/S
Silks
Socca
231 Ellsworth/S

Raw Bars

Absinthe
Bacchanal/S
Bandol
Belon
Black Cat
Blowfish Sushi
Blue Point
Bouchon/N
Cafe de Paris
Cafe Rouge/E
Eastside West
Eddie Rickenbacker's
Elite Cafe
ELROYS
Faz/S
Foreign Cinema
Globe
Grandeho's
Harry Denton's Starlight
LuLu

Marinus/S
MoMo's
Moonshine
Osome
PJ's Oyster Bed
Ricochet
Rocco's
Swan Oyster Depot
Tavolino
Ti Couz
Xanadu/E
Yabbies
Zibibbo/S
Zuni Cafe

Reservations Essential
Acquerello
Albona Rist.
Anjou
A.P. Stump's/S
Aqua
AsiaSF
Auberge du Soleil/N
Bella Vista/S
Brasserie Savoy
Cafe Jacqueline
Cafe Mozart
Camranh Bay/S
Carnelian Room
Catahoula/N
Cha Am Thai
Charles Nob Hill
Chez Panisse/E
Christophe/N
Cielo/S
Club XIX/S
Columbus Rist.
Curbside Too
Erna's Elderberry/S
Fleur de Lys
Flying Saucer
Fook Yuen/S
Foreign Cinema
Fountain Court
French Laundry/N
Fresh Cream/S
Fringale
Garibaldis/College/E
Gary Danko
Globe
Greens
Guaymas/N
Harry Denton's Starlight
Jordan's/E
Kuleto's Trattoria/S

L'Amie Donia/S
Little Italy
L'Olivier
Los Gatos/S
Mangiafuoco
Maria Therese
Matterhorn Swiss
Napa Valley Wine Train/N
Ondine/N
Osteria/S
Ovation
Pacific's Edge/S
Pasta Moon/S
Piatti/N
Plouf
Postrio
Ritz-Carlton Din. Rm.
Ritz-Carlton Terrace
Sierra Mar/S
Socca
Spago Palo Alto/S
Swagat/S
Tavolino
Trattoria Contadina
Venticello
Viognier/S
Wappo Bar/N
Waterfront
Wente Vineyards/E
Willowside Cafe/N
Yoshi's/E
Zaré
Zax
Zibibbo/S

Romantic Spots
Acquerello
Alegrias
Bella Vista/S
Buca Giovanni
Cafe Jacqueline
Cafe Majestic
Cafe Mozart
Casanova/S
Cassis
Charles Nob Hill
Chez Panisse/E
Chez Renee/S
Covey/S
El Paseo/N
Emile's/S
Erna's Elderberry/S
Fleur de Lys
Fresh Cream/S
Guernica/N

Jakarta
Jardinière
John Ash/N
Julius' Castle
La Folie
Lark Creek Inn/N
Le Mouton Noir/S
L'Olivier
Madrona Manor/N
Maharani
Masa's
Matterhorn Swiss
Meadowood Grill/N
Pacific's Edge/S
Prima/E
Rest. at Meadowood/N
Ritz-Carlton Din. Rm.
Rooster
Salute/E
Salute/N
San Benito Hse./S
Sent Sovi/S
Sierra Mar/S
Silks
Terra/N
231 Ellsworth/S
Venticello
Waterfront
Woodward's Garden
Zax

Saturday – Best Bets

(B=brunch; L=lunch;
best of many)
Absinthe (B,L)
Ajanta/E (L)
Alioto's (L)
Amber India/S (L)
Angkor Wat (L)
Anjou (L)
Aperto (B)
Aqui/S (L)
Armani Cafe (L)
A. Sabella's (L)
Autumn Moon/E (B)
Aux Delices (L)
Avenue 9 (L)
Baker St. Bistro (B,L)
Balboa Cafe (L)
Bandol (L)
Barney's (L)
Basta Pasta (L)
Battambang/E (L)
Beach Chalet (L)
Bette's Oceanview/E (B,L)

Bill's Place (L)
Bistro Don Giovanni/N (L)
Bistro Jeanty/N (L)
Bistro Zaré (B)
Bitterroot (L)
Black Cat (L)
Blackhawk Grille/E (L)
Blue Nile/E (L)
Bocca Rotis (B,L)
Bocce Cafe (L)
Bolero/N (L)
Bouchon/N (L)
Brannan's Grill/N (L)
Brava Terrace/N (L)
Brazio/E (L)
Breads of India/E (L)
Brix/N (L)
Bubba's Diner/N (B,L)
Buchanan Grill (B)
Buckeye Roadhse./N (L)
Buck's/S (B,L)
Buffalo Grill/S (L)
Cactus Cafe/N (L)
Cafe Akimbo (L)
Cafe Bastille (L)
Cafe Beaujolais/N (L)
Cafe Citti/N (L)
Cafe Claude (L)
Cafe de la Presse (B,L)
Cafe de Paris (B,L)
Cafe 817/E (L)
Cafe Fanny/E (L)
Cafe Flore (L)
Cafe For All Seasons (B,L)
Café La Haye/N (B)
Cafe Marcella/S (L)
Cafe Marimba (B,L)
Cafe Rouge/E (L)
Caffe Centro (B,L)
Caffe Delle Stelle (L)
Caffe Greco (L)
Caffe Proust (B,L)
California Cafe/E (L)
California Cafe/N (L)
California Cafe/S (B,L)
California Pizza Kit. (L)
California Pizza Kit./E (L)
Calzone's (B,L)
Casa Aguila (L)
Casanova/S (L)
Castagnola's (L)
Catahoula/N (L)
Cha Am Thai (L)
Cha Am Thai/E (L)
Cha Cha Cha (L)

Chateau Souverain/N (L)
Cheers (B)
Chef Chu's/S (L)
Chevys (L)
Chevys/E (L)
Chevys/N (L)
Chevys/S (L)
Chez Panisse Cafe/E (L)
Chow (L)
Cielo/S (L)
Citizen Cake (B,L)
Citron/E (L)
Clementine (B)
Clement St. B&G (B,L)
Cliff Hse. (L)
Club XIX/S (L)
Compadres/N (L)
Compadres/S (L)
Connecticut Yankee (B,L)
Cordon Bleu (L)
Crow's Nest/S (L)
Curbside (B,L)
Delancey St. (B,L)
Della Santina's/N (L)
Doidge's Cafe (B,L)
Domaine Chandon/N (L)
Dottie's True Blue (B)
Dragon Well (L)
Duarte's Tavern/S (L)
Duck Club/S (L)
E&O Trading (L)
Eastside West (B)
Ebisu (L)
Eddie Rickenbacker's (L)
El Balazo (L)
Ella's (B)
Enrico's (L)
Erna's Elderberry/S (B)
Esperpento (L)
Estampas Peruanas/S (L)
Fandango/S (L)
Farallon (L)
FatApple's/E (B,L)
Faz/E (L)
Faz/S (L)
Felix & Louie's/N (L)
Fior d'Italia (L)
Firewood Cafe (L)
Florio (B)
Fog City Diner (L)
Food Inc. (B,L)
Fook Yuen/S (L)
Fournou's Ovens (B)
French Laundry/N (L)
Fresca (L)

Fuzio (L)
Gaylord India (L)
Gaylord India/S (L)
General's Daughter/N (L)
Ginger Island/E (B,L)
Gordon Biersch (L)
Gordon Biersch/S (L)
Gordon's/N (B,L)
Gramercy Grill (B)
Grandeho's (L)
Grandview/S (L)
Great Eastern (L)
Greens (L)
Grill/S (L)
Guaymas/N (L)
Hamburger Mary's (B,L)
Harbor Village (L)
Hard Rock Cafe (L)
Heirloom/N (L)
Horizons/N (B,L)
Houston's (L)
Hungarian Sausage (B,L)
Iberia/S (L)
Il Fornaio (B,L)
Il Fornaio/E (B,L)
Il Fornaio/S (B,L)
Insalata's/N (L)
Iron Horse (L)
JoAnn's Cafe/S (L)
John Ash/N (L)
John's Grill (L)
Kate's Kitchen (B,L)
Katia's (L)
Kenwood/N (L)
Kincaid's Bistro/S (L)
La Cumbre (L)
La Cumbre/S (L)
La Mediterranée (B,L)
La Mediterranée/E (B,L)
La Note/E (B)
La Pastaia/S (L)
Lark Creek/E (L)
Lark Creek/S (L)
La Rondalla (L)
Las Camelias/N (L)
La Taqueria (L)
La Taqueria/S (L)
La Vie (L)
Le Central Bistro (L)
Le Cheval/E (L)
Left at Albuquerque (L)
Left at Albuquerque/S (L)
Left Bank/N (L)
Left Bank/S (L)
Leticia's (L)

Liberty Cafe (B)
Little City (B,L)
Little Joe's (L)
Live Fire/N (L)
Liverpool Lil's (B,L)
Los Gatos/S (L)
L'Osteria Del Forno (L)
LuLu (B,L)
Macaroni Sciue Sciue (L)
Magnolia Pub (B,L)
Maharani (L)
Maki (L)
Mama's on Washington (B,L)
Mama's Royal Cafe/E (B)
Mandarin (L)
Marin Joe's/N (L)
Marinus/S (L)
Mario's Bohemian (L)
Massawa (L)
Max's Diner (L)
Max's on Square (L)
Max's Opera Café (L)
Max's Opera Café/S (B,L)
Mazzini/E (L)
McCormick & Kuleto's (L)
Meadowood Grill/N (L)
Meetinghouse (B)
Mel's Drive-In (B,L)
Miss Millie's (B)
Mom is Cooking (L)
MoMo's (B)
Montage (L)
Montrio/S (L)
Mo's Burgers (B,L)
Moss Beach Distillery/S (L)
Mozzarella Di Bufala (L)
Mustards Grill/N (L)
Napa Valley Grille/N (L)
Napa Valley Wine Train/N (B,L)
Narai (L)
New Joe's (L)
New Pisa (L)
Nippon Sushi (L)
Nob Hill Cafe (L)
North Beach (L)
North Sea Village/N (L)
Northstar & Little Dipper (B,L)
Oak Town Cafe/E (B)
O Chamé/E (L)
Olema Inn/N (L)
Oliveto/E (L)
Ondine/N (B)
O'Reilly's (B)
Original Joe's (L)
Original Old Clam (L)

Pacific (B,L)
Pacific's Edge/S (L)
Palomino (B,L)
Pancho Villa (L)
Pane e Vino (L)
Park Chow (B,L)
Park Grill (B,L)
Pasta Moon/S (L)
Pasta Pomodoro (L)
Pasta Pomodoro/E (L)
Pasta Pomodoro/N (L)
Pauli's Cafe (B)
Perry's (B,L)
Phuping/E (L)
Piatti/N (L)
Piatti/S (L)
Piazza D'Angelo/N (B,L)
Picante Cocina/E (B,L)
Picaro (L)
Pier 23 Cafe (L)
Pinot Blanc/N (L)
Pintxos (L)
PJ's Oyster Bed (B)
Planet Hollywood (L)
Plearn Thai/E (L)
Pluto's (B,L)
Pluto's/S (L)
Prego (L)
Presidio Cafe (L)
Prima/E (L)
Primo Patio (B,L)
Puccini & Pinetti (L)
Pyramid Alehse./E (L)
Ravenous/N (L)
Rest. Peony/E (L)
Rio Grill/S (L)
Rist. Fabrizio/N (L)
Roosevelt Tamale (L)
Rose Pistola (L)
Rose's Cafe (B,L)
Rosti (L)
Rotunda (L)
Rumpus (L)
Rutherford Grill/N (L)
Salute/E (L)
Salute/N (L)
Sam's Anchor Cafe/N (B,L)
San Benito Hse./S (L)
Sand Dollar/N (L)
Santa Fe B&G/E (L)
Saul's/E (B,L)
Savanna Grill/N (L)
Savor (L)
Scoma's (L)
Scoma's/N (L)

Scott's (L)
Scott's/E (L)
Sears Fine Food (L)
Showley's/N (L)
Sierra Mar/S (L)
Slow Club (B)
Station Hse. Cafe/N (L)
Stinking Rose (L)
Stokes Adobe/S (L)
Suppenküche (B)
Swagat/S (B,L)
Swan Oyster Depot (B,L)
Sweet Heat (L)
Syrah/N (L)
Tadich Grill (L)
Tapestry/S (L)
Tarpy's Roadhse./S (L)
Tavolino (L)
Terra/N (L)
Thirsty Bear (L)
Thornhill Cafe/E (B,L)
Ti Couz (B,L)
Tin-Pan (B,L)
Tita's (B,L)
Tomales Bay/N (L)
Tomatina/N (B,L)
Tommy's Joynt (L)
Tortola (B,L)
Town's End (B)
Tra Vigne/N (L)
2223 Rest. (B)
Universal Cafe (B)
Valentine's Cafe (B)
Via Vai (L)
Vicolo (L)
Vinga (B)
Viognier/S (B)
Vivande Porta Via (L)
Vivande Rist. (B,L)
Wa-Ha-Ka (L)
Wappo Bar/N (B,L)
Washington Sq. B&G (B)
Wente Vineyards/E (L)
Wild Hare/S (L)
Wine Spectator/N (L)
World Wrapps (L)
World Wrapps/N (L)
World Wrapps/S (L)
XYZ (B)
Zachary's/E (L)
Zazie (B)
Zibibbo/S (B)
Zuni Cafe (L)

Sunday – Best Bets
(B=brunch; L=lunch;
D=dinner; plus all hotels
and most Asians)
Absinthe (B,L,D)
Ajanta/E (L,D)
Alamo Square (B,D)
Alioto's (L,D)
Amber India/S (L,D)
Aperto (B,D)
A.P. Stump's/S (B,D)
Aqui/S (L,D)
Armani Cafe (L)
A. Sabella's (L,D)
Autumn Moon/E (B,D)
Avenue 9 (B,L,D)
Baker St. Bistro (B,L,D)
Balboa Cafe (B,L,D)
Bandol (L,D)
Barney's (L,D)
Basta Pasta (L,D)
Beach Chalet (B,D)
Bette's Oceanview/E (B,L)
Bill's Place (L,D)
Bistro Don Giovanni/N (L,D)
Bistro Jeanty/N (L,D)
Bistro Viola/E (B,D)
Bistro Zaré (B,D)
Bitterroot (L,D)
Black Cat (L,D)
Blackhawk Grille/E (B,D)
Bocca Rotis (B,D)
Bocce Cafe (L,D)
Bolero/N (L,D)
Bouchon/N (L,D)
Brannan's Grill/N (L,D)
Brava Terrace/N (L,D)
Brazio/E (B,D)
Bubba's Diner/N (B,L,D)
Buchanan Grill (B,D)
Buckeye Roadhse./N (B,D)
Buck's/S (B,L,D)
Cafe Beaujolais/N (L)
Cafe Citti/N (L,D)
Cafe Claude (B,L)
Cafe de la Presse (B,L,D)
Cafe de Paris (B,L,D)
Cafe Fanny/E (L)
Cafe Flore (L,D)
Cafe For All Seasons (B,L,D)
Café La Haye/N (B)
Cafe Marimba (B,L,D)
Cafe Rouge/E (L,D)
Caffe Greco (L,D)
Caffe Proust (B,L,D)

California Cafe/E (B,L,D)
California Cafe/N (B,L,D)
California Cafe/S (B,L,D)
California Pizza Kit./E (L,D)
Calzone's (B,L,D)
Carnelian Room (B,D)
Carta (B,D)
Casa Aguila (L,D)
Casanova/S (B,L,D)
Castagnola's (L,D)
Cha Am Thai (L,D)
Cha Am Thai/E (L,D)
Cha Cha Cha (L,D)
Chateau Souverain/N (L,D)
Cheers (B,D)
Chevys (L,D)
Chevys/E (L)
Chevys/N (L,D)
Chevys/S (L,D)
Chow (L,D)
Citizen Cake (B,L)
Citron/E (L)
Clementine (B,D)
Clement St. B&G (B,D)
Cliff Hse. (B,L,D)
Club XIX/S (L,D)
Compadres/N (L,D)
Compadres/S (L,D)
Connecticut Yankee (B,L,D)
Crow's Nest/S (L,D)
Curbside (B,L,D)
Delancey St. (B,L,D)
Della Santina's/N (L,D)
Doidge's Cafe (B,L)
Domaine Chandon/N (L,D)
Dottie's True Blue (B)
Duarte's Tavern/S (L,D)
Eastside West (B,D)
El Balazo (L,D)
Ella's (B)
Empress of China (L,D)
Enrico's (L,D)
Erna's Elderberry/S (B,D)
Estampas Peruanas/S (L,D)
Fandango/S (B,L,D)
FatApple's/E (B,L,D)
Faz/E (L,D)
Faz/S (L,D)
Felix & Louie's/N (L,D)
Fior d'Italia (L,D)
Firewood Cafe (L,D)
Flea St. Cafe/S (B,D)
Florio (B,D)
Fog City Diner (L,D)
Fountain Court (L,D)

French Laundry/N (L,D)
Fresca (L,D)
Fuzio (L,D)
Garden Court (B,L)
Garibaldis/Presidio (B,D)
Gaylord India (B,D)
Gaylord India/S (L,D)
General's Daughter/N (B,L,D)
Ginger Island/E (B,L,D)
Gordon Biersch (L,D)
Gordon Biersch/S (L,D)
Gordon's/N (B,L)
Gramercy Grill (B,D)
Greens (B)
Grill/S (L,D)
Guaymas/N (B,L,D)
Hamburger Mary's (B,L,D)
Hard Rock Cafe (L,D)
Heirloom/N (L,D)
Horizons/N (B,L,D)
Houston's (L,D)
Hungarian Sausage (B,L,D)
Iberia/S (L,D)
Il Fornaio (B,L,D)
Il Fornaio/E (B,L,D)
Insalata's/N (B,L,D)
Iroha (L,D)
JoAnn's Cafe/S (L)
John Ash/N (B,D)
Kate's Kitchen (B,L)
Kenwood/N (L,D)
Kincaid's Bistro/S (L,D)
La Cumbre (L,D)
La Cumbre/S (L,D)
La Mediterranée (B,L,D)
La Mediterranée/E (B,L,D)
La Note/E (B)
La Pastaia/S (L,D)
Lark Creek/E (B,D)
Lark Creek Inn/N (B,D)
La Rondalla (L,D)
La Taqueria (L,D)
La Taqueria/S (L,D)
La Vie (L,D)
Left at Albuquerque (L,D)
Left at Albuquerque/S (L,D)
Left Bank/N (B,L,D)
Left Bank/S (L,D)
Le Soleil (L,D)
Leticia's (B,L,D)
Liberty Cafe (B,D)
Little City (B,L,D)
Little Joe's (L,D)
Live Fire/N (L,D)
Liverpool Lil's (B,L,D)

Long Life Noodle (L,D)
Long Life Vegi/E (L,D)
Los Gatos/S (B,L,D)
L'Osteria Del Forno (L,D)
LuLu (B,L,D)
Magnolia Pub (B,L,D)
Maharani (L,D)
Maki (L,D)
Mama's on Washington (B,L)
Mama's Royal Cafe/E (B)
Mandalay (L,D)
Mandarin (L,D)
Marin Joe's/N (L,D)
Marinus/S (L,D)
Mario's Bohemian (L,D)
Massawa (L,D)
Max's Diner (L,D)
Max's on Square (L,D)
Max's Opera Café (L,D)
Max's Opera Café/S (B,L,D)
Mazzini/E (L,D)
McCormick & Kuleto's (B,L,D)
Meetinghouse (B)
Mel's Drive-In (B,L,D)
Mifune (L,D)
Miss Millie's (B,D)
Mom is Cooking (L,D)
MoMo's (B,D)
Montage (L,D)
Moose's (B,D)
Mo's Burgers (B,L,D)
Moss Beach Distillery/S (B,L,D)
Mozzarella Di Bufala (L,D)
Mustards Grill/N (B,L,D)
Napa Valley Grille/N (B,L,D)
Napa Valley Wine Train/N (B,L,D)
New Joe's (L,D)
New Pisa (L,D)
Nola/S (L,D)
North Beach (L,D)
Northstar & Little Dipper (B,L,D)
Oak Town Cafe/E (B)
Oliveto/E (L,D)
O'Reilly's (B,D)
Original Joe's (L,D)
Original Old Clam (L,D)
Palace/S
Palomino (B,L,D)
Pancho Villa (L,D)
Pasta Moon/S (B,L,D)
Pasta Pomodoro (L,D)
Pasta Pomodoro/E (L,D)
Pasta Pomodoro/N (L,D)
Pauli's Cafe (B,D)
Phuping/E (L,D)

Piaf's (B,D)
Piatti/N (L,D)
Piatti/S (L,D)
Piazza D'Angelo/N (B,L,D)
Picante Cocina/E (B,L,D)
Picaro (L,D)
Pier 23 Cafe (B,L,D)
Pinot Blanc/N (L,D)
Pintxos (L,D)
PJ's Oyster Bed (B,D)
Planet Hollywood (L,D)
Plearn Thai/E (L,D)
Pluto's (B,L,D)
Pluto's/S (L,D)
Prego (L,D)
Presidio Cafe (L,D)
Pyramid Alehse./E (L,D)
Ravenous/N (L,D)
Rest. Peony/E (L,D)
Rick's (B,D)
Ricochet (B,D)
Rio Grill/S (B,L,D)
Roosevelt Tamale (L,D)
Rose Pistola (L,D)
Rose's Cafe (B,L,D)
Rosti (L,D)
Rotunda (B,L)
Rumpus (L,D)
Rutherford Grill/N (L,D)
Salute/E (B,D)
Sam's Anchor Cafe/N (B,L,D)
San Benito Hse./S (L,D)
Sand Dollar/N (L,D)
Santa Fe B&G/E (L,D)
Saul's/E (B,L,D)
Savanna Grill/N (L,D)
Savor (L,D)
Scoma's (L,D)
Scoma's/N (L,D)
Scott's/E (B,L,D)
Sears Fine Food (L)
Slanted Door (L,D)
Slow Club (B)
Sonoma Mission/Grille/N (B,D)
Station Hse. Cafe/N (L,D)
Stinking Rose (L,D)
Suppenküche (B,D)
Swagat/S (B,L,D)
Sweet Heat (L,D)
Tarpy's Roadhse./S (B,L,D)
Tavolino (L,D)
Terra/N (L)
Thornhill Cafe/E (B,L,D)
Ti Couz (B,L,D)
Tita's (B,L)

188

Tomales Bay/N (L,D)
Tommy's Joynt (L,D)
Tortola (L,D)
Town's End (B)
Tra Vigne/N (L,D)
2223 Rest. (B,D)
Universal Cafe (B,D)
Valentine's Cafe (B,D)
Vicolo (L,D)
Vinga (B,D)
Viognier/S (B,D)
Vivande Porta Via (L,D)
Vivande Rist. (B,L,D)
Wa-Ha-Ka (L,D)
Wappo Bar/N (B,L,D)
Washington Sq. B&G (B,D)
Wente Vineyards/E (B,L,D)
Wild Hare/S (L,D)
Wine Spectator/N (L,D)
World Wrapps (L,D)
World Wrapps/N (L,D)
World Wrapps/S (L,D)
Zachary's/E (L,D)
Zazie (B,D)
Zibibbo/S (B,D)
Zuni Cafe (B,L,D)

Senior Appeal

Alfred's Steak Hse.
Alioto's
Cafe For All Seasons
Cafe Majestic
Clement St. B&G
Covey/S
Emile's/S
Fleur de Lys
Fresh Cream/S
Garden Court
Harris'
House of Prime Rib
La Bergerie
Marin Joe's/N
Maye's Oyster Hse.
Scoma's
Sears Fine Food

Singles Scenes

Ace Wasabi's
Balboa Cafe
Beach Chalet
Biscuits & Blues
Bix
Black Cat
Buchanan Grill
Buckeye Roadhse./N
Cafe Flore

Calzone's
Caribbean Zone
Crow's Nest/S
Cypress Club
Elite Cafe
Gordon Biersch
Gordon Biersch/S
Guaymas/N
Hamburger Mary's
Il Fornaio
Il Fornaio/S
Infusion
Jakarta
Julie's Supper Club
Kuleto's
LuLu
MacArthur Park
Mecca
Palomino
Perry's
Pier 23 Cafe
Pluto's
Pluto's/S
Postrio
Prego
Sam's Anchor Cafe/N
Thirsty Bear
2223 Rest.
Washington Sq. B&G
Zuni Cafe

Sleepers

(Good to excellent food,
but little known)
Aqui/S
Cafe 817/E
Charanga
Chez Renee/S
Cordon Bleu
Covey/S
Cucina Jackson Fillmore/N
Duck Club/S
Dusit Thai
Eastside West
Elan Vital
Gordon's/N
Grandview/S
Great Eastern
Jasmine Hse.
Jocco's/S
Jordan's/E
Kasbah/N
La Traviata
Le Papillon/S
Madrona Manor/N

Maki
Mikayla/Casa Madrona/N
Mio Vicino/S
Narai
Osaka Grill
Palace/S
Paolo's/S
Pazzia
Primo Patio
Rue de Main/E
Sanraku
Seoul Garden
71 St. Peter/S
Showley's/N
Sierra Mar/S
Stokes Adobe/S
Tanuki
Tapestry/S
Thornhill Cafe/E
Tomales Bay/N
2030/S
Uzen/E
Yukol Place

Teflons

(Get lots of business, despite so-so food, i.e. they have other attractions that prevent criticism from sticking)
Alioto's
Basta Pasta
Beach Chalet
Bocce Cafe
Bubble Lounge
Cafe de la Presse
California Pizza Kit.
California Pizza Kit./E
Caribbean Zone
Chevys
Chevys/E
Chevys/N
Chevys/S
Cliff Hse.
ELROYS
Fuzio
Hard Rock Cafe
Long Life Noodle
Mel's Drive-In
Moss Beach Distillery/S
Pasta Pomodoro
Pasta Pomodoro/E
Pasta Pomodoro/N
Perry's
Pier 23 Cafe
Planet Hollywood

Sam's Anchor Cafe/N
Stinking Rose
Tommy's Joynt
World Wrapps
World Wrapps/N
World Wrapps/S

Tasting Menus
Acquerello
Aqua
Auberge du Soleil/N
Blowfish Sushi
Cafe Majestic
Campton Place
Carnelian Room
Catahoula/N
Chapeau!
Charles Nob Hill
Cielo/S
Domaine Chandon/N
Elan Vital
Erna's Elderberry/S
Fifth Floor
First Crush
Fleur de Lys
French Laundry/N
Gary Danko
Jardinière
La Folie
Lark Creek Inn/E
La Toque/N
Le Papillon/S
Masa's
mc²
Mikayla/Casa Madrona/N
North India
North Sea Village/N
One Market
Oodles
Pacific
Paolo's/S
Pinot Blanc/N
Postrio
Prima/E
Rest. at Meadowood/N
Rest. Marais
Ritz-Carlton Din. Rm.
Rubicon
Sent Sovi/S
Silks
Sonoma Mission Inn Grille/N
Spiedini/E
Splendido
Terra/N
Tommy Toy's
Wine Spectator/N

Teas
(See also *Hotel Dining*; the following are highly touted)
Citizen Cake
First Crush
Katia's
Rotunda

Teenagers & Other Youthful Spirits
Ace Wasabi's
Barney's
Benihana
Benihana/E
Benihana/S
Bill's Place
Cacti/N
Cactus Cafe/N
California Pizza Kit.
California Pizza Kit./E
Caribbean Zone
Enrico's
FatApple's/E
Gira Polli
Gira Polli/N
Hamburger Mary's
Hard Rock Cafe
Jakarta
La Cumbre
La Taqueria
Mario's Bohemian
Max's Diner
Max's Opera Café
Max's Opera Café/S
Mel's Drive-In
Mo's Burgers
Mozzarella Di Bufala
North India
Pancho Villa
Pauline's
Pazzia
Pier 23 Cafe
Planet Hollywood
World Wrapps
World Wrapps/N
World Wrapps/S
Yet Wah

Theme Restaurants
Ace Wasabi's
Blowfish Sushi
Caribbean Zone
Hard Rock Cafe
Planet Hollywood

Visitors on Expense Accounts
Big Four
Fior d'Italia
Greens
Harris'
Izzy's
McCormick & Kuleto's
Moose's
North Beach
One Market
Park Grill
Prima/E
Ritz-Carlton Din. Rm.
Rubicon
Scala's Bistro
Silks
Stars
Tadich Grill

Wheelchair Access
(Most places now have wheelchair access; call in advance to check)

Wine/Beer Only
Ace Wasabi's
Acquerello
Ajanta/E
Alamo Square
Albona Rist.
Alegrias
Alice's
Allegro
Antica Trattoria
Aperto
Aux Delices
Avenue 9
Baker St. Bistro
Baraonda
Barney's
Bay Wolf/E
Bella Trattoria
Bette's Oceanview/E
Bill's Place
Bistro Aix
Bistro Clovis
Bistro Vida/S
Bistro Viola/E
Bitterroot
Blue Nile/E
Blue Plate
Blue Point
Bocca Rotis
Bontà Rist.

Kasbah/N
Katia's
Khan Toke
Kincaid's Bistro/S
Kirala/E
Korea Hse.
La Bergerie
La Cumbre
La Cumbre/S
Lalime's/E
La Mediterranée
La Mediterranée/E
L'Amie Donia/S
La Note/E
Las Camelias/N
La Taqueria
La Taqueria/S
La Toque/N
La Traviata
La Vie
Le Charm
Le Soleil
Liberty Cafe
Lichee Garden
Little Italy
Little Joe's
London Wine Bar
Long Life Noodle
Long Life Vegi/E
Los Gatos/S
Macaroni Sciue Sciue
Madrona Manor/N
Magnolia Pub
Maharani
Maki
Mama's on Washington
Mama's Royal Cafe/E
Mandalay
Mangiafuoco
Manka's Inverness/N
Maria Therese
Mario's Bohemian
Marnee Thai
Massawa
Ma Tante Sumi
Meetinghouse
Mel's Drive-In
Mescolanza
Michelangelo Cafe
Mifune
Mikayla/Casa Madrona/N
Mio Vicino/S
Miss Millie's
Mo's Burgers
Mozzarella Di Bufala

Nan Yang Rockridge/E
Narai
Nava/E
Neecha Thai
Nob Hill Cafe
North India
North Sea Village/N
Northstar & Little Dipper
Oak Town Cafe/E
O Chamé/E
Olema Inn/N
Osaka Grill
Osteria
Osteria/S
Pacific Cafe
Pancho Villa
Pane e Vino
Park Chow
Parma
Pasta Moon/S
Pasta Pomodoro
Pasta Pomodoro/E
Pasta Pomodoro/N
Pauline's
Pauli's Cafe
Pazzia
Phuping/E
Picante Cocina/E
Picaro
Pintxos
Plearn Thai/E
PlumpJack Cafe
PlumpJack Cafe/N
Pluto's
Pluto's/S
Primo Patio
Pyramid Alehse./E
Radicchio
Ravenous/N
Rice Table/N
Rick & Ann's/E
Rist. Bacco
Rist. Fabrizio/N
Rist. Milano
Rivoli/E
Robata/N
Roosevelt Tamale
Rooster
Rose's Cafe
Rosti
Rue de Main/E
Sanppo
Sanraku
Saul's/E
Savor

Sent Sovi/S
71 St. Peter/S
Showley's/N
Slanted Door
Soizic/E
Stelline
Sukhothai
Suppenküche
Sushi Groove
Sushi Ran/N
Swan Oyster Depot
Syrah/N
Taiwan
Tanuki
Terra/N
Terra Brazilis
Thep Phanom
Thornhill Cafe/E
Tomales Bay/N
Tomatina/N
Tommaso's
Ton Kiang
Tortola
Town's End
Trattoria Contadina
Tu Lan
Uzen/E
Valentine's Cafe
Venezia/E
Via Vai
Vicolo
Vineria
Vivande Porta Via
Wappo Bar/N
Willowside Cafe/N
Woodward's Garden
Yabbies
Yank Sing
Ya-Ya Cuisine
Yuet Lee
Yukol Place
Zachary's/E
Zarzuela
Zax
Zazie
Zinzino
Zza's Trattoria/E

Winning Wine Lists
Acquerello
Aqua
Auberge du Soleil/N
Bay Wolf/E
Blackhawk Grille/E
Brava Terrace/N

Cafe Marcella/S
Carnelian Room
Casanova/S
Catahoula/N
Chapeau!
Chez Panisse/E
Chez Panisse Cafe/E
Chez Renee/S
Chez T.J./S
Covey/S
Cypress Club
Dal Baffo/S
El Paseo/N
ELROYS
Eos
Erna's Elderberry/S
Farallon
First Crush
Flea St. Cafe/S
Fleur de Lys
Fournou's Ovens
French Laundry/N
Gary Danko
girl & the fig/N
Greens
John Ash/N
Julius' Castle
La Pastaia/S
Lark Creek Inn/N
London Wine Bar
Masa's
Meetinghouse
Moose's
Mustards Grill/N
North Beach
One Market
Pacific's Edge/S
Park Grill
PlumpJack Cafe
PlumpJack Cafe/N
Postrio
Prima/E
Rest. at Meadowood/N
Rist. Ecco
Ritz-Carlton Din. Rm.
Rivoli/E
Rubicon
Silks
Sonoma Mission Inn Grille/N
Stars
Tarpy's Roadhse./S
Terra/N
231 Ellsworth/S
Wente Vineyards/E
Willowside Cafe/N

Wine Spectator/N
Zuni Cafe

Worth a Trip
EAST
Berkeley
  Chez Panisse
  Jordan's
Oakland
  Bay Wolf
  Oliveto
Walnut Creek
  Prima
NORTH
Boonville
  Boonville Hotel
Calistoga
  Catahoula
Larkspur
  Lark Creek Inn
Mendocino
  Cafe Beaujolais
Napa
  Auberge du Soleil
  Brava Terrace
  Domaine Chandon
  French Laundry
  Meadowood Grill
  Mustards Grill
  Napa Valley Wine Train
  Terra
Sonoma
  Bistro Ralph
SOUTH
Big Sur
  Sierra Mar
Half Moon Bay
  Pasta Moon
  San Benito Hse.
Monterey/Carmel
  Fresh Cream
  Pacific's Edge
  Tarpy's Roadhse.
Oakhurst
  Erna's Elderberry
Pebble Beach
  Roy's/Pebble Beach
San Jose
  Emile's
San Mateo
  231 Ellsworth
Saratoga
  Sent Sovi

Young Children
(Besides the normal fast-food
places; * indicates children's
menu available)
Alioto's*
Anzu*
Aqui/S*
A. Sabella's
Bandol
Barney's*
Beach Chalet*
Bette's Oceanview/E*
Bighorn Grill/E*
Bill's Place
Biscuits & Blues*
Bistro Viola/E*
Bocca Rotis*
Brazio/E*
Bubba's Diner/N*
Buckeye Roadhse./N*
Buck's/S*
Cactus Cafe/N*
Cafe Marimba*
Cafe Riggio*
Caffe Sport
California Cafe/N*
Capellini/S
Capp's Corner
Casanova/S*
Castagnola's
Cheers
Chez Panisse/E*
Chow*
Clement St. B&G
Crow's Nest/S*
Duck Club/S*
E&O Trading*
El Balazo*
Ernesto's
FatApple's/E
Faz/S
Felix & Louie's/N*
Firewood Cafe*
First Crush*
Fournou's Ovens
Frascati*
Fresca*
Garden Court
Ginger Island/E*
Gordon Biersch/S*
Grill/S*
Hamburger Mary's
Hard Rock Cafe
Horizons/N*
House of Prime Rib

I Fratelli*
Insalata's/N*
Izzy's
Jakarta
JoAnn's Cafe/S
Jordan's/E*
Kabuto Sushi
Kenwood/N
Kuleto's Trattoria/S*
La Ginestra/N
Lark Creek/E*
Lark Creek/S*
Lark Creek Inn/N*
Left Bank/S*
Little Joe's
Live Fire/N*
LuLu*
Marin Joe's/N
Max's Diner
Max's on Square*
Max's Opera Café
Max's Opera Café/S*
Meadowood Grill/N*
Mel's Drive-In
Mikayla/Casa Madrona/N*
Montrio/S*
Mo's Burgers
Moss Beach Distillery/S*
Mozzarella Di Bufala
Napa Valley Wine Train/N*
Nava/E*
New Joe's
New Pisa*
North India
One Market*
Pacific's Edge/S
Palomino
Park Chow*

Park Grill*
Pauline's
Pazzia
Perry's
Perry's Downtown*
Picante Cocina/E*
Planet Hollywood
Pluto's*
Pluto's/S*
Puccini & Pinetti*
Pyramid Alehse./E*
Rick's*
Ricochet*
Rio Grill/S*
Rosti*
Rutherford Grill/N*
Sam's Anchor Cafe/N*
Sand Dollar/N*
Saul's/E
Savanna Grill/N*
Savor*
Schroeder's
Scoma's*
Scoma's/N*
Scott's*
Scott's/S*
Splendido*
Station Hse. Cafe/N*
Stokes Adobe/S*
Tarpy's Roadhse./S*
Tomatina/N*
Tonga*
Tortola
Venezia/E*
Vinga*
Wente Vineyards/E*
Zza's Trattoria/E*

ALPHABETICAL PAGE INDEX*

* All restaurants are in the City of San Francisco unless otherwise noted (E=East of San Francisco; N=North of San Francisco; S=South of San Francisco).

Wine Vintage Chart 1985-1998

This chart is designed to help you select wine to go with your meal. It is based on the same 0 to 30 scale used throughout this *Survey*. The ratings (prepared by our friend **Howard Stravitz**, a law professor at the University of South Carolina) reflect both the quality of the vintage and the wine's readiness for present consumption. Thus, if a wine is not fully mature or is over the hill, its rating has been reduced. We do not include 1987, 1991 or 1993 vintages because, with the exception of cabernets, '91 Northern Rhônes and '93 red Burgundies and Southern Rhônes, those vintages are not especially recommended.

	'85	'86	'88	'89	'90	'92	'94	'95	'96	'97	'98
WHITES											
French:											
Alsace	25	20	23	28	28	24	28	26	24	25	24
Burgundy	24	25	19	27	22	23	22	27	28	25	24
Loire Valley	–	–	–	26	25	18	22	24	26	23	22
Champagne	28	25	24	26	28	–	–	24	26	24	–
Sauternes	22	28	29	25	26	–	18	22	23	24	–
California:											
Chardonnay	–	–	–	–	–	24	22	26	22	26	26
REDS											
French:											
Bordeaux	26	27	25	28	29	18	24	25	24	23	23
Burgundy	24	–	23	27	29	23	23	25	26	24	24
Rhône	26	20	26	28	27	15	23	24	22	24	26
Beaujolais	–	–	–	–	–	–	21	24	22	24	23
California:											
Cab./Merlot	26	26	–	21	28	26	27	25	24	25	26
Zinfandel	–	–	–	–	–	21	23	21	22	24	25
Italian:											
Tuscany	27	–	24	–	26	–	–	25	19	28	25
Piedmont	25	–	25	27	27	–	–	23	25	28	25

Bargain sippers take note: Some wines are reliable year in, year out, and are reasonably priced as well. They include: Alsatian Pinot Blancs, Côtes du Rhône, Muscadet, Bardolino, Valpolicella and inexpensive Spanish Rioja and California Zinfandel and are best bought in the most recent vintages.